AS PE FOR OCR

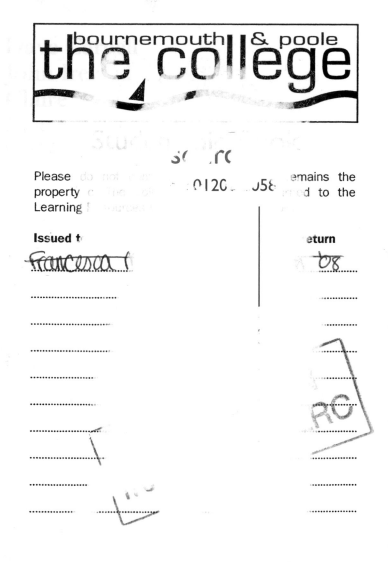

bournemouth & poole
the college

Please do not ... remains the
property ... d to the
Learning ...

01206 ...058

Issued t   eturn

Francesca   08

....

....

....

....

....

....

....

....

31843

Heinemann Educational Publishers
Halley Court, Jordan Hill, Oxford, OX2 8EJ
Part of Harcourt Education

Heinemann is the registered trademark of
Harcourt Education Limited.

© Carnell, Ireland, Jones, Mackreth, van Wely, 2002

First published 2002

07

11

British Library Cataloguing in Publication Data is available
from the British Library on request.

10-digit ISBN: 0 435499 54 8
13-digit ISBN: 978 0 435499 54 9

Typeset by J & L Composition, Filey

Original illustrations © Harcourt Education Limited 2002

Printed and bound in China by CTPS

Cover photographs: © Empics

Picture research by Peter Morris

Acknowledgements
Every effort has been made to contact copyright holders of
material reproduced in this book. Any omissions will be
rectified in subsequent printings if notice is given to the
publishers.

The publishers would like to thank the following for
permission to reproduce photographs:

Corbis/ Duomo/ William Sallaz: Figures 3.03, 6.05; Action
Plus/ Richard Francis: Figures 3.04, 8.09; Empics/ Tony
Marshall: Figures 3.05, 6.07, 6.09, 6.13, 6.17, 6.19, 7.08,
8.10, 9.05, 9.08 (bottom right and bottom left), 9.11, 11.05
(centre and bottom), 12.13, 14.01; Empics/ Neal Simpson:
Figures 3.06, 8.06, 9.16, 12.12; Empics/ Michael Steele:
Figures 3.07, 6.12, 8.01; SPL/Alfred Pasieka: Figure 1.05;
Empics/ Adam Davy: Figures 6.01, 6.04; Empics/ John
Buckle: Figures 6.02, 6.14, 8.05; Empics/ Mike Egerton:
Figures 6.06, 6.15, 6.20, 9.07, 11.07; Action Plus/ Glyn Kirk:
Figures 6.08, 7.04, 9.08 (bottom centre); Empics/ Matthew
Ashton: Figure 6.10; Action Plus Sport Images: Figure 6.11;

Empics/ Jed Leicester: Figure 6.18; Empics/ Ray Field:
Figure 6.21; Empics: Figure 7.05; Corbis/ Rick Gomez:
Figures 7.06, 11.01 (centre); Empics/ Stephen Pond: Figure
7.12; Photolibrary Wales/ Dave Newbould: Figure 14.02;
Trevor Clifford: Figures 8.08, 9.01, 9.03, 9.06, 10.10, 14.03,
14.04; Empics/ Claire Mackintosh: Figure 8.02; Corbis/Karl
Weatherley: Figure 8.03; Stone/ Steven Peters: Figure 9.02;
Peter Morris: Figure 9.08 (top); John Walmsley: Figure 9.04;
Action Plus/ Neale Haynes: Figure 9.09; Action Plus/ Neil
Tingle: Figures 9.15, 13.22, 13.29; Empics/ Steve Mitchell:
Figures 6.16, 13.21; Corbis/ Temp Sport/ Dimitri Lundt:
Figure 9.17; Corbis/ Mitchell Gerber: Figure 10.07; Corbis/
Ronnie Kaufman: Figure 10.08; Corbis/ Bob Krist : Figure
10. 14; Photolibrary Wales: Figure 11.01 (top); Robert
Harding/ Michael Philip Manheim: Figure 11.01 (bottom);
Corbis/ Anne Griffiths-Bell: Figure 11.04; Corbis/ Jim
Cummins: Figure 11.05 (top); Corbis/ Hubert Studler:
Figure 12.02; Empics/ David Worthy: Figure 12.01; Mary
Evans Picture Library: Figure 12.03; Corbis/ Sharna
Balfour, Gallo Images: Figure 12.06; Action Images: Figure
12.09; Corbis/ Wolfgang Kaelher: Figure 12.10; Empics/
Phil Walter: Figure 13.16.

The publishers have made every effort to trace the copyright
holders, but if they have inadvertently overlooked any, they
will be pleased to make the necessary arrangements at the
first opportunity.

Websites
Links to appropriate websites are given throughout the book.
Although these were up to date at the time of writing, it is
essential for teachers to preview these sites before using
them with pupils. This will ensure that the web address
(URL) is still accurate and the content is suitable for your
needs.

We suggest that you bookmark useful sites and consider
enabling pupils to access them through the school intranet.
We are bringing this to your attention, as we are aware of
legitimate sites being appropriated illegally by people
wanting to distribute unsuitable or offensive material. We
strongly advise you to purchase suitable screening software
so that pupils are protected from unsuitable sites and their
material.

If you do find that the links given no longer work, or the
content is unsuitable, please let us know. Details of changes
will be posted on our website.

> The strengthening exercises described in Chapter 2 are
> not dangerous or harmful provided they are carried out
> responsibly without unnecessary force, which might lead
> to injury, and closely adhering to health and safety
> guidelines. If in doubt about any of the exercises, avoid
> them altogether or seek medical advice. Neither the
> authors nor the publisher can be held responsible for any
> injury sustained while performing any of the exercises
> outlined in this book.

Tel: 01865 888058 www.heinemann.co.uk

Contents

Chapter 4: Part II – Control of Blood Supply 73

Chapter 5: Respiratory System 85

Unit 2: Movement skills

Chapter 6: Defining, Developing and Classifying Skills in PE 108

Chapter 7: Information Processing 129

Chapter 8: Control of Motor Skill in PE 144

Chapter 9: Learning Skills in PE 151

Unit 3: Contemporary studies in PE

Chapter 10: PE and Sport in Schools 166

Chapter 11: Concepts of Sport in Society   188

Chapter 12: Sport and Culture   200

Chapter 13: Sporting Issues Analysis   219

Unit 4: Performance and its improvement through Critical Analysis

Chapter 14: Performance and its Improvement through Critical Analysis   264

Introduction

This book is designed specifically for students following OCR's AS Physical Education (PE) course. It will support and reinforce the teaching you receive in your centre following the principle of applying theory to practical performance and relating practical performance to theory. The OCR course also embraces the principle that practical performance is essential to the understanding of theory – students will be assessed in their practical activities with those marks contributing to the overall AS grade.

The content of the book is presented in a form that is identical to the OCR specification arranged under the same sections and sub-headings. This means that the content will probably be in the same order as you are taught it in your centre. The information is presented in a practical context wherever possible as an aid to your understanding and to prepare you for your examination questions.

Organisation of the book

The book is divided into four units that represent the areas in which you will be examined.

1 Anatomy and physiology.
2 Movement skills.
3 Contemporary studies in PE.
4 Performance and its improvement through critical analysis.

The units are divided into chapters. Each chapter has an introduction which explains the content and how the theories relate to each other and to practical activities.

Wherever possible theory will be applied to practical activities in order that you become accustomed to this approach. This is how you will be taught and examined.

Throughout each chapter you will find a series of tasks which are designed to help you understand, apply and remember the topics they relate to. You will also find that some of the tasks cover work that you will need to include in your Personal Performance Portfolio (PPP).

Important definitions are highlighted in 'KEYWORDS' boxes to make it easier for you to find them. You will also find 'HOT TIPS' included throughout – these are meant to give you guidance as to how to improve your knowledge in order to get better grades in your AS exams.

At the end of each chapter there will be some sample questions for you to do. In most cases these will be from past examination papers and will not only allow you to test your knowledge and understanding but will also give you an idea of the type and difficulty of the questions you will have to answer in your AS examinations.

How you will be examined

You have three units to complete, two of which have examination papers with the third being a coursework unit in which your teachers will assess you. Units 1 and 2 are examined in both January and the summer, but Unit 3 can only be taken in the summer.

UNIT 1 (OCR UNIT 2562)

This unit is worth 40% of your AS marks. It consists of a $1\frac{1}{2}$-hour examination paper consisting of four compulsory questions.
There are:

- two anatomy and physiology questions
- two acquiring and performing movement skills questions.

Each question is worth a total of 15 marks but is broken down into smaller sections. Each of the smaller questions has the number of marks it is worth clearly indicated.

HOT TIPS

Take care when answering the questions in this exam. Plan your answers, make sure that you write in sentences, use paragraphs and check your spelling. Those three marks for quality of language can make a difference to your grade.

UNIT 2 (OCR UNIT 2563)

This unit is worth 30% of your AS marks. It consists of a $1\frac{1}{4}$-hour examination paper consisting of two compulsory questions. Each question is worth a total of 21 marks but is broken down into smaller sections. Each of the smaller sections has the number of marks clearly indicated. In addition there are three marks available for the quality of your language, including spelling, grammar, punctuation, sentence construction and use of paragraphs.

UNIT 3 (OCR UNIT 2564)

This unit is worth 30% of your AS marks. This is the practical (coursework) unit and is split into two parts.

- Practical activities (20%) – you are assessed in two practical activities.
- Personal Performance Portfolio (PPP) (10%) – a piece of written work relating to one of the activities you have been assessed in.

Exam tips

1 Read the questions thoroughly so that you understand what they are asking you and what you have to do.

2 Relate your answer to the number of marks available for that question. Remember that you usually have to make one point in your answer for each mark that is available.

3 Wherever possible apply the theory to a practical activity and make sure that you name that activity.

4 Make sure that in your anatomy and physiology, and skill answers you use the appropriate technical terms.

5 In the contemporary studies questions make sure that you plan your answers – particularly in the questions that have 5–8 marks available.

6 In the contemporary studies questions make sure that your spelling, grammar and punctuation are correct, and that you write in sentences and use paragraphs where appropriate.

7 Make sure that you plan the use of your time properly.

8 In the exam you will write your answers on the question paper. The number of lines available gives you an indication of the length of answer required.

9 Make sure that you revise all aspects of each area. Do not think that just because a topic was in a previous exam it will not be in yours.

Chapter 1 **Joints and Movement**

Learning Objectives

At the end of this chapter you should be able to:
- Identify the bones that articulate at different joints in the body.
- Understand how to classify joints according to the movement they allow.
- Describe the structure and function of the characteristics common to synovial joints.
- Name and give examples of the six types of synovial joint.
- Use anatomical terminology to identify and describe common joint movements.
- Analyse a range of sporting techniques in terms of the joint movements.

Introduction

All sporting techniques, from the powerful executions of a shot putter to the elegant routine performed by a gymnast on the beam, require a considerable range of movement. Our joints are the sites on the body that allow these movements to take place. However, although joints allow our skeleton to move, they also hold it together, and therefore joints are very important features of our body. In this chapter, we will first identify where our joints are located and how they might be grouped according to the range of movement they allow. We will look in more detail at the types of joint that allow a considerable range of movement and see how the structures of these types of joint provide the skeleton with both strength and protection. Finally, we will learn to describe anatomically the movements that occur at the joints and use this knowledge to analyse sporting performances.

KEY WORDS

Joint

A place on the body where two or more bones meet.

Introduction to the Skeleton

The average human adult has 206 bones that are joined to ligaments and tendons to form a protective and supportive framework for the attachment of muscles. You do not need to know the names of all these bones, but you will probably know many of them already. You will need to know the main bones in the body and you should use Figure 1.03 to familiarise yourself with their names.

Classification of Joints

Joints are classified by structure and function. For AS level anatomy and physiology we need not concern ourselves with the details of structural classification. However, we will link the terminology used in structural classification to that of functional classification.

KEY WORDS

Ligament

A tough band of fibrous, slightly elastic connective tissue that attaches one bone to another. It binds the ends of bones together to prevent dislocation.

Tendon

A very strong connective tissue that attaches skeletal muscle to bone.

HOT TIPS

In your examination you would never need to be able to label a skeleton, but you would be expected to know the bones that articulate at the following joints: wrist, radio-ulnar, elbow, shoulder, spine, hip, knee and ankle.

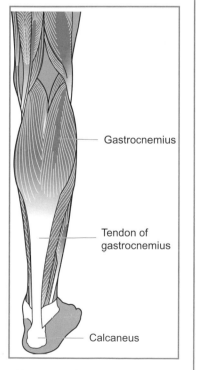

Fig. 1.02 The tendon of the gastrocnemius attaches to the calcaneus bone.

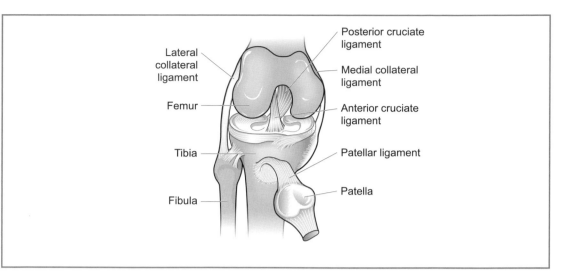

Fig. 1.01 The four ligaments of the knee joint and the patellar ligament.

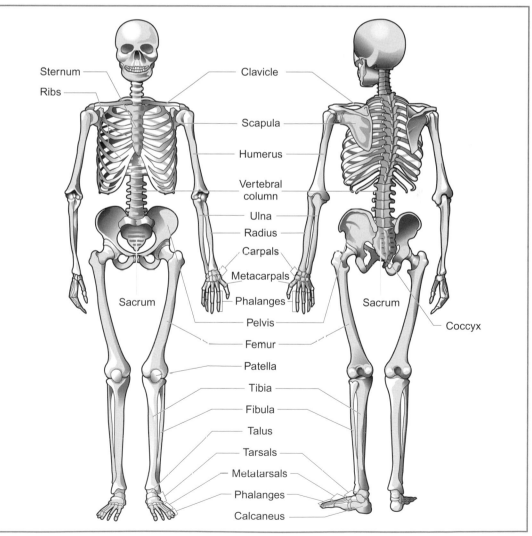

Fig. 1.03 A labelled diagram of anterior and posterior skeleton.

TASK 1

1   Use Fig. 1.03 to help you identify the bones that articulate at the joints indicated on the illustration below.

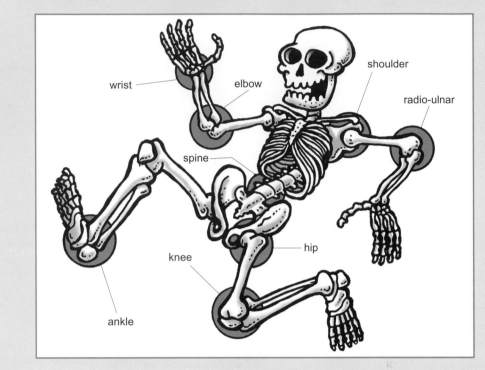

2   Record your answers in a table similar to the one below.

Joint	Helpful hints	Names of articulating bones
Wrist	List *three* bones.	
Elbow	List *three* bones.	
Radio-ulnar	This is an easy one!	
Shoulder	List only *two* bones. Find out the names of the *bony features* that articulate.	
Spine	Name the bones that make up the spine and list *five* areas of the spine. Name the very *top two* bones in the spine.	
Hip	List only *two* bones. Find out the names of the *bony features* that articulate.	
Knee	Be careful here! List *only two* bones.	
Ankle	Tricky! List *three* bones, but not the tarsals.	

Joints are classified in three ways as summarised in the table below:

Structural classification

- fibrous or fixed joints   ⟶
- cartilaginous joints   ⟶
- synovial joints.   ⟶

Functional classification

- immovable joints
- slightly movable joints
- freely moveable joints.

Class of joint	Example	Movement	Diagram
Fibrous	Joints between the bones of the skull or joints between the sacrum and the coccyx at the bottom of the spine.	None	
Cartilaginous	Joints between bodies of adjacent vertebrae in the cervical, thoracic and part of the lumbar spine.	Slight	
Synovial	Joints between the bones of the arms and the legs.	Free	

Freely movable joints are located in the limbs of the **appendicular skeleton,** while immovable and slightly movable joints are more commonly found in the central core of the skeleton or the **axial skeleton.** The appendicular skeleton provides a framework for muscle attachment and movement.

KEY WORDS

Appendicular skeleton

The bones of the upper and lower limbs and their girdles that join to the axial skeleton.

Axial skeleton

This forms the long axis of the body and includes the bones of the skull, spine and rib cage. Its functions are to protect, support and carry other body parts.

TASK 2

1 List the individual bones that make up the appendicular skeleton.

2 The skeleton below is incomplete. Name the bony region that is missing and give two of its functions.

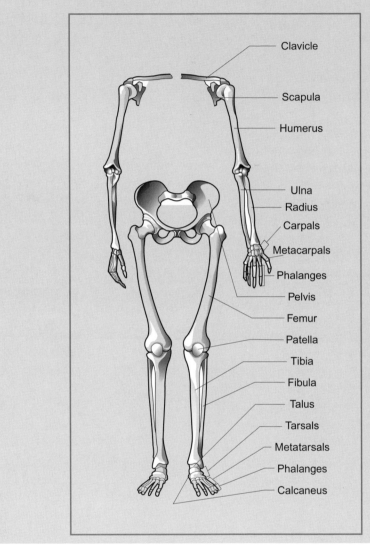

Synovial Joints

In PE and Sport, movement is very important. The synovial joints interest us most because they allow the greatest freedom of movement.

General Structure

Synovial joints have four distinguishing features, shown in figures 1.04 and 1.05 and analysed in the table below.

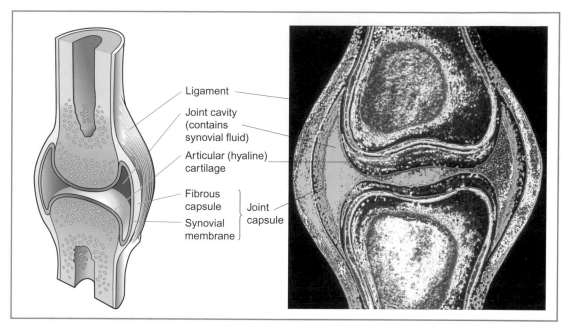

Figs. 1.04 and 1.05 The four features of a synovial joint.

Feature	Structure	Function
Articular/hyaline cartilage	Glassy-smooth cartilage that is quite spongy. It covers the ends of the bones at the joint.	• To prevent friction between the articulating surfaces of the bones at the joint. • To absorb compression placed on the joint and protect the bone ends from being crushed.
Two-layered joint capusle	The outer layer is a tough fibrous layer called the **fibrous capsule**. The inner layer is the **synovial membrane** that covers all the internal joint surfaces except for the articular cartilage.	• To strengthen the joint so that the bones are not pulled apart. • To secrete synovial fluid.
Synovial fluid	A slippery fluid the consistency of egg-whites that is contained within the joint cavity.	• To reduce friction between the articular cartilages. • To nourish the articular cartilage. • To rid the joint of any waste debris.
Ligament	A band of strong fibrous tissue.	• To connect one bone to another bone.

KEY WORDS

Bursa (pl. bursae)

A flattened fibrous sac lined with synovial membrane that contains a thin film of synovial fluid. They function to prevent friction at sites in the body where ligaments, muscles, tendons or bones might rub together.

In addition to the basic components described in the table above, some synovial joints have other structural features. Three common additional characteristics are bursae, menisci and pads of fat. See figure 1.06 on page 10.

KEY WORDS

Meniscus (pl. menisci)

A wedge of white fibrocartilage (a tough and flexible type of cartilage) that improves the fit between adjacent bone ends, making the joint more stable and reducing wear and tear to the joint surfaces.

Pad of fat

A fatty pad that provides cushioning between the fibrous capsule and a bone or muscle.

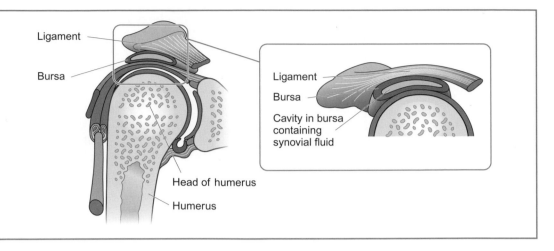

Fig. 1.06 Shoulder joint showing position of bursa to prevent friction between the ligament and the head of the humerus.

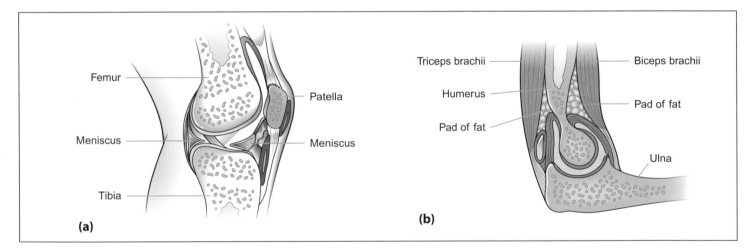

Fig. 1.07 (a) Knee joint showing two semi-lunar menisci situated to improve the way in which the femur fits with the tibia; and (b) elbow joint showing two pads of fat that provide cushioning between the fibrous capsule and the adjoining muscles.

TASK 3

From your knowledge of the general structure of synovial joints:

1. List *two* features that increase joint stability and give their specific function.

2. List *two* features that protect the skeleton and give their specific function.

Types of Synovial Joint

Although synovial joints have many common structural characteristics, the shapes of the articulating surfaces in joint capsules varies considerably and this determines how much movement is allowed at a particular joint.

Synovial joints can be further classified into six groups according to the shape of the articulating surfaces, as shown in the following illustration.

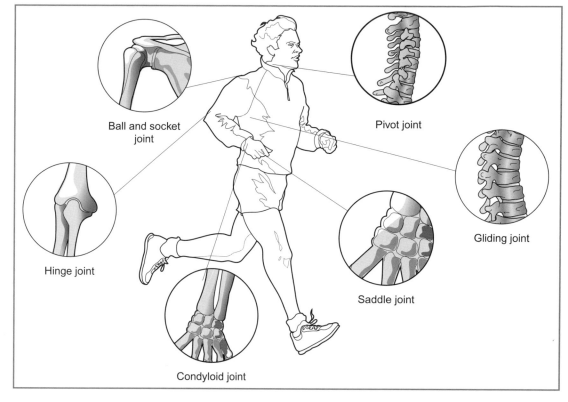

Fig. 1.08 The six types of synovial joint found in the body.

Ball and Socket Joint

Examples are the shoulder and hip joints. The ball shaped head of one bone articulates with a cuplike socket of an adjacent bone and allows the greatest range of movement of all the joints.

Hinge Joint

Examples are elbow, knee and ankle joints. The cylindrical-shaped protrusion of one bone articulates with a trough-shaped depression of an adjacent bone. Movement is restricted to bending and straightening only.

Pivot Joint

Examples are radio-ulnar and atlas/axis joints. The rounded, pointed or concave structure of one bone articulates with a ring-shaped structure of an adjacent bone. Movement is restricted to one bone rotating about its longitudinal axis.

Condyloid Joint

An example is the wrist joint. Similar to the ball and socket joint but it has much flatter oval articulating surfaces forming a much shallower joint. It allows the second-greatest range of movement.

Gliding Joint

An example is in the spine between adjacent bony processes. The articulating surfaces are basically flat and of approximately the same size. It allows a limited amount of gliding motion in all directions.

Saddle Joint

An example is the thumb joint. Similar to the condyloid joint, but the articulating surfaces are shaped like a saddle and both have concave and convex areas. The concave surface of one bone articulates with the convex surface of the adjacent bone and vice versa. It allows a degree of movement in most directions.

TASK 4

Place the six types of synovial joint on a continuum in terms of the range of movement they allow.

Greatest range   **Least range**

⬅━━━━━━━━━━━━━━━━━━━━━━━━━━━━━➡

TASK 5

The spine is a very interesting joint. It has a total of 26 bones, extends from the skull to the pelvis and forms the axis of the trunk. It also carries out the very important function of protecting the spinal cord. The spine is divided into *five* regions and contains examples of *four* different types of joint.

1   Identify the five regions of the spine labelled A, B, C, D and E in the diagram.

2   Name the features labelled 1, 2 and 3 in the diagram.

3   Identify the four types of joint found in the spine, stating clearly where they are found and the range of movement that they allow.

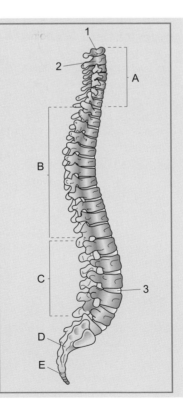

Anatomical Terminology and Movements

The movements at any particular joint are possible because of its structure and the skeletal muscles that contract to pull the bone into a different position. This is explained in more detail on page 20, but for now we must understand that every skeletal muscle is attached to bone at a minimum of two points on opposite sides of a joint. When the muscle contracts across a joint, one point of attachment is pulled towards the other, causing joint movement.

All anatomical movements relate to the **anatomical position** and it is very important that you are familiar with this. Movements can occur *away from* or *back towards* the anatomical position. Therefore, most movements have an accompanying movement that moves the same joint in the opposite direction and are therefore best listed in pairs. There are many types of movement in anatomy, but the ones described below are the relevant ones for AS Level PE.

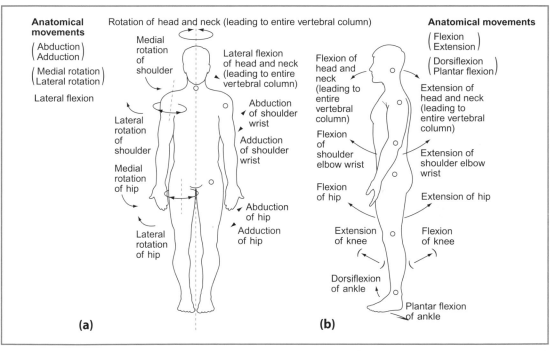
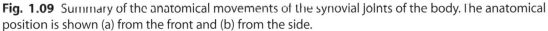

Fig. 1.09 Summary of the anatomical movements of the synovial joints of the body. The anatomical position is shown (a) from the front and (b) from the side.

Flexion and Extension

Flexion of a joint makes a body part move in a *forwards* direction from the anatomical position. **Extension** of a joint makes a body part move in a *backwards* direction. Flexion and extension can occur at the following joints: the wrist, the elbow, the shoulder, the spine, the hip and the knee.

TASK 6

1 Working with a partner, identify both flexion and extension of the wrist, elbow, shoulder, spine, hip and knee joints.

2 For each of the twelve movements you have identified, give a sporting technique that demonstrates the movement. For example, flexion of the wrists occurs in the follow-through of a set shot in basketball.

Horizontal Flexion and Horizontal Extension

HOT TIPS

Remember horizontal flexion and horizontal extension – the fingers are already pointing at the horizon.

Horizontal flexion and **horizontal extension** are movements of ball and socket joints, but tend to only be observable in the shoulder joint during sporting techniques. Horizontal flexion occurs when the shoulder is already flexed with the arm parallel to the ground and the shoulder joint moves towards the middle of the body. Horizontal extension occurs when the shoulder joint with the arm parallel to the ground moves away from the middle of the body.

TASK 7

1 Working with a partner identify horizontal flexion and horizontal extension of the shoulder joint.

2 For each of the two movements you have identified, give a sporting technique that demonstrates the movement. For example, horizontal flexion of the shoulder occurs in the throwing arm during the execution phase of a discus throw.

HOT TIPS

Think about the word 'abducted' when something or somebody is taken away.

Think about the word 'add' in maths when you always add one number to another.

Abduction and Adduction

Abduction of a joint makes a body part move *away from* the midline of the body in the anatomical position. **Adduction** of a joint makes a body part move *towards* the midline of the body. Abduction and adduction can occur at the following joints: the wrist, the shoulder and the hip.

HOT TIPS

Bending the spine from side to side as during a warm up *cannot* be described as abduction and adduction. It is termed **lateral flexion**.

TASK 8

1 Working with a partner identify abduction and adduction of the shoulder and hip joints.

2 For each of the four movements you have identified, give a sporting technique that demonstrates the movement. For example, abduction of the hips occurs when performing the upward phase of a straddle jump.

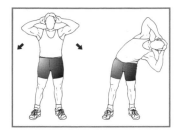

Rotation

Rotation of a joint is when a body part turns about its long axis *from the anatomical position*. For example, when using a screwdriver, rotation is occurring at the shoulder joint as the arm turns about an axis that travels straight through the arm from the shoulder to the wrist. Rotation does not have a separate opposite movement because it can be medial or lateral which are opposite movements. Rotation can occur at the following joints: the radio-ulnar, the shoulder, the spine and the hip.

HOT TIPS

Remember the difference between pronation and supination by thinking how you would carry a bowl of soup ('sup'ination) in the palm of your hand!

Pronation and Supination

Pronation and **supination** are anatomical terms unique to the radio-ulnar joint and are separate terms to describe rotation of the forearm. In the anatomical position the radio-ulnar joint is supinated. Pronation of the radio-ulnar joint makes the palm move to face backwards or downwards. Supination of the radio-ulnar joint is with the palm facing forwards or upwards.

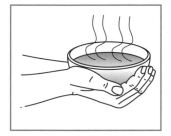

TASK 9

1   Working with a partner, identify:

 (a) rotation of the shoulder, spine and hip joints
 (b) pronation of the radio-ulnar joint
 (c) supination of the radio-ulnar joint.

2   For each of the five movements you have identified, give a sporting technique that demonstrates the movement. For example, pronation of the radio-ulnar joint occurs in the execution and recovery phases of a top-spin forehand drive in tennis.

Circumduction

Circumduction of a joint makes a body part move *from the anatomical position*, describing a cone shape. The joint performing circumduction stays still while the furthest end of the body part moves in a circle. Circumduction can occur at the following joints: the wrist, the shoulder and the hip.

HOT TIPS

To help recognise the difference between rotation and circumduction movements, identify the long axis of the moving body part and imagine there is a pen being held at the end. If the body part is rotating, the pen will draw a dot. If it is performing circumduction, the pen will draw a circle.

TASK 10

1   Working with a partner, identify circumduction of the wrist, shoulder and hip joints.

2   For each of the three movements you have identified, give a sporting technique that demonstrates the movement. For example, circumduction of the wrist occurs when turning a skipping rope.

Dorsiflexion and Plantar Flexion

Dorsiflexion and **plantar flexion** are anatomical terms unique to the ankle joint. Dorsiflexion of the ankle joint makes the foot move towards the shin as when you walk on your heels. Plantar flexion of the ankle joint makes the foot move away from the shin as when you walk on your tiptoes.

TASK 11

1   Working with a partner, identify dorsiflexion and plantar flexion of the ankle joint.

2   For each of the two movements you have identified, give a sporting technique that demonstrates the movement. For example, plantar flexion of the ankle occurs at take-off in a racing dive at the start of a swimming race.

The table below summarises the movements of the major joints of the body. Those in brackets are not as important for your course.

Joint	Possible movements
Wrist	• Flexion and Extension • (Abduction and Adduction) • (Circumduction)
Radio-ulnar	• Rotation i.e. Pronation and Supination
Elbow	• Flexion and Extension
Shoulder	• Flexion and Extension • Horizontal flexion and Horizontal extension • Abduction and adduction • Rotation • Circumduction
Spine	• Flexion and extension • Lateral flexion • (Rotation)
Hip	• Flexion and extension • Abduction and adduction • Rotation • (Circumduction)
Knee	• Flexion and extension
Ankle	• Dorsiflexion and plantar flexion

TASK 12

For revision purposes, copy and complete the table on page 17 onto a sheet of A4 and insert it in your file. The stars indicate the number of points you need to make to ensure you do not miss out any important information!

Joint	Joint type	Articulating bones	Movements possible at joint
Wrist	★	★★★	★★(★★★)
Radio-ulnar	★	★★	★★
Elbow	★	★★★	★★
Shoulder	★	★★	★★★★★★★
Spine	★★★★	★	★★★(★)
Hip	★	★★	★★★★★(★)
Knee	★	★★	★★
Ankle	★	★★★	★★

Revise as you go! Test your knowledge and understanding

- List the bones of the axial skeleton and give one function of the appendicular skeleton.
- Identify the bones that articulate at the shoulder and knee joints.
- Identify the class of joint located at:
  - the joints between the bodies of adjacent vertebrae
  - the joints between the bones of the skull
  - the joints of the leg (hip, knee and ankle).
- Sketch a diagram of the knee joint to show the location of: articular cartilage, joint capsule, synovial membrane, synovial fluid, femur and tibia.
- Describe the structure and function of the joint capsule.
- Describe the structure and function of a bursa and a pad of fat.
- Identify the type of synovial joint located at the hip joint, the elbow joint and the radio-ulnar joint.
- The shoulder joint is constructed to allow considerable range of movement. One of these movements is flexion that occurs during the ball toss in a tennis serve. Identify the other five types of movement that can occur at this joint and give an example of a sporting movement for each.
- Identify the missing information at **A, B, C, D, E** and **F** in the following table:

Joint	Joint type	Articulating bones	Movements possible
Elbow	A	Humerus, radius and ulna	B
C	Pivot	Radius and ulna	Pronation and supination
Hip	Ball and socket	D	E
Ankle	F	Tibia, fibula and talus	Dorsiflexion and plantar flexion

- Identify the movement performed at each of the joints listed in brackets for the techniques stated below:
  - upward phase of a sit up (spine, hip)

- downward phase of a pull up (shoulder, elbow)
- preparation phase of a vertical jump (shoulder, hip, knee, ankle)
- execution phase of a one-handed top spin backhand drive in tennis (shoulder, elbow, radio-ulnar, wrist).

Sharpen up your exam technique!

1 Briefly describe the actions of the playing arm at the shoulder, elbow and wrist during the preparation, execution and recovery of a forehand drive in tennis. Use the table below.

	Preparation	**Execution**	**Recovery**
Shoulder			
Elbow			
Wrist			

(6 marks)

HOT TIPS

For any question on joint movement *always* answer in table form to help you identify clearly the joint movements taking place and will also save you time.

2 Identify the movement occurring at the spine during the performance of a forehand drive in tennis. What are the other movements possible at the spine?

(3 marks)

3 The table below is a joint analysis of the start position for the sprint.

Joint	**Joint type**	**Articulating bones**	**Movement**
X	Hinge	Femur and tibia	Flexion
A	Ball and socket	B	C
Y	Hinge	D	Dorsiflexion

Provide the missing information for letters **A**, **B**, **C**, and **D**. (4 marks)

4 Describe the structure of the hip joint. How does it allow flexibility of movement as well as joint stability? (4 marks)

5 Identify the joint types found in the spinal column and relate their structure to the type of movement and function that they perform. (6 marks)

6 Provide the missing information for the table below based on a physical activity of your choice. (3 marks)

Example	**Joint**	**Joint type**	**Articulating bones**	**Movement**
A	Ankle	B	C	Plantar flexion

7 How does the structure of the knee joint affect performance during sporting activities?

(3 marks)

Chapter 2 **Muscles and Movement**

Learning Objectives

At the end of this chapter you should be able to:
- Describe the function of agonists, antagonists and fixators, and the role they play in muscle function.
- Identify the location and function of the major muscles of the human body giving examples of strengthening exercises for each.
- Understand the difference between concentric, eccentric and isometric muscular contraction.
- Carry out a full movement analysis of a variety of sporting techniques.
- Distinguish between the three types of skeletal muscle fibre in the body and explain how each one benefits specific types of physical activity.
- Recognise the considerable benefits of a warm up on skeletal muscle.

Introduction

Muscles are vital components of our bodies and considerable demands are placed upon them. We are equipped with three types of muscle (**skeletal, cardiac and smooth**). This chapter deals solely with the structure and function of **voluntary skeletal** muscles, but cardiac and smooth muscles are considered in Chapters 4 and 5.

Skeletal muscle

This attaches to and moves the skeleton. It is often termed striated muscle because it has obvious stripes on it caused by the long muscle fibres of which it is composed. It is also called voluntary muscle because it is the *only* type of muscle under our conscious control.

Skeletal muscle is the body's most abundant tissue, comprising about 23% of the female body weight and about 40% of the male body weight. The first part of this chapter looks at the different ways in which these muscles function as members of a group to accomplish sporting movements with the maximum efficiency. We will examine the gross anatomy, i.e. finding out the location and function, of the individual skeletal muscles you need to know about for your course, and how to strengthen them to make your movements more economical. This leads on to the different ways skeletal muscle can contract to exert a force on an object or bone. We can then use this knowledge to carry out a full movement analysis for specific sporting techniques.

The next part of this chapter looks at the role that muscle fibres play in their contribution to movement. This movement could be very powerful such as that demonstrated by a weight lifter, or more endurance based such as that required by a marathon runner. We will look at the different types of muscle fibres and how each is adapted to suit certain types of exercise. The chapter finishes with the beneficial effects of a warm up to the functioning of the muscular system.

 KEY WORDS

Origin

Point of attachment of a muscle that remains relatively fixed during muscular contraction.

Insertion

Point of attachment of a muscle that tends to move toward the origin during muscular contraction.

Antagonistic muscle action

As one muscle shortens to produce movement, another muscle lengthens to allow that movement to take place.

Agonist muscle/prime mover

The muscle that is directly responsible for the movement at a joint.

Antagonist muscle

The muscle that has an action opposite to that of the agonist and helps in the production of a coordinated movement.

Fixator muscle

The muscle that allows the agonist to work effectively by stabilising the origin of the agonist, so that the agonist muscle can pull against the bone without it moving to achieve an effective contraction.

TASK 1

1 Identify *three* differences between skeletal muscle and cardiac muscle.
2 Identify *three* differences between skeletal muscle and smooth muscle.

Muscles and Movement

There are over 600 skeletal muscles in the human body, most of which extend from one bone to another, are attached in at least two places and cross at least one joint. From Chapter 1, we know that muscles are attached to bones by **tendons.** These points of attachment at either end of the muscle form the **origin** and the **insertion.** It is important to remember that muscles can only *pull*, they can never *push*. When a muscle contracts, the pulling of one bone towards another across a movable joint causes movement.

Chapter 1 explained that movements go together in pairs. As skeletal muscles are responsible for the movements, the muscles are also arranged in pairs, for example the biceps brachii and triceps brachii. This is often termed **antagonistic muscle action.** Whatever movement one muscle can bring about, there is another muscle that is responsible for the opposite movement.

Functions of Skeletal Muscle

Muscles perform a specific role as members of a group to produce movement. When working together, they can take one of three roles: the **agonist muscle** or **prime mover,** the **antagonist muscle** or the **fixator muscle.**

In the action of the upward phase of the biceps curl, the biceps brachii, the triceps brachii and the trapezius work together as a group to produce the most efficient movement possible and in doing so they carry out very specific functions, which are summarised in the table opposite.

Muscle	Function	Explanation
Biceps brachii	Agonist/prime mover	The biceps brachii muscle pulls the lower arm upwards when its insertion moves towards its origin.
Triceps brachii	Antagonist	The triceps brachii muscle relaxes or lengthens to allow the biceps brachii muscle to shorten.
Trapezius	Fixator	The trapezius muscle applies a force to stabilise the scapula in order to hold the origin of the biceps brachii still.

TASK 2

1   Apply the functions played by the biceps brachii, triceps brachii and trapezius to the downward phase of the biceps curl. Discuss your observations with the rest of the class.

2   Can you identify the position of any other muscles in the body that might be acting as fixators during this exercise?

Location, Action and Strengthening Exercises

We will focus on the major muscles. Figure 2.01 shows the anterior and posterior views of the musculature of the human body. Learning these muscles is quite demanding. The best way may be to take one joint at a time and for each muscle examine the following:

HOT TIPS

Remember these muscles are arranged in pairs, so whatever movement one muscle can do, it will have a partner muscle that can reverse that movement.

- its location in the body (as in the anatomical position)
- the origin and insertions of the muscle (you will never be examined on this)
- the joint movement that occurs when the ends of the muscle get closer together (i.e. when the muscle contracts and the origin moves towards the insertion)
- one strengthening exercise for the muscle.

It is worth noting here that many muscles are capable of producing more than one joint movement but in the tables below only the main movements of each muscle have been identified to keep things relatively simple. These are the muscles that you will be expected to know about for your course.

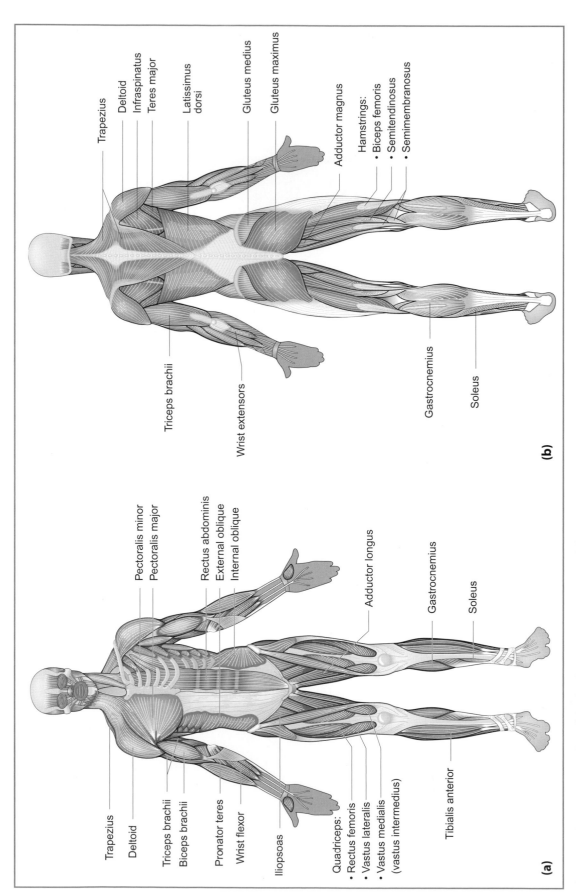

Fig. 2.01 The major muscles of the body: (a) anterior view and (b) posterior view.

Wrist Joint

Muscle	Wrist flexors	Wrist extensors
Location	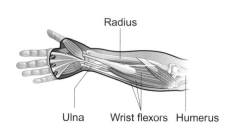	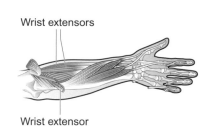
	Anterior forearm	**Posterior forearm**
Origin	Humerus, radius and ulna	Humerus, radius and ulna
Insertion	Carpals, metacarpals and phalanges	Metacarpals and phalanges
Action	Flexion of wrist joint	Extension of wrist joint
Strengthening exercises	**Wrist curls**	**Reverse wrist curls**

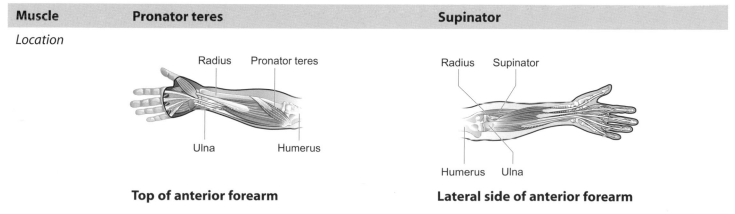

- Sit with forearms resting on a bench.
- With the radio-ulnar joint supinated, grip the weight.
- Curl wrists up towards body.
- Exhale as you complete the movement.
- Return to starting position.

- Sit with forearms resting on a bench.
- With the radio-ulnar joint pronated, grip the weight.
- Curl wrists back towards body.
- Exhale as you complete the movement.
- Return to starting position.

Radio-ulnar Joint

Muscle	Pronator teres	Supinator
Location		
	Top of anterior forearm	**Lateral side of anterior forearm**

continued

Origin	Humerus and ulna	Humerus and ulna
Insertion	Radius	Radius
Action	Pronation of radio-ulnar joint	Supination of radio-ulnar joint
Strengthening exercises	**Dumbbell curls** (downward phase)	**Dumbell curls** (upward phase)

- Sit on a bench holding a dumbbell in each hand with palms facing towards the body.
- Raise one arm at a time.
- Turn palm upwards during upward phase.
- Exhale as you complete the movement.
- Turn palm inwards during downward phase.

Elbow Joint

Muscle	**Biceps brachii**	**Triceps brachii**
Location		

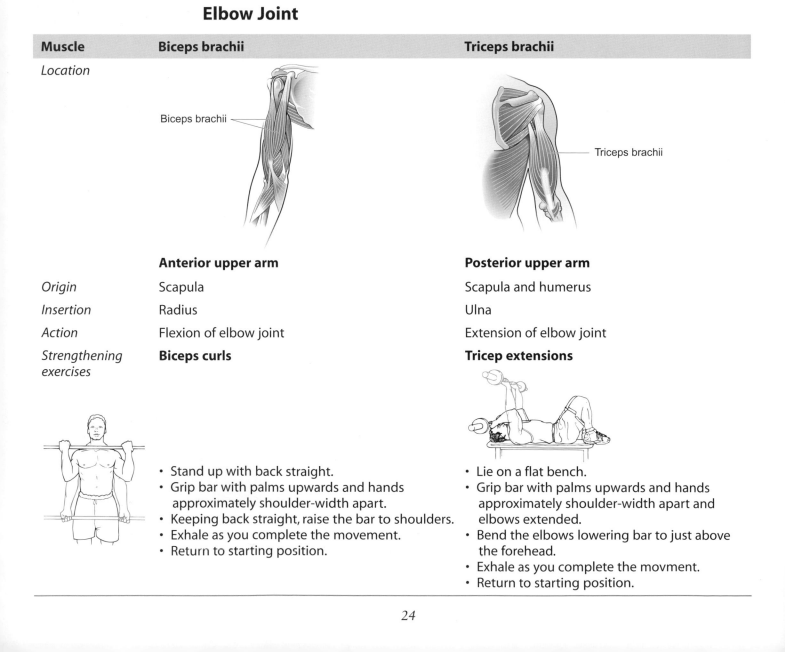

	Anterior upper arm	**Posterior upper arm**
Origin	Scapula	Scapula and humerus
Insertion	Radius	Ulna
Action	Flexion of elbow joint	Extension of elbow joint
Strengthening exercises	**Biceps curls**	**Tricep extensions**

Biceps curls:
- Stand up with back straight.
- Grip bar with palms upwards and hands approximately shoulder-width apart.
- Keeping back straight, raise the bar to shoulders.
- Exhale as you complete the movement.
- Return to starting position.

Tricep extensions:
- Lie on a flat bench.
- Grip bar with palms upwards and hands approximately shoulder-width apart and elbows extended.
- Bend the elbows lowering bar to just above the forehead.
- Exhale as you complete the movment.
- Return to starting position.

HOT TIPS

Consider deltoid muscle in
three sections as shown below.

TASK 3

Describe *one* other exercise to strengthen the biceps brachii muscle and another
to strengthen the triceps brachii muscle. Name *two* types of sports performer
who might benefit from strengthening these muscles.

Posterior deltoid — Middle deltoid — Anterior deltoid

Shoulder Joint

Major muscles you need to know are the **subscapularis** and
infraspinatus, teres major and **teres minor, deltoid** and **latissimus dorsi,
pectoralis major** and **trapezius**. Each section of the deltoid can bring
about a different action: the **anterior deltoid** produces **flexion**, the
middle deltoid produces **abduction** and the **posterior deltoid** produces
extension of the shoulder. You have therefore already found an agonist
for three of the eight movements of the shoulder joint by just
remembering one muscle!

Muscle	Subscapularis and teres major	Infraspinatus and teres minor
Location		

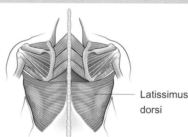

Latissimus dorsi

Cover scapula beneath trapezius

Origin	Scapula	Scapula
Insertion	Humerus	Humerus
Action	Medial rotation of shoulder	Lateral rotation of shoulder
Strengthening exercise	**Bent-over lateral raises**	

- Bend forwards with feet a comfortable distance apart and knees slightly bent. Keep the back straight.
- Hold a dumbbell in each hand with elbows slightly bent.
- Raise arms out to the side keeping a constant angle at the elbow joint.
- Exhale as you complete the movement.
- Return to starting position.

Muscle	Deltoid	Latissimus dorsi
Location	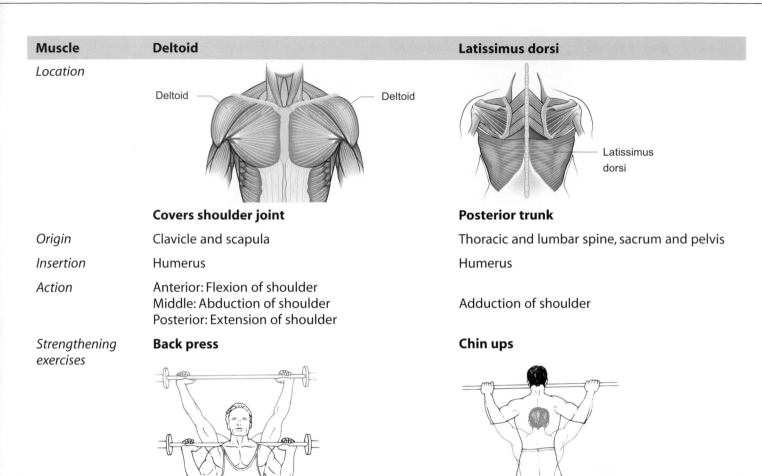	
	Covers shoulder joint	**Posterior trunk**
Origin	Clavicle and scapula	Thoracic and lumbar spine, sacrum and pelvis
Insertion	Humerus	Humerus
Action	Anterior: Flexion of shoulder Middle: Abduction of shoulder Posterior: Extension of shoulder	Adduction of shoulder
Strengthening exercises	**Back press**	**Chin ups**

Back press

- Sit on a bench with back straight.
- Rest bar across top of shoulders behind neck.
- Lift bar directly above head without arching your back.
- Exhale as you complete the movement.
- Return to starting position.

Chin ups

- Hang from a bar with arms straight and hands quite wide apart.
- Pull up until you can see over the bar.
- Exhale as you complete the movement.
- Return to starting position.

continued

Muscle	Pectoralis major	Trapezius
Location	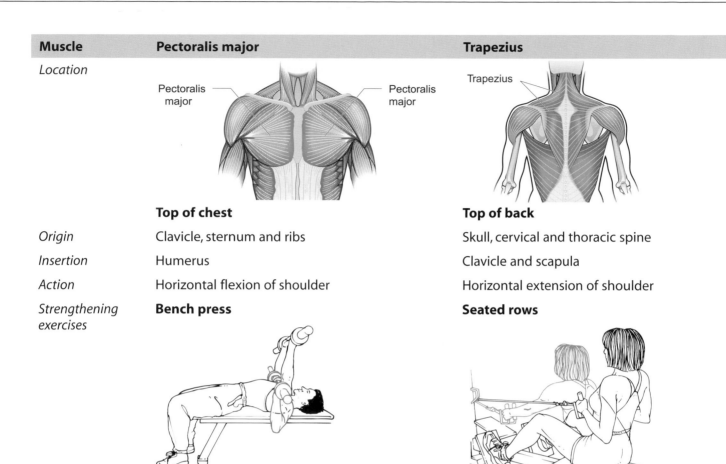 **Top of chest**	**Top of back**
Origin	Clavicle, sternum and ribs	Skull, cervical and thoracic spine
Insertion	Humerus	Clavicle and scapula
Action	Horizontal flexion of shoulder	Horizontal extension of shoulder
Strengthening exercises	**Bench press**	**Seated rows**

Bench press:
- Lie flat on back on a bench with feet flat on the floor.
- Grip bar across chest with arms bent and hands a comfortable distance apart.
- Raise the bar directly upwards until arms straight.
- Exhale as you complete the movement.
- Return to starting position.

Seated rows:
- Sit facing the rowing ergometer machine with feet against the foot rests.
- Grip the handle bar.
- Extend the knees, pull handle towards chest, ensuring that elbows are at shoulder height and travel as far back as possible.
- Exhale as you complete the movement.
- Return to starting position under control.

TASK 4

1 Working with a partner, try to find the eight major muscles of the shoulder joint on each other.
2 Identify each muscle that you find with a sticky label and carry out the movements of the shoulder joint that will occur as a result of these muscles shortening.

Spine

Major muscles you need to know are the **rectus abdominis** and **erector spinae group**, and the **external obliques** and **internal obliques**.

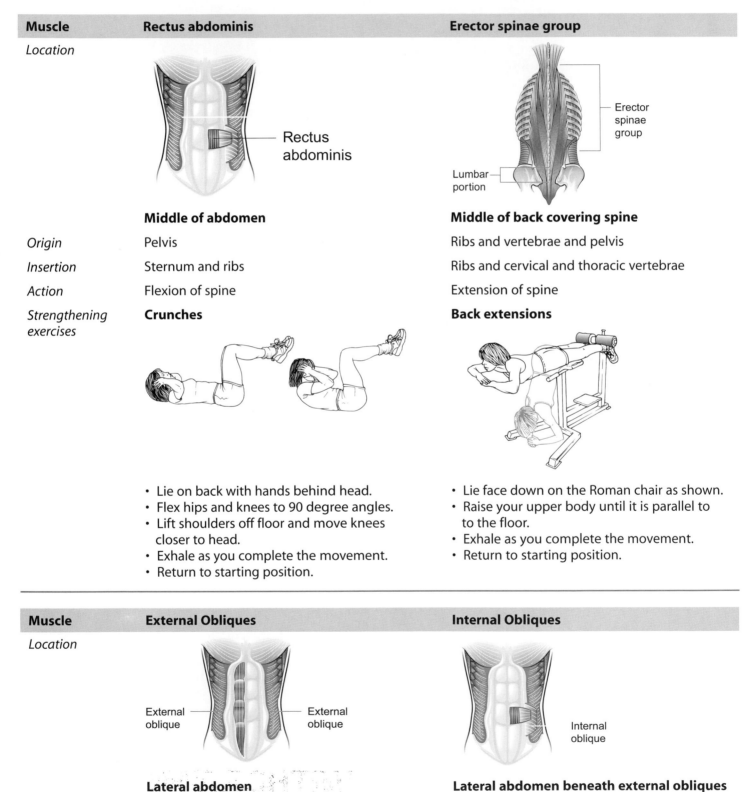

Muscle	Rectus abdominis	Erector spinae group
Location	**Middle of abdomen**	**Middle of back covering spine**
Origin	Pelvis	Ribs and vertebrae and pelvis
Insertion	Sternum and ribs	Ribs and cervical and thoracic vertebrae
Action	Flexion of spine	Extension of spine
Strengthening exercises	**Crunches**	**Back extensions**

Crunches:
- Lie on back with hands behind head.
- Flex hips and knees to 90 degree angles.
- Lift shoulders off floor and move knees closer to head.
- Exhale as you complete the movement.
- Return to starting position.

Back extensions:
- Lie face down on the Roman chair as shown.
- Raise your upper body until it is parallel to to the floor.
- Exhale as you complete the movement.
- Return to starting position.

Muscle	External Obliques	Internal Obliques
Location	**Lateral abdomen**	**Lateral abdomen beneath external obliques**

continued

Origin	Ribs		Pelvis
Insertion	Pelvis		Ribs
Action	Lateral flexion and rotation of spine		Lateral flexion and rotation of spine
Strengthening exercise	**Broomstick twists**		

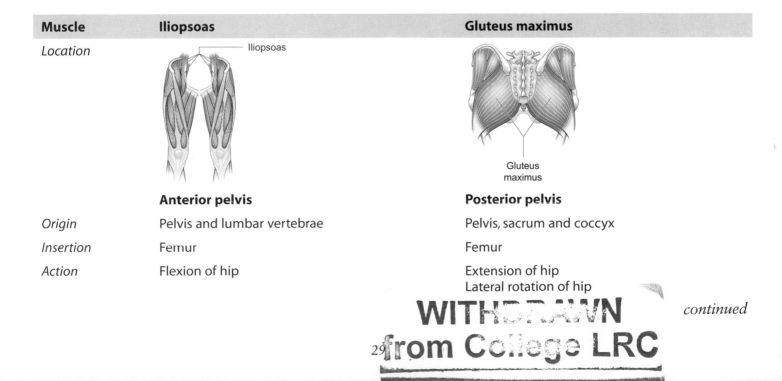

- Stand or sit, holding a broomstick across the top of the back of your shoulders.
- Rotate the upper body from side to side, trying to keep the hips still.

HOT TIPS

The fibres of the external and internal obliques run at 90 degrees to each other. This means that as you rotate your left shoulder forward in the exercise above you will be working your left external oblique and your right internal oblique.

Hip Joint

Major muscles you need to know are the **iliopsoas** and **gluteus maximus**, and the **gluteus medius** and **minimus**, and **the adductor group**.

Muscle	Iliopsoas	Gluteus maximus
Location	**Anterior pelvis**	**Posterior pelvis**
Origin	Pelvis and lumbar vertebrae	Pelvis, sacrum and coccyx
Insertion	Femur	Femur
Action	Flexion of hip	Extension of hip Lateral rotation of hip

continued

Strengthening exercises

Sit ups

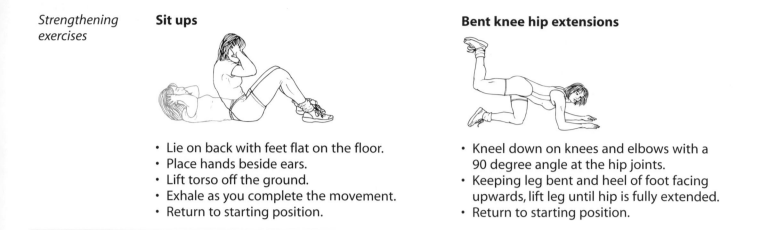

- Lie on back with feet flat on the floor.
- Place hands beside ears.
- Lift torso off the ground.
- Exhale as you complete the movement.
- Return to starting position.

Bent knee hip extensions

- Kneel down on knees and elbows with a 90 degree angle at the hip joints.
- Keeping leg bent and heel of foot facing upwards, lift leg until hip is fully extended.
- Return to starting position.

Muscle	Gluteus medius and minimus	Adductor group
Location	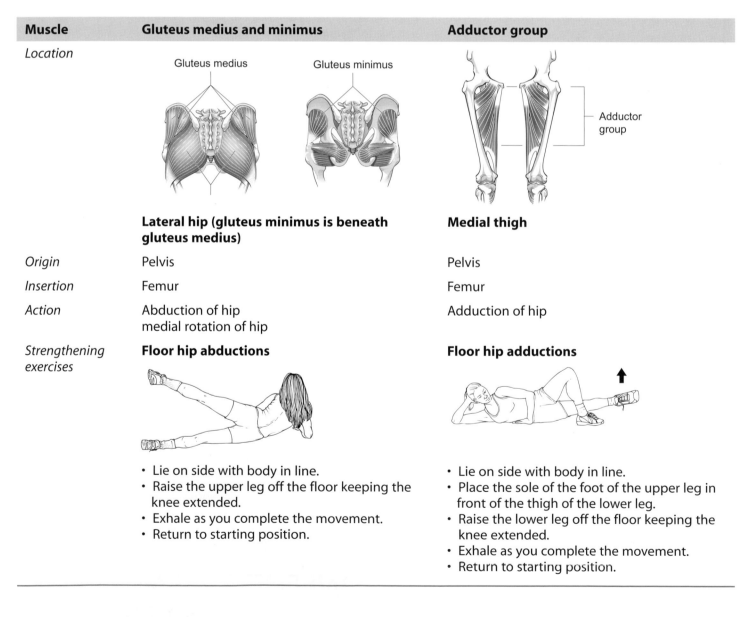 Gluteus medius / Gluteus minimus **Lateral hip (gluteus minimus is beneath gluteus medius)**	Adductor group **Medial thigh**
Origin	Pelvis	Pelvis
Insertion	Femur	Femur
Action	Abduction of hip medial rotation of hip	Adduction of hip
Strengthening exercises	**Floor hip abductions** • Lie on side with body in line. • Raise the upper leg off the floor keeping the knee extended. • Exhale as you complete the movement. • Return to starting position.	**Floor hip adductions** • Lie on side with body in line. • Place the sole of the foot of the upper leg in front of the thigh of the lower leg. • Raise the lower leg off the floor keeping the knee extended. • Exhale as you complete the movement. • Return to starting position.

Knee Joint

Major muscles you need to know are the **hamstring** and **quadriceps groups**.

Muscle	Hamstring group (biceps femoris, semitendinosus, semimembranosus)	Quadriceps group (rectus femoris, vastus lateralis, vastus medialis, vastus intermedius)
Location	 **Posterior thigh**	Rectus femoris · Vastus intermedius (deep to rectus femoris and not visible in figure) · Vastus lateralis · Vastus medialis — Quadriceps **Anterior thigh**
Origin	Pelvis and femur	Pelvis and femur
Insertion	Tibia and fibula	Tibia
Action	Flexion of knee joint	Extension of knee joint
Strengthening exercises	**Leg curls**	**Dumbbell squats**

· Lie face down on leg curl apparatus with knees extended as shown.
· Raise feet upwards bringing heels as close as possible to your gluteus maximus.
· Exhale as you complete the movement.
· Return to starting position.

· Stand up with back straight.
· Grip a dumbbell in each hand with arms by sides.
· Looking straight ahead squat down until thighs are parallel to the floor.
· Exhale as you complete the movement.
· Return to starting position.

HOT TIPS

You must be able to name the individual muscles that make up these groups. Remember that the hamstring group consists of *three* and the quadriceps group consists of *four* muscles.

TASK 5

Identify and describe *one* other exercise to strengthen the hamstring group of muscles and another to strengthen the quadriceps group of muscles. Name *two* types of sports performers who might benefit from these strengthened muscles.

Ankle Joint

Major muscles you need to know are the **tibialis anterior** and **gastrocnemius** and **soleus**.

Muscle	Tibialis anterior	Gastrocnemius and soleus
Location	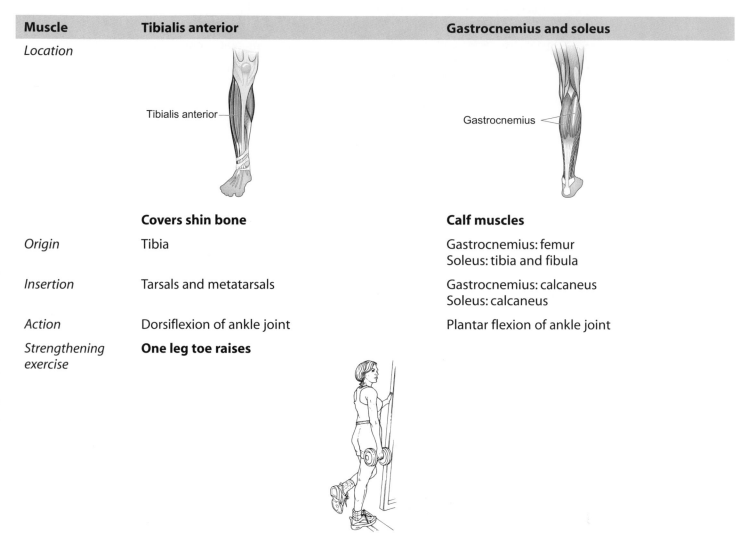 Covers shin bone	Calf muscles
Origin	Tibia	Gastrocnemius: femur Soleus: tibia and fibula
Insertion	Tarsals and metatarsals	Gastrocnemius: calcaneus Soleus: calcaneus
Action	Dorsiflexion of ankle joint	Plantar flexion of ankle joint
Strengthening exercise	One leg toe raises	

- Stand on one foot, placing ball of foot on a step.
- Holding a dumbbell on the same side as supporting foot, raise heel upwards as far as possible.
- Exhale as you complete the movement.

TASK 6

Cut out some photographs of sports performers from magazines or newspapers and label as many of the muscles identified in this chapter as possible.

TASK 7

For revision purposes, copy and complete the following tables and insert them in your file.

Upper limb	Joint movement	Agonist muscle	Antagonist muscle
Wrist joint	Flexion Extension		
Radio-ulnar joint	Pronation Supination		
Elbow joint	Flexion Extension		
Shoulder joint	Flexion Extension Horizontal flexion Horizontal extension Abduction Adduction Lateral rotation Medial rotation		

Spine	Joint movement	Agonist muscle	Antagonist muscle
Spine	Flexion Extension Lateral flexion Rotation		

Lower limb	Joint movement	Agonist muscle	Antagonist muscle
Hip joint	Flexion Extension Abduction Adduction Lateral rotation Medial rotation		
Knee joint	Flexion Extension		
Ankle joint	Dorsiflexion Planar flexion		

KEY WORDS

Isotonic muscular contraction

Where a muscle is exerting a force and changing length. If the muscle is *shortening* during this movement, this is termed concentric contraction. If a muscle is *lengthening*, this is termed eccentric contraction.

Isometric muscular contraction

Where a muscle is exerting a force but there is no change in muscle length.

Types of muscular contraction

There are two main types of muscular contraction: **isotonic** and **isometric**. Isotonic muscular contraction can occur in two ways, **concentric** and **eccentric**. The diagram on page 34 shows, therefore, that there are in fact *three* types of muscular contraction that we need to study and these are explained in more detail in the following table.

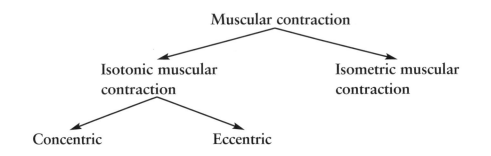

Type of contraction	Description	Practical example from PE
Concentric contraction (Isotonic)	• Muscle shortens under tension. • Insertion moves towards origin. • Occurs in agonist muscle.	**Biceps curl** Concentric contraction occurs in the biceps brachii during the upward phase of the exercise. The biceps brachii shortens to pull the forearm upwards and is the agonist muscle for this action of flexion of the elbow.
Eccentric contraction (Isotonic)	• Muscle lengthens under tension. • Insertion moves away from origin. • Occurs in antagonist muscle. • Only occurs if the antagonist is acting as a brake to help control the joint movement.	**Biceps curl** Eccentric contraction occurs in the biceps brachii during the downward phase. The biceps brachii lengthens to allow the forearm to lower and is the antagonist muscle for this action of extension of the elbow. It applies a brake to this movement to allow the lowering phase to occur under control.
Isometric contraction	• There is an increase in muscle tension but no change in its length. • There is no movement of the origin or the insertion. • Occurs in the fixator muscle. • Occurs in muscles carrying out other functions if they are working against a resistance that cannot be overcome.	**Biceps curl** Isometric contraction occurs in the trapezius muscle during the upward and downward phases of the biceps curl. The trapezius exerts a force to stabilise the scapula to hold the origins of the biceps brachii and triceps brachii muscles in place. There is no change in the length of the trapezius muscle as it acts as a fixator in this exercise.

HOT TIPS

If the answer is 'yes' to all three of these questions, you have eccentric muscular contraction:

Is the muscle lengthening? Is the muscle the antagonist muscle for the movement taking place? Is the muscle trying to apply a brake to the movement?

TASK 8

Challenge a partner to a monkey grip arm wrestle, i.e. hold your arm in front of you with elbow flexed, then join hands with a partner in the same position and try to extend their elbow. Try to choose somebody in your class who is about the same body build as you so you will be fairly evenly matched. As you are carrying out this challenge, consider the following questions and then discuss your findings with the rest of the group.

1 What type of muscular contraction is occurring in the biceps brachii if you are: • losing • winning • equally matched?

2 What other physiological changes may be occurring in the body while you are arm wrestling?

TASK 9

Complete a full joint and muscle analysis for a specific phase of a discrete skill in your chosen PPP activity, for example, the execution phase of the push pass in hockey. Include a photograph of you performing this skill at the correct phase.

Your analysis table should include as much information as possible on your skill and a suggested format is shown below.

Joint	Joint type	Articulating bones	Action	Agonist muscle	Type of contraction	Antagonist muscle
Right wrist						
Right radio-ulnar						
Right elbow						
Right shoulder						
Spine						
Right hip						
Right knee						
Right ankle						
Left wrist						
Left radio-ulnar						
Left elbow						
Left shoulder						
Left hip						
Left knee						
Left ankle						

Muscle Fibre Types

An athlete's ability to excel at endurance or speed work will depend largely on the type of training they undertake. However, it will also depend on their muscles' ability to produce a certain speed and strength of contraction.

If we were to dissect one of the skeletal muscles and study its cross section under the microscope, we would see that it is made up of bundles of muscle fibres.

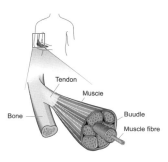

The cross sectional structure of skeletal muscle.

TASK 10

On a single set of axes, sketch graphs to illustrate the tensions generated for type I, type IIa and type IIb muscle fibres against time. Label the x axis 'time' and the y axis 'force'.

Structure and Function of Muscle Fibre Types

The variations in the structure and function of the three types of muscle fibre are best described in the table below.

	Slow oxidative fibres (SO; type I)	Fast oxidative glycolytic fibres (FOG; type IIa)	Fast glycolytic fibres (FG; type IIb)
Structural variations			
Colour	Red	Red to Pink	White (pale)
Size	Small	Intermediate	Large
No. of mitochondria	Many	Many	Few
No. of capillaries	Many	Many	Few
Myoglobin concentration	High	High	Low
Glycogen stores	Low	Intermediate	High
Functional variations			
Contractile speed	Slow	Fast	Fast
Contractile strength	Low	Intermediate	High
Fatigue resistance	High	Moderate	Low
Aerobic capacity	High	Moderate	Low
Anaerobic capacity	Low	High	High
Location	e.g. gastrocnemius of marathon runner	e.g. gastrocnemius of 1500m runner	e.g. gastrocnemius of 110m hurdler
Best suited activities	e.g. endurance type activities	e.g. activities involving walking, running and sprinting	e.g. speed/power type activities

Due to these, slow twitch muscle fibres function predominantly during submaximal exercise, whereas fast twitch muscle fibres are recruited as the exercise intensity increases.

Muscle Fibre Type and Athletic Performance

In the leg muscles of highly trained distance runners, 80% of the muscle may be composed of slow twitch fibres. In contrast, the leg muscles of sprinters may comprise of 75% of fast twitch muscle fibres. Middle distance runners would probably have more equally proportioned quantities of each. The following table shows the percentage of fibre type distribution of slow twitch and fast twitch muscle fibres in a variety of male and female athletes.

In conclusion, it is important to remember that champions cannot be predicted simply from their percentage make up of slow and fast twitch muscle fibres. Other factors, such as training and the efficiencies of the cardiovascular and respiratory systems, are of equal importance.

Slow twitch muscle fibre

Designed for aerobic work, it uses oxygen to produce a small amount of force over a long time. Marathon runners have a high percentage in their leg muscles. Also known as SO or type I fibres.

Fast twitch muscle fibre

Designed for anaerobic work, it produces a large amount of force in a very short time. Shot putters have a high percentage in their arm muscles. There are two types: fast oxidative glycolytic (FOG) or type IIa fibres and fast glycolytic (FG) or type IIb fibres.

HOT TIPS

More recent research has identified a third type of fast twitch fibre, known as type IIc fibres, although relatively little is known about them. The average skeletal muscle is made up of approximately 50% type I fibres, 25% type IIa fibres and 25% type IIb fibres. It is thought that some of this last 25% might include up to 3% of type IIc fibres.

HOT TIPS

Muscle fibre type is determined using biopsy, which involves a hollow needle being inserted into the muscle to extract a small sample of muscle tissue. This can then be analysed to determine the percentage of slow twitch to fast twitch fibres.

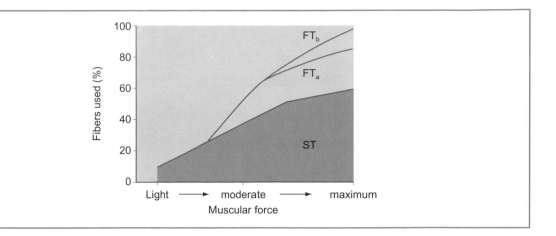

Recruitment of slow twitch and fast twitch muscle fibres.

Athlete	Gender	Muscle	Slow twitch (%)	Fast twitch (%)
Sprinters	M	Gastrocnemius	24	76
	F	Gastrocnemius	27	73
Distance runners	M	Gastrocnemius	79	21
	F	Gastrocnemius	69	31
Shot putters	M	Gastrocnemius	38	62
Canoeists	M	Posterior deltoid	71	29

TASK 11

Relate this task to a world-class sprinter and keep the completed work in your folder.

1 Cut out a picture of your chosen performer.
2 Predict the percentage of slow twitch muscle to fast twitch muscle fibres in their hamstring muscles.
3 Predict the percentage of slow twitch to fast twitch muscle fibres in their external oblique muscles.
4 Justify your predictions, making your comments as specific as possible in terms of the structure and function of the muscle fibre characteristics.

Physiological Effects of a Warm Up on Skeletal Muscle

There is no question that time spent on a warm up will improve performance and you will have looked at warm up techniques when compiling your PPP. We need to look at the benefits of such a warm up on the speed and strength of muscular contraction. These benefits, due to an increase in temperature of the muscles, are as follows:

KEY WORDS

Warm up

Light aerobic exercise that takes place prior to exercise, normally including some light exercise to elevate the heart rate, some mobilising exercises for the joints, some stretching exercise for the muscles and some easy rehearsal of the skills to follow.

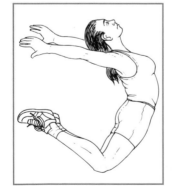

- greater strength of contraction due to improved elasticity of muscle fibres.
- faster speed of contraction due to an increased speed of nerve transmission to the muscle fibres.
- faster speed of contraction and relaxation of the muscle fibres due to a higher muscle temperature.
- increased speed of strength of contraction due to an improvement in coordination between antagonistic pairs because of a reduction in muscle viscosity.
- increased speed and strength of contraction due to an increase in enzyme activity in warmer muscle fibres.
- reduced risk of injury despite an increase in speed of strength of contraction due to an increase in blood flow and oxygen to the muscle.

Revise as you go! Test your knowledge and understanding

- Describe where on the body you would locate the pectoralis major, tibialis anterior, iliopsoas and latissimus dorsi muscles.
- List the agonist and antagonist muscles for the following actions:
    - abduction of the shoulder
    - supination of the radio-ulnar joint
    - extension of the elbow joint
    - extension of the spine
    - flexion of the knee.
- Explain the function of the external and internal obliques when the spine rotates to take the right shoulder forward and the left shoulder backward.
- Other than the exercise given in this chapter, identify and describe one exercise to strengthen the pectoralis major muscle.
- Identify the agonist, antagonist and fixator muscles for the following movements:
    - step ups (flexion of knee)
    - step ups (extension of hip)
    - sit ups (flexion of spine)
    - press ups (flexion of elbow).
- Explain what is meant by the terms 'concentric', 'eccentric' and 'isometric' muscle action and give a sporting example for each.
- A pull up is a controlled movement using the major muscle groups of the upper body. Describe the role of the biceps brachii and the triceps brachii during both the upward and downward phases of the pull up.
- The athlete in the diagram is performing the hang technique during the flight phase of the long jump. Identify the agonist muscle acting on each of the following joints as the athlete moves into the hang position: spine, hip and knee.
- What are the three types of muscle fibre found in skeletal muscle?
- Identify *two* structural and *two* functional differences in the characteristics of slow twitch and fast twitch muscle fibres.
- Why do elite marathon runners have a high percentage of red muscle fibres in their legs?

- Give *two* physiological benefits of a warm up on the speed and strength of muscular contraction.

Sharpen up your exam technique!

1 The figures to the left show an athlete performing a maximal leg and hip press.
   (a) Name two of the muscles acting on the knee joint as the bar is moved upwards. (2 marks)

   (b) Describe the types of muscular contraction taking place in the active muscles at the front and back of the thigh during the upward movement and while the bar is being held up. (3 marks)

2 A muscle can perform different types of muscular contraction. The table below gives an example of concentric muscle action.

Action performed	Joint	Active muscle	Type of contraction	Muscle function
Biceps curl (upward phase)	Elbow	Biceps brachii	Concentric	Prime mover

Using the biceps curl as an example and the table as a guide, analyse another type of muscular contraction taking place during this movement. (4 marks)

3 The table below is a joint and muscle analysis of the upward phase of a sit up.

Joint type	Articulating bones	Movement produced	Working muscle
1	Thoracic and lumber vertebrae	A	B
2	C	D	Iliopsoas

Provide the missing information for letters **A**, **B**, **C** and **D**. (4 marks)

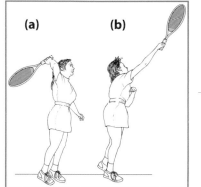

(a)   **(b)**

4 The figures to the left show part of an overhead striking movement. Identify the changes in movement around the joints of the arm from position (a) to position (b), and identify the muscle responsible for each movement.
   (6 marks)

5 The elbow joint produces movement in a wide variety of activities in PE.
   (a) Identify the agonist and fixator during extension of the elbow joint and give a sporting example of this movement. (3 marks)
   (b) Identify the type of muscular contraction occurring at the agonist and give one exercise that could be used to strengthen that muscle.
   (2 marks)

6 A jump is a fundamental motor skill used in PE.
   (a) Identify a prime mover involved and the type of muscular contraction being performed at the ankle joint during the take off phase of a jump. (2 marks)
   (b) How does the role of this muscle change during the landing phase of the jump and what type of contraction is now being performed? (2 marks)

7 The diagram to the left shows the performance of a bench press. Explain the meaning of the statement 'muscles are arranged in antagonistic pairs' and use the upward phase of the bench press to illustrate your answer. (4 marks)

8 Applying knowledge from your practical activities, complete the movement analysis table below. Identify the missing information **A, B, C, D** and **E**. (5 marks)

Joint	Joint type	Articulating bones	Movement produced	Prime mover	Antagonist
Ankle	A	Talus, tibia, fibula	B	C	Tibialis anterior
Radio-ulnar	D	Ulna, radius	Supination	E	Pronator teres

9 The table opposite shows the percentage of slow twitch muscle fibres in the muscle groups of male (M) and female (F) athletes and non-athletes.
   (a) Discuss the reasons for the variations in the percentages of slow twitch muscle fibres in the various groups of athletes. (3 marks)
   (b) The swimmers have a high percentage of slow twitch fibres in the deltoid muscle. Identify *two* structural and *two* functional characteristics of slow twitch fibres. (4 marks)

10 Using an example from PE or sport, show how the functions of either a slow oxidative fibre or a fast glycolytic fibre have an effect on performance. (4 marks)

11 Why would a warm up help the performance of activities involving strong, fast muscular contractions? (2 marks)

Athletic group	Shoulder (deltoid)	Calf (gastrocnemius)	Thigh (vastus lateralis)
Long distance runners		79% (M) 69% (F)	
Canoeists	71% (M)		
Triathletes	60% (M)	59% (M)	63% (M)
Swimmers	67% (M) 69% (F)		
Sprint runners		24% (M) 27% (F)	
Cyclists			57% (M) 51% (F)
Weight lifters	53% (M)	44% (M)	
Shot putters		38% (M)	
Non-athletes			47% (M) 46% (F)

Chapter 3 **Mechanics, Motion and Movement**

Learning Objectives

At the end of this chapter you should be able to:

- Describe the difference between linear, angular and general motion.
- Understand the effect of the application of forces to sporting techniques.
- Apply all three of Newton's Laws of Motion to many sporting examples.
- Describe the mechanical principles that determine different levels of stability and explain why some sports techniques require minimum stability while others require maximum stability.
- Apply your knowledge of mechanics to the analysis of sporting techniques and the correction of errors.

Introduction

In this chapter we will be looking in detail at the subject of motion and movement, which is concerned with the mechanics of movement in sport. You will have learned about the mechanical principles that are used in our everyday lives from your GCSE science lessons, and in this chapter we will see that these same principles can be applied to sport. We will be looking at how the application of the laws of **motion, force, Newton's Laws of Motion** and **centre of mass** can help to produce an improved performance. A basic knowledge of these laws of mechanics is necessary for the *analysis* of movement. Once you can apply these laws with confidence to sporting techniques you will be able to *suggest corrections* to increase the likelihood of successful and efficient movement.

Motion

Motion is movement and is divided into three main categories:

Linear motion
Angular motion } General motion (bola)

KEY WORDS

Linear motion

When a body moves in a straight or curved line, with all its parts moving the same distance, in the same direction and at the same speed.

Linear Motion

Examples of Linear Motion from Sport

One example of linear motion in a straight line could be a tobogganist. All parts of the body and the toboggan are moving in a straight line, the same distance, in the same direction at the same speed.

Fig. 3.01 Linear motion of a tobogganist in a straight line.   **Fig. 3.02** Linear motion of a shot put in a curved line.

Linear motion in a curved line is very rare in human motion but can be seen in a shot put (*if* no spin is imparted at release). All parts of the shot are moving in a curved line, the same distance, in the same direction at the same speed.

Angular Motion

The definition of angular motion is perhaps more difficult to understand. To produce angular motion, the movement must occur around a fixed point or axis, for example, like a bicycle wheel turning about its axle or a door opening on its hinges. When we apply this concept to the human body we often talk of athletes spinning, circling, turning and somersaulting, which implies that the athlete or part of the athlete is moving through a circle or part of a circle about a particular point. However, the most obvious examples of angular motion are the limbs in our own bodies because they move around our joints, which are fixed points. Consider flexion and extension of your elbow joint. You will notice that the lower arm is moving through part of a circle about a particular point – your elbow joint, which in this example is the axis of rotation.

TASK 1
Carry out the particular angular movements below and for each case identify:
- the body part showing angular motion
- the axis of rotation.

1   Tap your foot up and down on the floor as you might when listening to music.
2   Raise your arm above your head as you might when answering a question from your teacher and lower it again.
3   Carry out five sit-ups.
4   While sitting on chairs, kick a ball between yourself and a partner.
5   Keeping your upper arm completely still so that your shoulder does not move, draw a series of zigzags on the board.

Examples of Angular Motion from Sport

Angular motion of the arm can be seen when swimming front crawl. During one complete stroke cycle the arm moves a complete circle about the axis of rotation – the shoulder joint.

Fig. 3.03 Swimmer showing angular motion of the arm about the shoulder joint.

Fig. 3.04 Gymnast showing angular motion of his whole body about the high bar.

Angular motion of the whole body is more difficult to exemplify, but a perfect example would be the giant circle on the high bar in Men's Olympic Gymnastics. The gymnast moves in a complete circle about the axis of rotation – the bar.

KEY WORDS

General motion

A combination of linear and angular motion.

General Motion

Examples of General Motion from Sport

Most movements in sport are combinations of linear and angular motion and therefore this third type of motion is the easiest to exemplify. The approach run of a javelin thrower shows general motion. During the approach the javelin and the torso of the athlete are showing linear motion by moving in a straight line with all parts moving the same distance, in the same direction at the same speed. However, the arms and legs of the athlete are showing angular motion as the non-throwing

Fig. 3.05 Javelin thrower showing general motion.

Fig. 3.06 Wheelchair athlete showing general motion.

TASK 2

1   Using as many different sports as you can think of, list:
   (a)   *three* examples of pure linear motion
   (b)   *three* examples of pure angular motion
   (c)   *five* examples of general motion.

Make sure you describe each example in sufficient detail that the form of motion being displayed can be easily recognised.

2   There are very few examples of linear motion in a curved line from PE or sport. Other than the shot put, can you think of one other example?

3   Using the activity you are studying for your PPP, give two examples for each of the three types of motion studied in this chapter. Try to describe each example rather than just state a particular movement.

arm rotates around part of a circle about the shoulder joint, the upper legs about the hip joints, the lower legs about the knee joints and the feet about the ankle joints.

A second example of general motion is a wheelchair athlete. The body of the athlete and their chair are displaying linear motion as they move along the track, but the swinging action of the athlete's arms and the turning of the chair's wheels exhibit angular motion.

KEY WORDS

Force

A push or a pull that alters, or tends to alter, the state of motion of a body.

Force

A force can perform the following functions:

*   Cause a body at rest to move, for example when we take a penalty flick in hockey, the force we apply with the stick on the ball causes it to start moving towards the goal.
*   Cause a moving body to:
    –   change direction, for example when we return a tennis serve, the force we apply with the racket causes the ball to return to the server's side of the net
    –   accelerate, for example at the end of the 1500m race, the force we apply to the track enables us to accelerate toward the finish line faster than our opponents
    –   decelerate, for example at the bottom of a ski run, the force we apply to the snow enables us to slow down.
*   Change an object's shape, for example when we jump on a trampoline, the force of our body weight causes a distortion on the bed.

The extent to which the forces mentioned achieve the examples above depends on where the force is applied and the size and direction of the applied force. The size and direction of the force will obviously affect the change of motion and this will be explained further when we look at Newton's Laws of Motion (pages 46–47).

The line of application of the force will also affect the subsequent motion and this is better looked at when we have an understanding of the centre of mass (pages 47–49).

> ### TASK 3
> Using examples from each of your two assessed activities, identify and describe five effects that a force can have.

Newton's Laws of Motion

You will have noticed that there is a direct link between motion and force, which can simply be stated as, '*Without force, there can be no motion.*' This close relationship is explained by Newton's Laws of Motion.

Newton's First Law of Motion

This is often termed the 'Law of Inertia' and states that:

> ❛ *A body continues in a state of rest or of uniform velocity unless acted upon by an external force.* ❜

Application

Consider the hockey ball during the penalty flick. A body (the hockey ball) continues in a state of rest (on the penalty spot) unless acted upon by an external force (the muscular forces on the hockey stick).

Newton's Second Law of Motion

This is often termed the 'Law of Acceleration' and states that:

> ❛ *When a force acts on an object, the rate of change of momentum experienced by the object is proportional to the size of the force and takes place in the direction in which the force acts.* ❜

Application

Again, consider the hockey ball during a penalty flick. When a force acts on an object (the muscular forces applied to the stick on the ball) the rate of change of momentum experienced by the object (the acceleration of the hockey ball) is proportional to the size of the force (the ball will accelerate faster with a greater push of the stick) and takes place in the direction in which the force acts (the ball accelerates towards the hockey goal).

Newton's Third Law of Motion

This states that:

> ❛ *For every action there is an equal and opposite reaction.* ❜

Fig. 3.07 Rugby player showing Newton's Third Law of Motion to change direction.

This is saying that whenever an object exerts a force on another, there will be an equal and opposite reaction exerted by the second on the first.

Application

Consider a rugby player swerving to their right to avoid a tackle. For every action (the rugby player pushes the ground to their *left* with their feet) there is an equal and opposite reaction (the ground exerts an equal force to the *right* allowing the player to swerve in that direction).

TASK 4

1   Ask a friend, relative or teacher to give you the name of an obscure sport that they may have heard of or seen on the television. If you are not familiar with this sport then they will need to be able to describe it to you. Write down applications of each of Newton's three Laws of Motion in this sport.

2   Using the activity you are studying for your PPP, give examples that show applications of Newton's three Laws of Motion. Give at least two applications for each law.

KEY WORDS

Centre of mass

The point at which the body is balanced in all directions.

Centre of Mass

The **mass** of a body is the amount of material of which it is made, so it is quite easy to say that a shot put will have a greater mass than a football, as it is solid and therefore made from more as well as heavier material. The centre of mass of a body is the point where all of its mass could be considered to be concentrated.

In uniform symmetrical objects in which the mass is evenly distributed, the centre of mass is found at the geometrical centre of that object, for example a shot put, a discus or a tennis ball. At this point, half of the mass is above and half is below, half the mass is in front and half is behind, half the mass is to the left and half is to the right of the centre of mass. However, centre of mass is not always as simple to locate, as it is an imaginary point that can lie outside the body. Consider a ring doughnut – its centre of mass will be at its centre which is in the middle of the hole!

In the human body, the centre of mass is not a fixed point located in a specific part of the body. Its location will vary depending on body position and, as we will see, it can also be a point outside the actual body.

Locating an Athlete's Centre of Mass

Athletes' bodies are not uniform symmetrical shapes with mass evenly distributed from head to foot. They are made up of bone, muscle, fat and tissue, all of which vary in mass. To complicate things further, athletes demonstrate a considerable range of body positions. In the simplest situation, for an athlete standing upright with their arms by their sides, the centre of mass for a male is about two to three centimetres above the navel and for a female it is slightly lower. This is because, in general, males tend to have more body mass concentrated in their shoulders and upper body whereas females tend to have more concentrated at their hips.

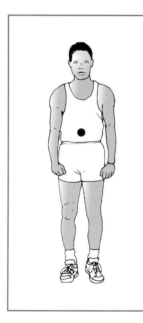

Fig. 3.08 Male athlete showing position of centre of mass.

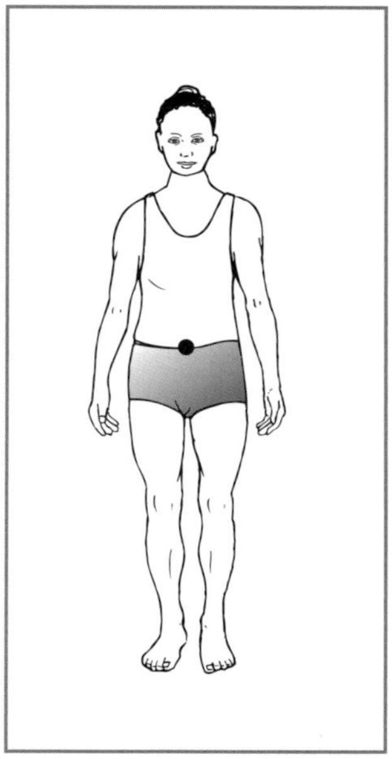

Fig. 3.09 Female athlete showing position of centre of mass.

Fig. 3.10 Athlete showing how the position of the centre of mass alters with changes in body shape.

As soon as the athlete moves from this symmetrical position, their centre of mass also shifts, meaning that an athlete's centre of mass rarely stays in the same position for very long. If the athlete raises their arms, the centre of mass will be higher to ensure that the body remains balanced in all directions from it. If the athlete raises their arms while holding a barbell the centre of mass will be raised even further as a majority of the mass is now concentrated at the top of the body.

Fig. 3.11 Trampolinist showing that the position of the centre of mass can move outside the body.

In extreme body shapes such as a good pike jump in trampolining or a bridge in gymnastics, the centre of mass is a point that lies outside the body. In the case of the trampolinist, the athlete's arms and legs have moved so far forward that the centre of mass has also had to move forward so much that it has temporarily moved outside the body.

TASK 5

Cut out five action pictures from the sports pages of newspapers and identify the position of the athletes' centres of mass in each case.

KEY WORDS

Stability

Relates to how difficult it is to disturb a body from a balanced position.

Line of gravity

A line extending from the centre of mass vertically down to the ground. See figure 3.12.

Stability

An athlete who is kneeling on all fours is more stable than an athlete who is standing on one foot because the first will require a greater force to tip them over. Stability is important in sport as a stable body position will enable an athlete to resist motion, whereas an unstable one will enable an athlete go into action.

The stability of an athlete is determined by a number of mechanical principles that depend on the following:

- position of athlete's centre of mass
- athlete's base of support
- position of the athlete's **line of gravity**
- mass of the athlete.

TASK 6

With a partner, complete the activities outlined below.

1   Ask a partner to take up the following stances:
   (a)   standing with feet apart, one in front of the other
   (b)   standing with feet together
   (c)   kneeling on all fours, with knees and hands spread
   (d)   standing with feet together on tip toe
   (e)   standing in a stalk stand
   (f)   standing with feet apart to the sides.

2   For each of the positions, push your partner with a consistent force:
   (a)   from the side   (b)   from behind   (c)   from in front.

3   Repeat (1) and (2) above, but this time ask your partner to try to resist.
4   Stand with the backs of your shoulders, hips and heels against a flat wall. Bend forwards and try to touch your toes with your hands.
5   Summarise your findings in a table.

continued

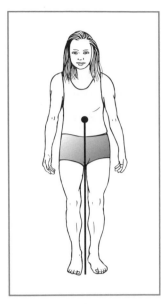

Fig. 3.12 Athlete showing the position of their centre of mass and line of gravity.

KEY WORDS

Direct force

A force whose line of application passes through the centre of mass of a body causing the resulting motion to be linear.

Eccentric force

A force whose line of application passes outside the centre of mass of a body causing the resulting motion to be angular.

6   Discuss your findings with the rest of your class and try to write down the principles that influence stability under the following headings.
- The position of the athlete's centre of mass.
- The athlete's base of support.
- The position of the athlete's line of gravity.
- The mass of the athlete.

7   Using the principles you found in Task 5, place them on a continuum:

STABLE   LESS STABLE   UNSTABLE

← →

8   List *three* stable and *three* unstable positions from PE and sport.

Relationship between Centre of Mass and Application of Force

The direction of the application of a force in relation to the centre of mass will determine whether the subsequent motion of a body is linear or angular.

Linear Motion

If the line of action of the force passes through the body's centre of mass, the resulting motion will be linear. For example, when an athlete performs a vertical jump they apply an action force on the ground with their legs, which applies a reaction force that passes directly through the athlete's centre of mass. This enables the athlete to jump straight up and straight down again with their centre of mass following a linear path. A force that passes through the centre of mass of a body is called a **direct force**.

Angular Motion

If the line of action of the force passes outside the body's centre of mass, the resulting motion will be angular. For example, when an athlete performs a forward somersault on the trampoline, they pike slightly at the hips bringing their centre of mass forwards. They then apply a force on the bed whose reaction force passes behind their centre of mass causing them to rotate forwards. A force that passes outside the centre of mass of a body is called an **eccentric force**.

TASK 7

1   Throw a tennis ball into the air without it spinning. Try to get the ball to travel straight up and down so that it demonstrates linear motion.

Draw a diagram to show the ball's centre of mass, the point of application of the force and the direction in which the force acts. What is the scientific name given to the force resulting in linear motion?

2   Throw the same tennis ball into the air but this time try to get to spin so that it demonstrates angular motion.

Draw a diagram to show the ball's centre of mass, the point of application of the force and the direction in which the force acts. What is the scientific name given to the force resulting in angular motion?

3   Throw the tennis ball into the air a few more times but try to vary the amount of spin the ball displays. Suggest what you must do in order to get the maximum amount of spin.

Revise as you go! Test your knowledge and understanding

- Define 'general motion' and give two examples of it from PE or Sport.
- What does the word 'force' mean? List four things that a force can do and using an activity of your choice, give an example for each.
- Define Newton's second Law of Motion and give two examples of how this law is applied to an activity of your choice.
- Define 'centre of mass'. Explain the difference in the position of the centre of mass between an athlete performing a straight jump and a pike jump on a trampoline.
- Why do you think that a man's centre of mass is higher than a woman's?
- List four factors that affect a body's stability.
- Define an unstable position. What happens to your line of gravity when you fall?
- Explain why a handstand is a more demanding balance than a headstand.

Sharpen up your exam technique!

1   Explain how an athlete can use their knowledge of balance to achieve the most effective sprint start.   (3 marks)

2   It is helpful for a gymnast to understand the influence of the centre of mass when performing a balance. Using a named balance, describe the factors that would affect its performance.   (4 marks)

3   The application of force is essential to maximise performance. Using a physical activity of your choice, explain how an understanding of force can improve performance.   (4 marks)

4   A jump is a fundamental motor skill used in PE. Draw and label a diagram to show the order of lever being used at the ankle joint during the take off phase of a jump.   (2 marks)

5   The effect that a force has when applied to a sports performer can determine the type of motion produced. In each case, use an example from PE to show how you would produce: (a) linear motion   (b) angular motion.   (4 marks)

6   Using examples from your practical activities, explain how knowledge of Newton's Laws of Motion would improve performance.   (3 marks)

Chapter 4: Part I **Cardiovascular System**

Learning Objectives

At the end of this chapter you will be able to:
- Understand the interaction between the cardiovascular and respiratory systems.
- Identify and describe the internal and external structures of the heart, in relation to the cardiac cycle and conduction system.
- Describe and explain the events during the cardiac cycle directly linked to the conduction system of the heart.
- Provide definitions and resting values for stroke volume, heart rate and cardiac output.
- Describe and explain changes in heart rate, stroke volume and cardiac output during sub-maximal and maximal activity.
- Explain how changes in heart rate are regulated by neural, hormonal and intrinsic factors during exercise.
- Investigate, measure and graphically represent heart rate response to varying intensities of workload and during recovery.

Introduction

KEY WORDS

Aerobic

A process taking place in the presence of oxygen.

Anaerobic

A process taking place in the absence of oxygen.

Aerobic System – an overview

Exercise that relies predominantly on the supply and use of oxygen to supply the energy for prolonged performance is termed 'endurance' or '**aerobic**' work. The **aerobic system** which provides the energy for this prolonged work consists of three distinct body systems: the heart, vascular and respiratory systems. These three systems closely interact to ensure a constant distribution of oxygen around the body, particularly to the muscles during exercise.

The marathon and long distance cycling are clear examples of aerobic exercise requiring a good supply of oxygen, but less obvious are sports with different positions/roles. Midfield players in sports like football, hockey or the centre in netball can be termed aerobic as they require performers to run for prolonged periods, whereas forwards or a goalkeeper in the latter sports predominantly sprint or jump, actvities which are dependent on energy supply with insufficient oxygen and conversely termed **anaerobic** work.

So why do we need an understanding of the structure and function of the cardiovascular/respiratory systems? An athlete's **aerobic capacity** – the ability to supply and use oxygen to provide the energy for prolonged periods – is limited by the efficiency of the three aerobic systems. Put simply, an athlete with a low aerobic capacity will be less able to supply sufficient oxygen/energy for their muscles to run, cycle or swim during predominantly aerobic sports or exercise.

Figure 4.1.1 below shows the interaction between these three body systems. Remember, during exercise, the primary aim of the aerobic system is to ensure our working muscles have an adequate supply of oxygen to supply the energy for prolonged performance.

HOT TIPS

Remember, examination questions about the close interaction between heart, vascular and respiratory systems very often require you to combine information from the three systems, particularly the heart and vascular system.

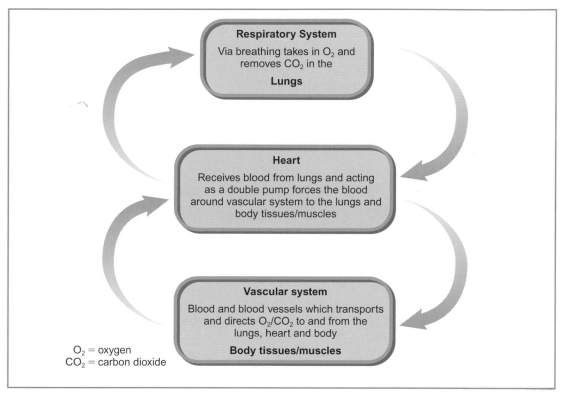

Fig. 4.1.1 The interaction between the vascular, heart and respiratory systems.

Review of Heart Structure and Function

You will have learned about heart structure and function in your KS4 study. However, the following sections will help you review your knowledge so that you can describe and explain the events of the cardiac cycle, linked to the conduction system of the heart.

KEY WORDS

Deoxygenated

Blood depleted of oxygen.

Oxygenated

Blood saturated/loaded with oxygen.

Skeletal muscles require a good supply of oxygen to supply the energy to perform physical activity. Figure 4.1.1 shows that blood vessels of the vascular system transport the oxygen in the blood away from the heart, but where does the force or pressure to circulate the blood around the body come from? This is the primary function of the heart.

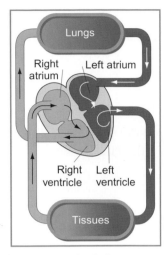

Fig. 4.1.2 The left (oxygenated) and right (deoxygenated) dual action pumps.

The heart acts as a 'dual action pump' – two separate pumps that work simultaneously to pump blood to two different destinations. The right side pumps **deoxygenated** blood towards the lungs and the left side pumps **oxygenated** blood toward the rest of the body – see Figure 4.1.2.

Before we look further at how the heart works as a dual pump, it is essential to have a basic knowledge of its structure in order to describe, understand and explain how it functions.

The heart is located within the **thoracic cavity**, underneath the ribs of the chest, and is the approximate size of a clenched fist. Clench your right fist and place your extended thumb on top of your sternum. Your fist represents the approximate size and location of your heart just left of centre. See Figure 4.1.3.

Internal/External Structure of the Heart

Chambers of the Heart

The heart consists of two pumps, separated by a muscular wall called the **septum**. The left and right pumps each consist of two chambers, an **atrium** and a **ventricle**, which make up the four chambers of the heart.

The left and right atria are the upper, low-pressure chambers that principally collect and store blood before pumping it below into the left and right ventricles. Having only to pump blood directly below, to the ventricles, the muscular walls of the atria are relatively thin compared with those of the ventricles.

The left and right ventricles are the lower, high-pressure chambers that generate the force/pressure required to pump blood around the whole body. The greater force generated requires a greater contraction, therefore the muscular walls of ventricles are thicker than the atria walls. Similarly, the right ventricle only pumps blood to the lungs, whereas the left ventricle pumps blood around the whole body and consequently the left ventricle has a thicker muscular wall than the right one.

Heart Valves

Four one-way valves are situated within the heart and function to:
* control the forward direction of blood flow through the heart
* prevent the backflow of blood within the heart chambers.

KEY WORDS

Pulmonary

Linked to the lungs.

Two **atrioventricular** (AV) valves separate the atria from the ventricles. The right AV valve is called the **tricuspid valve** and the left AV valve, the **bicuspid valve**. The two remaining valves are called the **semilunar** (SL) **valves**. The right SL valve is called the **pulmonary** valve, and exits the right ventricle into the **pulmonary artery**. The left SL valve, called the **aortic valve**, exits the left ventricle into the aorta. See Figure 4.1.3.

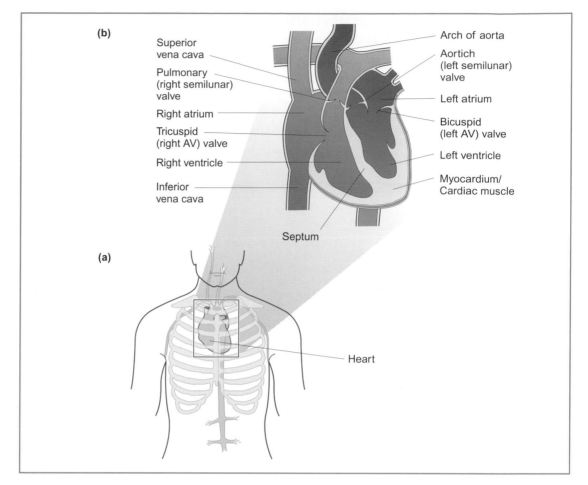

(b)

Superior
vena cava

Pulmonary
(right semilunar)
valve

Right atrium

Tricuspid
(right AV) valve

Right ventricle

Inferior
vena cava

Arch of aorta

Aortich
(left semilunar)
valve

Left atrium

Bicuspid
(left AV) valve

Left ventricle

Myocardium/
Cardiac muscle

Septum

(a)

Heart

Fig. 4.1.3 Location of the heart within the thoracic cavity (a) and the internal and external sructures of the heart (b).

Blood Vessels of the Heart

The heart interacts with the blood vessels of the vascular system to transport blood to and from the heart. These blood vessels are more easily remembered by learning how they link with the internal structures of the heart. The points below show which blood vessels (in bold) transport blood to/from the internal structures of the heart.

1 **Superior/inferior venae cavae** – deoxygenated blood from body to right atrium.
2 **Pulmonary artery** – deoxygenated blood from the right ventricle to the lungs.
3 **Pulmonary veins (x 4)** – oxygenated blood from lungs to the left atrium.
4 **Aorta** – oxygenated blood from left ventricle to whole body.

The heart wall is made of cardiac muscle and, like skeletal muscle, requires a good supply of blood oxygen to and from the heart for it to function as a pump. The blood vessels supplying oxygenated blood to the heart are called coronary arteries and blood vessels removing deoxygenated blood are called coronary veins.

The coronary circulation follows on from the aorta in point 4 above.

5 **Coronary arteries** – left and right branches from the aorta encircle and supply the heart muscle with oxygen and glucose.

6 **Coronary veins** – alongside the coronary arteries, drain deoxygenated blood directly back into the right atrium via the coronary sinus.

TASK 1

1 Suggest reasons why the heart never fatigues.

2 Does the heart work aerobically or anaerobically?

TASK 2

Imagine you are a red blood cell returning to the aorta at the superior/inferior venae cavae. Describe the structural features you pass through on route. Include where you are and what you are carrying.

Heart's Conduction System Linked to the Cardiac Cycle

Now that you have reviewed the structural features of the heart, it is time to look at how the heart functions as a dual action pump. You will have a basic understanding from KS4 that each individual pump of the heart represents one heartbeat, but the more technical term used is the **cardiac cycle**, i.e. the mechanical events of one heartbeat. However, because the heart generates its own electrical impulse to control these mechanical events, we need to consider the electrical conduction system first.

Conduction System

The electrical impulse responsible for stimulating the heart to contract is called the **cardiac impulse.** The heart is said to be **myogenic** – it generates its own electrical impulse. Figure 4.1.4 shows the location of the structures involved in the conduction system and the path of the cardiac impulse through the heart.

The cardiac impulse is initiated from the **sino-atrial** (SA) node located in the posterior wall of the right atrium and is often termed the **pacemaker**. The impulse travels through the atria walls causing both atria to contract. The ventricles are insulated from the atria and cannot be stimulated at this point. The cardiac impulse reaches and activates the AV node in the right atrium which passes the impulse down into the **bundle of His** located within the septum of heart. The AV node actually helps delay the impulse allowing the contraction of the atria to finish before the ventricles begin to contract. The bundle of His splits into left and right branches and spreads the impulse down to the bottom of the heart and then up and

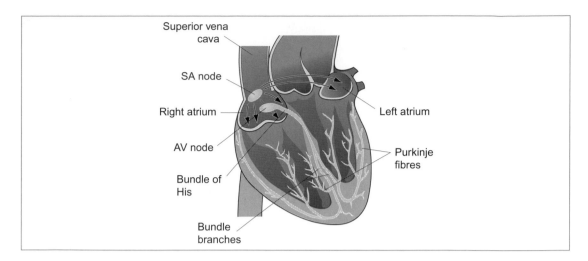

Fig. 4.1.4 Structures involved in the conduction of the cardiac impulse.

around the walls of both ventricles' walls via a network of **purkinje fibres,** causing both ventricles to contract. The ventricles relax and the cycle is repeated with the next cardiac impulse initiated from the SA node.

TASK 3

1 Sketch a rough diagram of the heart and label its four chambers.
2 Draw and number (in order) the structures involved in conducting the cardiac impulse through the heart – use arrows to represent the route.
3 Complete a bulleted flow table alongside your diagram relating the information in the above text to the corresponding numbers in your diagram.

Cardiac Cycle

HOT TIPS

Remember that the events during the cardiac cycle occur simultaneously – what takes place on the right is occurring at the same time on the left side of the heart.

The cardiac cycle represents the mechanical events of one heartbeat. At rest, one complete cycle lasts 0.8 seconds (secs) and is repeated approximately 72 times a minute (min). The cardiac cycle consists of two phases that represent the contraction and relaxation of the heart muscle.

1 **Diastole** lasting 0.5 seconds, represents the relaxation phase.
2 **Systole** lasting 0.3 seconds, represents the contraction phase.

The flow diagram below summarises the phases and sequence of events occurring during the cardiac cycle.

HOT TIPS

You will be required to link the conduction system to the events of the cardiac cycle.

TASK 4

Complete a more detailed flow diagram to indicate and describe where the conduction system in Task 3 intersects the cardiac cycle flow diagram above.

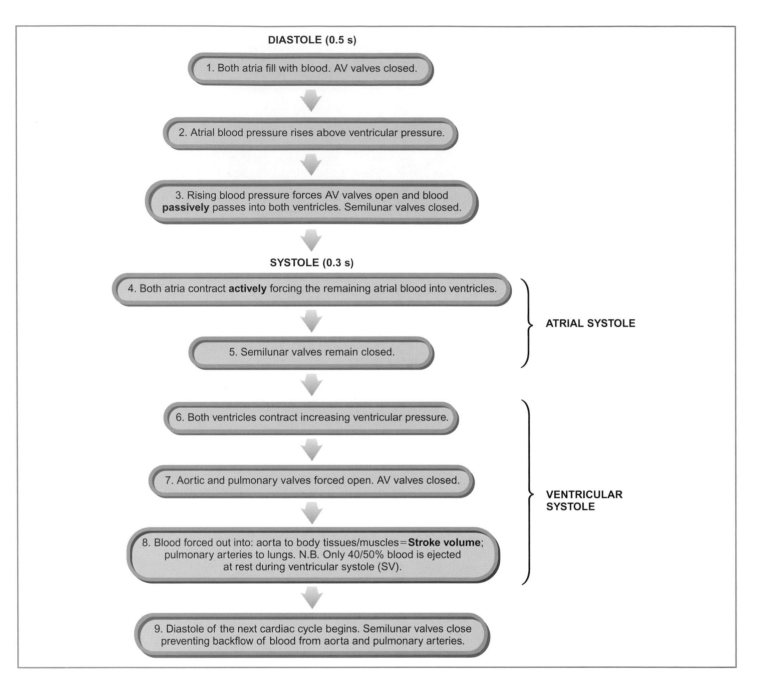

DIASTOLE (0.5 s)

1. Both atria fill with blood. AV valves closed.

2. Atrial blood pressure rises above ventricular pressure.

3. Rising blood pressure forces AV valves open and blood **passively** passes into both ventricles. Semilunar valves closed.

SYSTOLE (0.3 s)

4. Both atria contract **actively** forcing the remaining atrial blood into ventricles.

5. Semilunar valves remain closed.

ATRIAL SYSTOLE

6. Both ventricles contract increasing ventricular pressure.

7. Aortic and pulmonary valves forced open. AV valves closed.

8. Blood forced out into: aorta to body tissues/muscles=**Stroke volume**; pulmonary arteries to lungs. N.B. Only 40/50% blood is ejected at rest during ventricular systole (SV).

VENTRICULAR SYSTOLE

9. Diastole of the next cardiac cycle begins. Semilunar valves close preventing backflow of blood from aorta and pulmonary arteries.

Resting Heart Rate – volumes and definitions

We have previously identified the primary function of the heart as a dual action pump. But how can we measure its performance and ability to pump and circulate blood around the body? Simple, measure its output – how much blood the heart pumps out per minute. The output of blood is calculated by measuring both the heart rate and volume of blood pumped with each heartbeat (stroke volume). Knowledge of how the heart rate and stroke volume interact is vital in measuring the performance of the heart. Let us now look at them in more detail.

Heart Rate

Heart rate (HR) represents the number of times the heart ventricles beat in one minute. The average resting HR is 72 beats per minute (bpm). Your approximate maximal HR is calculated by subtracting your age from 220.

$$220 - Age = Max\ HR$$

KEY WORDS

Bradycardia

A resting HR below 60.

Hypertrophy

Increase in size of heart muscle wall.

Stroke volume

Blood ejected from heart ventricles every beat.

A low resting HR may indicate a high level of aerobic/endurance fitness and highly trained endurance athletes have been reported to have a HR as low as 28bpm. A resting HR below 60 is termed **bradycardia**, meaning slow HR; it is due to an increase in stroke volume caused by an increase in size of the heart muscle wall called **hypertrophy**.

Stroke Volume

When we looked at the cardiac cycle, we observed that ventricular systole provides the force required to pump blood out of each ventricle. The volume of blood ejected each time a ventricle contracts is called the **stroke volume** (SV). In other words, SV is the difference in the volume of blood in the ventricle, *before* and *after* ventricle contraction. The following terms are used to measure S.V.

End-diastolic volume (EDV) – *before*, refers to the volume of blood in the ventricle at the end of the relaxation filling phase.

End-systolic volume (ESV) – *after*, refers to the volume of blood remaining in the ventricles at the end of contraction phase.

The average resting values for EDV and ESV show how we can calculate the average resting stroke volume as 70 millilitres (ml), about half a glass of wine. See figure 4.1.5.

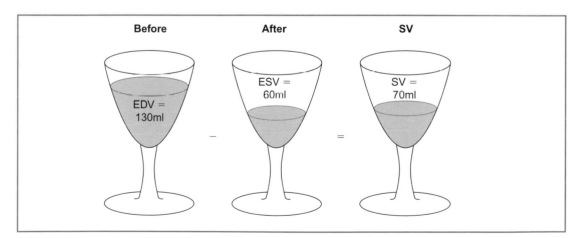

Fig. 4.1.5 Calculation of the average SV at rest. Notice that only 40/50% of the blood in the ventricles is pumped out at rest.

TASK 5

If we know the average resting HR is 72bpm and SV is 70ml we can calculate a third volume by multiplying the above two figures. Calculate this figure and attempt to give a definition to describe this volume.

Cardiac Output

If you have understood the relationship between SV and HR, your definition should read something like: the volume of blood ejected by the heart ventricles in one minute.

This is called your **cardiac output** (Q) and if you calculated the task above correctly you should already know the average resting value is around 5 litres per minute (L/min).

The relationship between Q, SV and HR is summarised as follows:

$$Q = SV \times HR$$

$$(L/min) = (ml \text{ per beat}) \times (beats \text{ per min})$$

HOT TIPS

Remember 1000ml = 1L. When calculating blood volumes, always present figures from 1000ml and above in litres if referring to SV and L/min if referring to Q.

TASK 6

If an athlete has a resting Q of 5L/min, but a resting HR of 60, what is their resting SV? Suggest reasons to explain why SV has increased.

TASK 7

1   Interpret the information in the table below.
2   Suggest reasons as to how and why HR decreases and SV increases in a trained athlete compared to a untrained athlete.

	HR	×	SV	=	Q
Definition	The number of ventricular contractions in one minute		The volume of blood ejected from the heart when the ventricles contract.		The volume of blood ejected from the heart ventricles in one minute.
Untrained	70bpm		70/72ml		5,000ml (5 litres)
Trained	50bpm		100ml		5,000ml (5 litres)

Heart Rate Response to Exercise

In the last section we looked at SV, HR and Q at rest, but what happens to them during exercise? When an athlete begins to cycle or run, their breathing rate quickens increasing their oxygen consumption in response to the increasing demand for oxygen by the working muscles. It is the role of the heart to increase its output in order to boost the rate at which oxygen is delivered to the working muscles. Having identified that Q is a product of SV and HR, we now need to understand how they respond to meet the increasing demand for oxygen, during exercise. Refer to the appropriate graph as you read through the following sections to help you understand the response of SV, HR and Q to exercise.

Stroke Volume Response to Exercise

When an athlete starts running, their SV increases linearly as their running speed/intensity increases, but only up to 40–60% of their maximal running speed. After this point, SV values reach a plateau and this suggests that maximal SV values are reached during **sub-maximal** exercise (40–60%). SV increases from values around 70–80ml per beat at rest to maximal values of around 120–140ml per beat during exercise (see Figure 4.1.6). The wine glass analogy will help you understand how SV increases (see Figure 4.1.7). Remember that only 40–50% of the EDV is actually pumped out at rest – the remainder acts as a reserve volume which during exercise is utilised to increase SV and therefore Q.

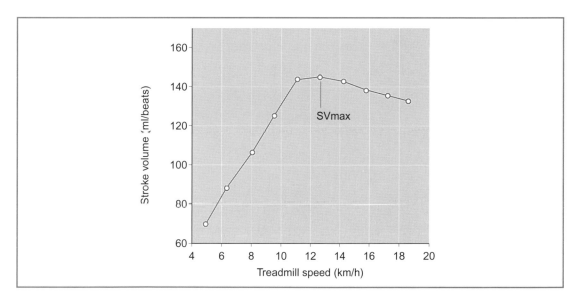

Fig. 4.1.6 Stroke volume response to increasing exercise intensity.

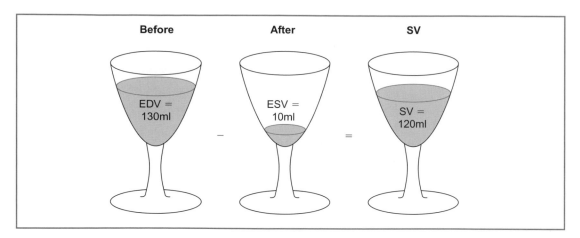

Fig. 4.1.7 Calculation of the average SV during exercise.

To understand why SV increases, we need to identify the factors that determine SV. Put simply, SV is determined by the heart's ability to fill and empty each beat. The heart's ability to fill is dependent upon:

KEY WORDS

Venous return

Blood returning to the heart.

Ventricular contractility

Capacity of heart ventricles to contract.

- **venous return** – SV primarily increases due to an increase in blood returning to the heart (venous return)
- the ventricles are able to stretch further and enlarge.

Together, these increase the filling capacity of the heart and hence the **EDV**.

The heart's capacity to empty is dependent upon:
- a greater EDV provides a greater stretch on the heart walls
- a greater stretch increases the force of ventricular systole (contraction of ventricles).

Together this increases **ventricular contractility** which almost completely empties the blood from the ventricles, whereas, only 40–50% of the blood in the ventricles is pumped out at rest. At rest venous return is lower and therefore less filling and emptying takes place.

Let us continue the example of the runner above. If the runner increases their running speed towards their maximal exercise intensity level, above 40–60%, they will need to increase their Q further. However, their SV has already reached its plateau (maximal value) during sub-maximal work, so what happens to allow Q to increase further? Remember that Q is made up of SV × HR. Hence, any further increase in Q must be due to a further increase in HR.

TASK 8

1   Suggest reasons to explain why:
    (a) SV reaches maximal values during sub-maximal work and
    (b) SV may even decrease as heart rate increases towards maximal levels. Refer back to the timing of the cardiac cycle and see if this helps your reasoning.

2   Compare Figure 4.1.5 with Figure 4.1.7. Describe the changes in EDV, ESV and SV from rest to during exercise conditions. What are the benefits of an increased SV in regard to improving aerobic performance?

Heart Rate

Before, during and after exercise HR is continually changing, but may do any of the following depending upon the exercise undertaken. See figure 4.1.14 on page 70.

- Increase well above resting values even before exercise is started. This is termed the **anticipatory rise** and is a result of the early release of **adrenalin** which stimulates the SA node to increase HR.
- Increase as exercise intensity increases but slow down just prior to maximal HR values. See Figure 4.1.8.
- Decrease as exercise intensity decreases.
- Reach a **plateau** during sub-maximal work and represent the optimal **steady state** HR for meeting the demand for oxygen at that specific intensity of work. If you are out running and you can happily chat away to your running partner, you are likely to be running at a sub-maximal steady state. However, any further increase or decrease in intensity, such as running up a hill, will require a new steady state HR.
- Decrease rapidly immediately after exercise stops due to a decrease in the demand for oxygen by the working muscles.
- Gradually and more slowly decrease, but still remain elevated, towards resting values to allow the body to recover – termed the **oxygen debt**.

We will look at HR response to sub-maximal and maximal exercise in more detail later in this chapter in regard to how HR is regulated.

KEY WORDS

Oxygen debt

Additional oxygen consumption during recovery, above that usually required when at rest.

Cardiac Output

Cardiac output, being the product of SV and HR (Q = SV x HR), similarly increases directly in line with exercise intensity from resting values of 5L/min up to maximal values of 20–40L/min in highly trained endurance athletes such as marathon runners and cyclists (See Figure 4.1.9). Cardiac output primarily increases to supply the increased demand for oxygen from our working muscles.

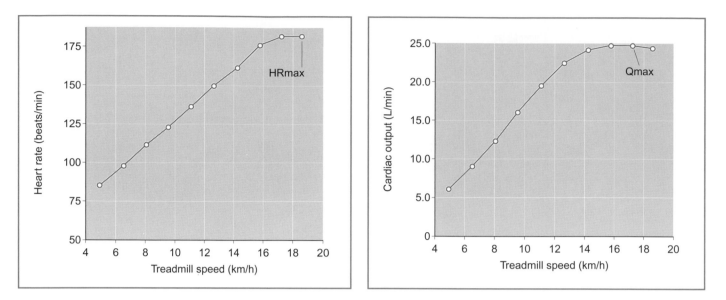

Fig. 4.1.8 Change in heart rate during exercise.

Fig. 4.1.9 Change in cardiac output during exercise.

		EXERCISE INTENSITY	
DEF	**Resting**	**Sub-maximal** **(Moderate)**	**Maximal**
SV	60/80ml 80/110ml	80/100ml untrained 160/200ml trained	100/120ml untrained 160/200ml trained
HR	70/72bpm	Up to 100/130bpm	220 – your age
Q	5L/min	Up to 10L/min	20–40L/min

The table above gives a summary of HR, Q and SV related to exercise intensity. Note that the calculation of SV, HR and Q values at moderate exercise intensity are averaged between resting and maximal values.

Stroke volume, Heart Rate and Cardiac Output in Summary

At the onset of exercise, Q is increased by an increase in both HR and SV. When the intensity of the exercise exceeds 40–60% of an athlete's maximal exercise intensity, SV begins to plateau and any further increase in Q is a result of an increase in HR. See figure 4.1.10.

Heart Rate Regulation and Control

Figure 4.1.10(a) shows that the heart is capable of increasing or decreasing cardiac output to meet the demand for oxygen made by the working muscles, but how is the heart regulated to control these changes? Heart control involves a series of very complex mechanisms that need simplifying to make them easier to understand.

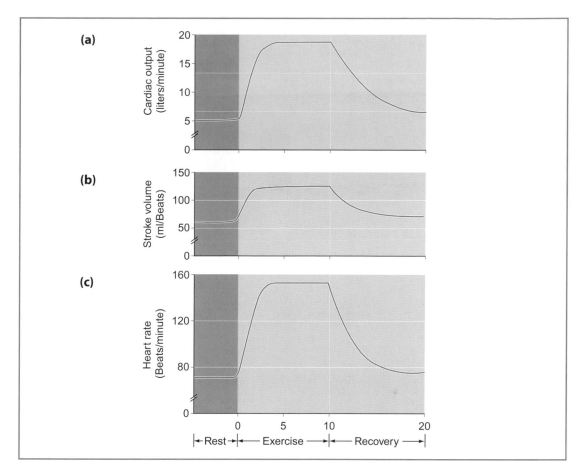

Fig. 4.1.10 Response of HR (c) and SV (b) to control Q (a) from rest, exercise and recovery.

TASK 9

Test your knowledge and understanding of SV, HR and Q by applying them to body position both at rest and during the activities in the table below.

1 What happens to HR as exercise intensity increases?
2 What happens to SV from supine to standing and standing to increasing exercise intensity?
3 What happens to Q from supine to standing?
4 Why does the swimmer have a higher SV?
5 Why has the cyclist the lowest SV of the three trained athletes?

Summary of cardiac function

Active untrained male	HR (bpm)	SV (ml)	Q (L/min)
From: reclining/supine	50	95	5.2
To: sitting	55	70/80	4.7
Standing/upright	60	60/70	4.2

continued

Walking	90	80/90	9
Jogging	140	110	15
Trained athletes			
Fast paced running	190	130	25
Cycling	185	120	22
Swimming	170	135	23

Source: Wilmore pp229–30

TASK 10

Investigate HR response to different body positions.

1 Use a HR monitor or take HR values manually at the radial (wrist) or carotid (neck) pulse.

2 Measure and record your HR whilst lying flat (prone), sitting, standing and during light exercise. Wait 2–3 minutes before measuring after changing posture. If you measure manually count for 10 seconds, starting from zero, and multiply by 6.

3 Complete the table below and plot your data onto a graph.

Activity	HR
Prone (lying flat)	
Sitting	
Standing	
Light exercise	

4 Describe the changes in HR due to changes in body position from prone to exercising positions. Give reasons to account for these changes.

5 Compare HR values between members of your group. Why are there differences?

Cardiac Control Centre

The **medulla oblongata** in the brain contains the **cardiac control centre (CCC)**, which is primarily responsible for regulating the heart. The CCC is controlled by the **autonomic** nervous system (ANS), meaning it is under involuntary control and consists of **sensory** and **motor nerves** from either the sympathetic or parasympathetic nervous system. **Sympathetic** nerves increase HR whilst **parasympathetic** nerves decrease HR. But how does the CCC actually regulate HR?

Each cardiac cycle is controlled by the conduction system by the SA node initiating the cardiac impulse causing the heart to contract. The CCC quite simply initiates the sympathetic or parasympathetic nervous systems to stimulate the SA node to either increase or decrease HR. See Figure 4.1.12.

Factors Affecting the Cardiac Control Centre

Three main factors affect the activity of the CCC (see Figure 4.1.11):

1 **Neural** control – (primary control factor)   2 **Hormonal** control
3 **Intrinsic** control.

KEY WORDS

Motor nerves

Nerves which stimulate muscle tissue causing motor movement.

Sensory nerves

Nerves which transmit information to Central Nervous System, e.g. from receptors to the CCC.

Receptors

Sense organs that pick up stimuli, which are relayed to the brain (medulla oblongata).

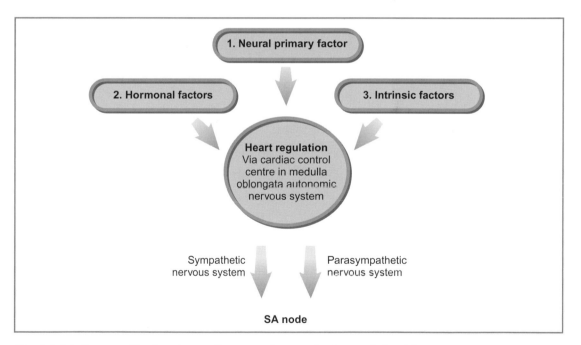

Fig. 4.1.11 Factors affecting the cardiac control centre in the medulla oblongata.

Neural Control

During exercise the CCC is stimulated by the following sensory receptors:

- **proprio-receptors** in muscles, tendons and joints inform the CCC that motor (movement) activity has increased

- **chemoreceptors** sensitive to chemical changes, in muscles, aorta and carotid arteries, inform the CCC that lactic acid and carbon dioxide (CO_2) levels have increased and oxygen (O_2) and pH levels have decreased
- **baroreceptors** sensitive to stretch within blood vessel walls, in aorta and carotid arteries inform the CCC that blood pressure has increased.

The CCC responds to the neural information above by stimulating the SA node, via the sympathetic cardiac **accelerator nerve** to increase HR and SV.

After exercise stops, all the neural factors above are reversed gradually and the CCC increases stimulation via the parasympathetic **vagus nerve** for the SA node to **decrease** heart rate.

HOT TIPS

The CCC response during and after exercise looks at the effects of the sympathetic and parasympathetic nervous systems in isolation to simplify and ease learning. However it is worth noting that the CCC balances the control of both the inhibitory effects of the vagus nerve to decrease HR with the stimulation of the accelerator nerve to increase HR. Hence, the stimulation of the vagus nerve is decreased simultaneously with the increased stimulation of the accelerator nerve. The net effect is a much more rapid increase in HR than if just one of the above occurred.

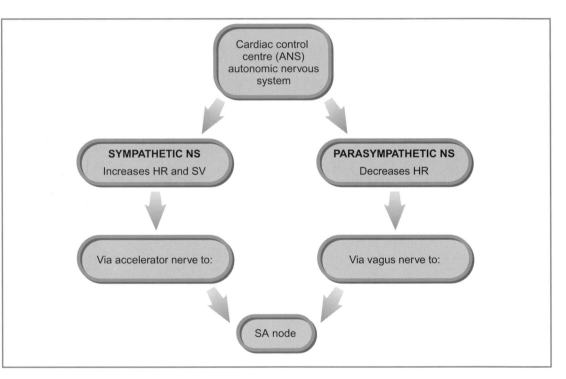

Fig. 4.1.12 Sympathetic and parasympathetic control of HR via the ANS.

Hormonal Control

Before and during exercise, **adrenalin** is released within the blood stream. Adrenalin stimulates the SA node to increase both HR and the strength of ventricular contraction which therefore increases SV.

Intrinsic Control

During and after exercise there are a number of intrinsic/internal factors that affect HR control. During exercise:

- **temperature** increases, which increases the speed of nerve impulses, which in turn increases HR
- **venous return** increases HR which directly increases EDV and therefore SV (Starling's Law).

After exercise:

- temperature decreases and HR decreases
- venous return decreases, which in turn decreases SV (Starling's Law).

KEY WORDS

Venous return

Blood returning to the heart.

Starling's Law

SV dependant upon venous return = any increase in VR causes an increase in SV and Q.

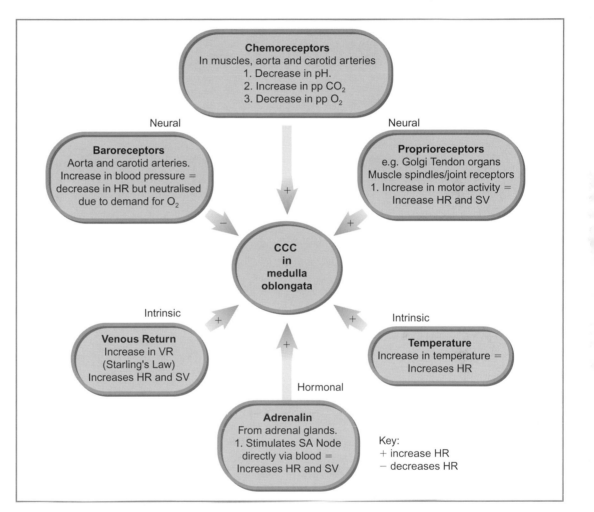

Fig. 4.1.13 Summary of neural, hormonal and intrinsic factors affecting the activity of the CCC.

Heart Regulation during Exercise

We have already established that during exercise the HR increases to supply the increasing demand for oxygen from our working muscles and help remove by-products of respiration. Having identified the factors affecting the CCC and how it controls HR, you must now learn to apply this knowledge and be able to describe and explain how HR is regulated, at optimal levels to supply the oxygen, for both sub-maximal and maximal exercise.

TASK 11

Using your knowledge of HR, the factors affecting CCC and how HR is regulated, describe and explain the changes in HR response at each stage in Figure 4.1.14 for both sub-maximal and maximal exercise.

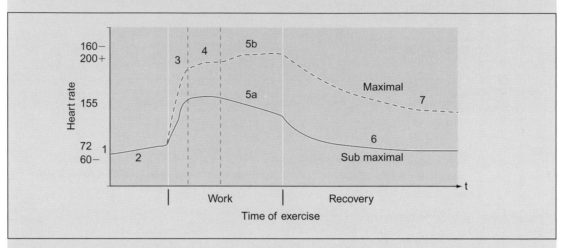

Fig. 4.1.14 The typical HR response to sub-maximal and maximal work. Stages 1–7 show the significant changes that occur.

HOT TIPS

If the table is set up in EXCEL, the graph will automatically format as you input your HR values.

TASK 12

1 Complete the following exercise to record your HR response to varying work intensities.

2 Use a HR monitor to obtain the HR values or take them manually at the radial (wrist) or carotid pulse (neck).

3 Cycle, row or run for three minutes attempting to keep within each of the three HR intensities, as follows:

   • Low = 120–30   • Medium = 135–50   • High = 155–70.

4 Complete the table below and plot your data on the graph.

5 Using your knowledge and understanding of HR response to exercise, factors affecting the CCC and heart regulation, describe and explain your own/your partner's HR response to the three work intensities.

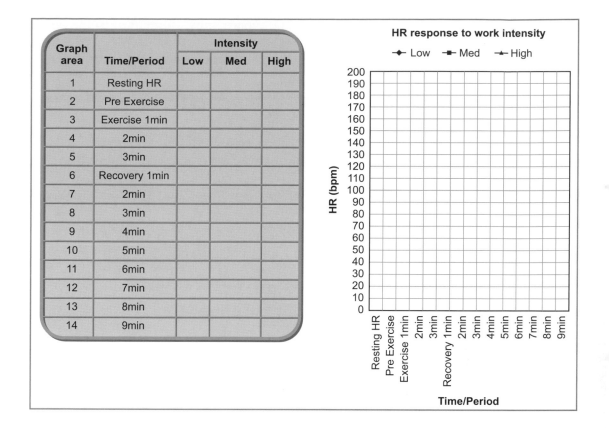

Graph area	Time/Period	Intensity		
		Low	Med	High
1	Resting HR			
2	Pre Exercise			
3	Exercise 1min			
4	2min			
5	3min			
6	Recovery 1min			
7	2min			
8	3min			
9	4min			
10	5min			
11	6min			
12	7min			
13	8min			
14	9min			

Some Useful Guidelines

- Use the table in Task 11 to help identify the area of HR response you are referring to.
- Compare your HR response with the typical HR response to sub-maximal and maximal exercise identified in Figure 4.1.14.
- Use/link stages 1–7 in Figure 4.1.14 to correspond with the table above.
- Ensure you refer to all three work intensities, although it may be helpful to refer to two or more workloads if their responses are similar.
- Attempt to explain any differences between your own and the typical responses to sub-maximal and maximal exercise in Figure 4.1.14. For example, how accurate were your testing procedures in terms of reliability and validity?

Revise as you go! Test your knowledge and understanding

- Sketch a diagram to show the interaction between the heart, respiratory and vascular systems. Use arrows to indicate the direction in which they interact.
- Describe the events and timing of the cardiac cycle.
- Sketch a diagram of a heart to show the route and structures involved in the conduction system of the heart.
- Define the terms HR, SV and Q.

- Explain the term 'hypertrophy' in relation to the heart and its affect on resting HR and SV.
- Use the terms EDV and ESV to account for the difference between SV at rest and during exercise.
- How does the heart's capacity to fill and empty help explain the factors that determine SV values?
- The cardiac cycle is made up of two phases, namely systole and diastole. Describe the flow of blood through the heart during each phase.
- Describe the neural factors affecting the activity of the CCC.
- Describe and explain the contribution of hormonal and intrinsic mechanisms in the control of HR.
- An 18-year-old swimmer uses maximal effort to complete 100m front crawl in a personal best time of 60 seconds. Sketch a graph to show their HR response prior to, during and for ten minutes after the race.

Sharpen up your exam technique!

1   A fit 18-year-old student participates in a fun run and runs 5 miles in 35 minutes. Sketch a graph to show the changes in heart rate prior to, during and for a 10-minute recovery period. (4 marks)

2   Explain the effects of the release of adrenalin on heart rate prior to exercise and why it is beneficial to an athlete's performance. (3 marks)

3   Explain how cardiac output is increased during exercise. Why is this beneficial to performance? (4 marks)

4   The table below shows the response of a student's heart to exercise.

Activity level	HR (bpm)	SV (ml)	Q(L)
Rest	50	100	A
Exercise	200	160	B

Define the term 'cardiac output' and calculate the values for A and B, showing all calculations used. (3 marks)

5   Describe how the conduction system of the heart controls the cardiac cycle. (4 marks)

Chapter 4: **Part II –**
Control of Blood Supply

Learning Objectives

At the end of this chapter you will be able to:
- Draw and explain the pulmonary and systemic circulatory networks and the factors linked with venous return.
- Describe and explain the distribution of cardiac output at rest and during exercise via the vascular shunt mechanism and the role of the vasomotor centre.
- Describe and explain how carbon dioxide and oxygen are carried within the vascular system.
- Describe and explain the effects of a warm-up and cool-down period on the vascular system.

Introduction

Figure 4.1.1 on page 53 shows how the vascular system consists of blood and blood vessels which transport and direct oxygen (O_2) and carbon dioxide (CO_2) to and from the lungs, heart and body tissues. Cardiac output is distributed to the various organs/tissues of the body according to their need/demand for oxygen. In essence, blood represents the substance that actually carries the oxygen and carbon dioxide while the vast system of blood vessels represents a system of tubing that directs and delivers the flow of blood toward the body tissues.

Circulatory Networks

The heart consists of two separate pumps which pump blood to two different locations via two circulatory networks of blood vessels. See Figure 4.2.1.

1. **Pulmonary circulation – deoxygenated** blood from the right ventricle of the heart to the lungs and **oxygenated** blood back to the left atrium.
2. **Systemic circulation** – oxygenated blood from the left ventricle to the body tissues and deoxygenated blood back to the right atrium.

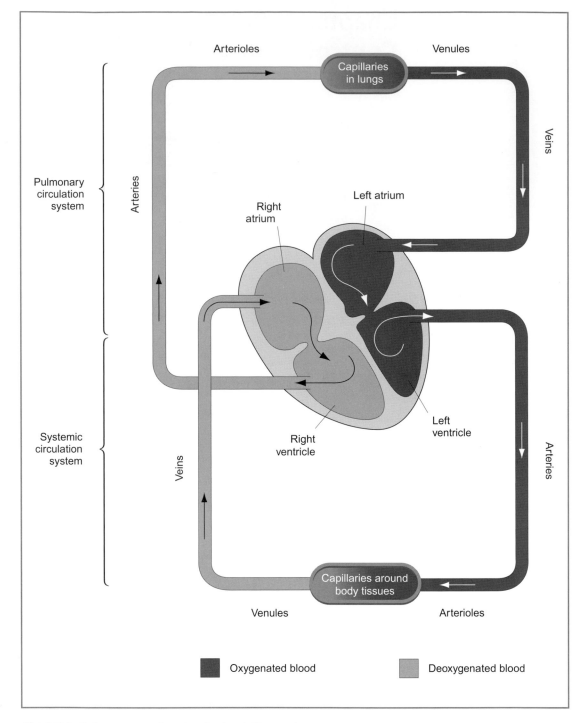

Fig. 4.2.1 Pulmonary and systemic circulation systems.

Blood Vessels of the Systemic Circulation

The interaction and additional detail of blood vessels involved in the systemic circulation are more easily learned as a flow diagram. See Figure 4.2.2.

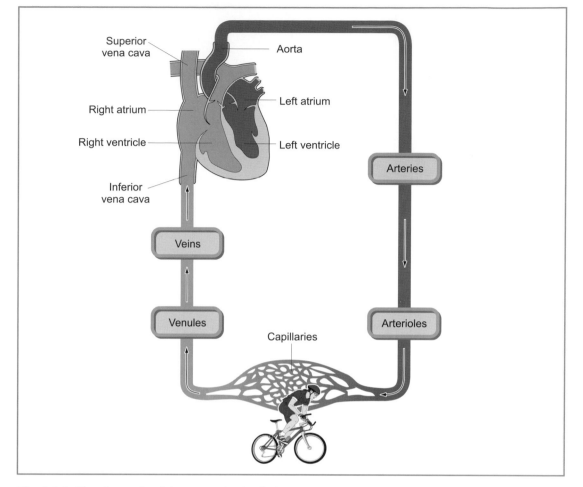

Fig. 4.2.2 Blood vessels of the systemic circulation.

Arteries are the largest blood vessels, and as they spread away from the heart, they reduce in size to become **arterioles** and finally **capillaries**, the narrowest blood vessels. Capillaries flow into larger **venules** and then even larger **veins** before entering the right atrium from either the **inferior vena cava** from the lower body, or **superior vena cava** from the upper body.

Blood Vessels of the Pulmonary Circulation

We previously learned about the blood vessels of the pulmonary circulation when we looked at the blood vessels of the heart (see pages 55–56), namely the **pulmonary artery** from the right ventricle to the lungs and the **pulmonary vein** from the lungs to the left atrium (see Figure 4.2.3).

Considering that arteries, normally, carry oxygenated blood and veins carry deoxygenated blood, what is unusual about pulmonary circulation? The pulmonary artery is the only artery carrying deoxygenated blood and the pulmonary vein is the only vein to carry oxygenated blood.

Remember that pulmonary arteries/veins do not carry the blood normally associated with arteries and veins. Exam questions often use the location of either the pulmonary artery or vein as a starting point to test your knowledge of heart structure.

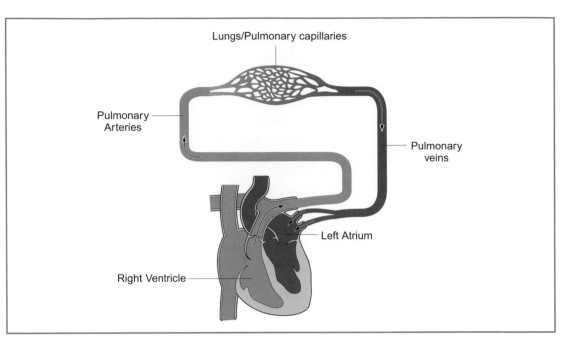

Fig. 4.2.3 Blood vessels of the pulmonary circulation.

Blood Vessel Structure

There are three main groups of blood vessels:

1 **Arteries/arterioles** – which transport oxygenated blood away from the heart towards tissues/muscles.
2 **Capillaries** – which bring the blood directly in contact with the tissues where oxygen and carbon dioxide are actually exchanged.
3 **Veins/venules** – which transport deoxygenated blood back towards the heart.

Note that this is with the exception of the pulmonary arteries and veins.

You are not required to know the detail of the three layers of blood vessels. However you are required to know some structural differences to explain how blood vessels differ in their function, summarised as follows.

* All blood vessels have three layers except for single-walled capillaries.
* Arteries and arterioles have a large middle layer of **smooth muscle** to allow them to **vasodilate** and **vasoconstrict** to alter their shape/size to regulate blood flow.
* Arterioles have a ring of smooth muscle surrounding the entry to the capillaries into which they control the blood flow. Called **pre-capillary sphincters**, they can vasodilate and vasoconstrict to alter their shape/size to regulate blood flow.
* Capillaries have a very thin, one cell thick, layer to allow gaseous exchange.
* Larger veins have **pocket valves** to prevent the backflow of blood and direct it in one direction back to the heart.

Smooth muscle

Involuntary muscle found in blood vessel walls.

Vasodilate

Widening of arterial blood vessels.

Vasoconstrict

Narrowing of arterial blood vessel walls.

Venodilate

Widening of venous blood vessels.

Venoconstrict

Narrowing of venous blood vessel walls.

- Venules and veins have a much thinner muscular layer, allowing them to **venodilate** and **venoconstrict** to a lesser extent, and a thicker outer layer to help support the blood that sits within each pocket valve.

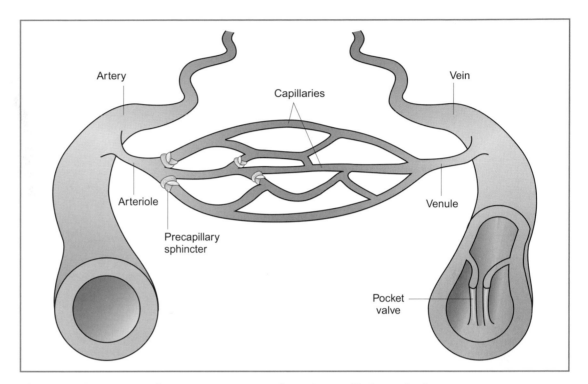

Fig. 4.2.4 Comparison of common structures of arteries, capillaries and veins.

Venous Return

Venous Return (VR) is the transport of blood from the capillaries through venules, veins and then either the superior or inferior vena cava back to the right atrium of the heart. We know that the main function of the heart is to pump blood around the body, so why is it important to understand how and why blood returns to the heart? Let us look at the dynamics of venous return in more detail to find out why.

Starling's Law of the Heart

Starlings Law of the Heart states that stroke volume is dependent upon venous return. Hence, if VR increases, stroke volume (SV) increases; if VR decreases, SV decreases. Remember that SV directly affects cardiac output (Q), so if SV increases then Q increases. So VR is important because it determines SV and Q.

At rest VR is sufficient to maintain SV and Q to supply the demand for oxygen. However, during exercise the pressure of blood in the veins is too low to maintain VR and SV and Q therefore decrease. The body needs additional mechanisms to help push the blood against gravity through the veins back to the heart to increase VR and therefore SV.

Venous Return mechanisms

There are five mechanisms that help to maintain VR.

1 **Pocket valves** – One-way valves in the veins prevent backflow of blood and direct it towards the heart. See Figure 4.2.5(a).
2 **Muscle pump** – Veins are situated between skeletal muscles, which when contracting and relaxing, help to push or squeeze blood back towards the heart. See Figure 4.2.5(b).
3 **Respiratory pump** – During exercise, breathing becomes deeper and/or faster, which causes pressure changes in the thorax and abdomen. This increases the pressure in the abdomen, squeezing the large veins in that area and forcing the blood back to the heart. See Figure 4.2.6.
4 **Smooth muscle** – Contraction and relaxation of smooth muscle in the middle layer of the vein walls also helps to push blood through the veins and towards the heart. See Figure 4.2.5(c).
5 **Gravity** – Blood from the upper body is aided by gravity as it descends to the heart.

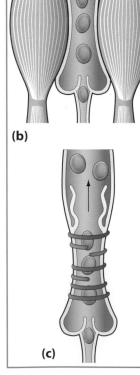

(a)

(b)

(c)

Fig. 4.2.5 Venous return mechanisms: (a) pocket valve; (b) muscle pump; (c) smooth muscle.

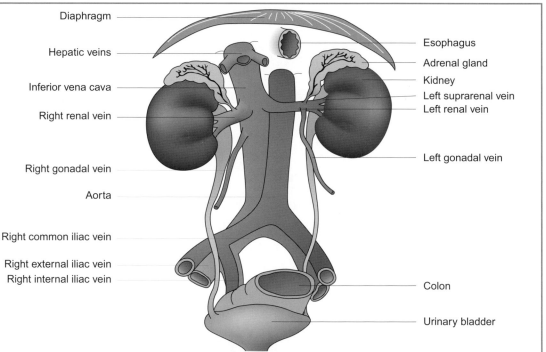

Fig. 4.2.6 Respiratory pump.

Blood pooling

VR requires a force to push the blood back towards the heart. If there is insufficient pressure the blood will sit in the pocket valves of the veins. This **blood pooling** (see Figure 4.2.7) is often described as a feeling of heavy legs. Increased cardiac output (Q) sent to the muscles in the legs actually pools or sits here with insufficient pressure to return it to the heart.

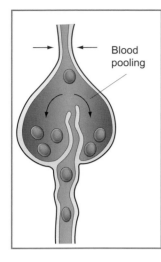

Fig. 4.2.7 Blood pooling.

Pocket valves, gravity and smooth muscle are quite sufficient to maintain VR during rest but not during or immediately after exercise. The additional mechanisms of the skeletal and respiratory pump are needed to ensure VR is maintained. How can we maintain the muscle and respiratory mechanisms? An active cool down helps to maintain these two important mechanisms. An elevated respiration rate maintains the respiratory pump and continued skeletal muscle contractions maintain the effect of the skeletal muscle pump. All these mechanisms help maintain VR and redistribute Q to prevent blood pooling.

TASK 1

Consider the following scenario which is a problem faced by all athletes. A cyclist completes an exhausting high intensity training programme and immediately stops, climbs off the bike and stands against the wall whilst recovering. Feeling light headed or dizzy they faint, falling to the floor. Use your knowledge of VR to explain this sequence of events and give your recommendations to avoid reoccurrance.

Distribution of Cardiac Output at Rest and during Exercise

We have already identified that cardiac output (Q) increases during exercise, but how does the cardiovascular system redistribute the blood to the working muscles which demand an increased supply of oxygen? The process of redistributing Q is called the **vascular shunt mechanism**. Let us first consider the distribution of Q, and then where and how it is redistributed during exercise. Consider the table below.

Distribution of Q during rest, light, moderate and maximal exercise								
Tissue	Rest		Light		Moderate		Maximal	
	(%)	(ml)	(%)	(ml)	(%)	(ml)	(%)	(ml)
Liver	27	1350	12	1100	3	600	1	300
Kidneys	22	1100	10	900	3	600	1	250
Brain	14	700	8	750	4	750	3	750
Heart	4	200	4	350	4	750	4	1000
Muscle	20	1000	47	4500	71	12500	88	22000
Skin	6	300	15	1500	12	1900	2	600
Other	7	350	4	400	3	500	1	100
Total	100	5000	100	9500	100	17600	100	25000

We are primarily concerned with the distribution of Q to the working muscles and in this respect the following conclusions can be made from the table above:

- **At rest:**
  - only 15–20% resting Q is supplied to muscles
  - the remaining Q (80–85%) supplies body organs.
- **During exercise:**
  - increased Q (80–85%) is supplied to the working muscles as exercise intensity increases
  - decreasing percentage of Q is supplied to body organs
  - blood supply to the brain is maintained
  - increased blood supply to the skin surface during lighter work, but decreased as exercise intensity increases.

Figure 4.2.8 simplifies the data in the table above to show the redistribution of Q from organs to muscle tissues during exercise.

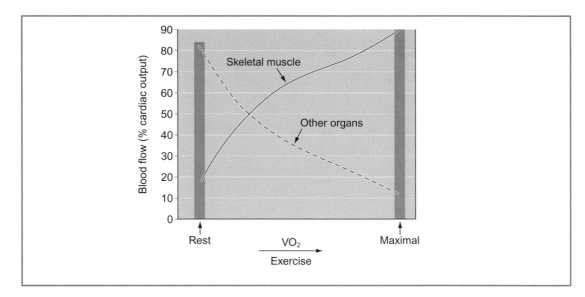

Fig. 4.2.8 Redistribution of cardiac output between organs and muscles during exercise.

Let us use the scenario of the cyclist who fainted after a bout of training to exemplify the distribution of Q due to the changing demands for oxygen from the body tissues/organs.

At rest and prior to training, the cyclist's Q was spread around the body organs and tissues related to their resting needs for oxygen. When exercise began, skeletal muscle in the legs increased its demands for oxygen and blood flow was increased. In contrast, the tissues/organs not directly required during exercise (liver, kidneys, intestines etc.) had their blood flow reduced. Initially blood flow to the skin surface increased to help decrease rising temperature, but as the intensity of exercise increased the ever-increasing demand for more oxygen by the muscles overrode the need to decrease temperature, and blood flow to the skin decreased. Once exercise stopped, Q was gradually redistributed back towards resting levels as the body recovered.

Remember that our cyclist fainted. In immediately stopping and standing, blood pooling occurred in the pocket valves of the veins in the cyclist's legs due to insufficient pressure to maintain venous return against gravity. By immediately stopping, the cyclist switched off the muscle and respiratory pump mechanisms of venous return. As venous return decreased, SV and therefore Q decreased (Starling's Law) and reduced blood pressure thus threatening the blood supply to the brain which simply responded by making the cyclist dizzy/faint. The cyclist fell which lowered the head, which aided venous return and therefore blood pressure and Q, restoring blood flow to the brain. Recall that an active cool-down is essential to maintain venous return and prevent blood pooling.

Vasomotor Control Centre

The vascular shunt mechanism redistributes Q during rest and exercise, but how is this controlled? The **Vasomotor Control Centre** (VCC) located in the **medulla oblongata** of the brain stimulates the sympathetic nervous system to either vasodilate or vasconstrict the precapillary sphincters and arterioles supplying muscles and organs. Vasomotor control works very much in the same manner as in the **CCC**. The VCC receives information from:

- **chemoreceptors** in muscles, aorta and carotid arteries. These inform the VCC that lactic acid and carbon dioxide levels have increased and oxygen and pH levels have decreased
- **baroreceptors** in aorta and carotid arteries. These inform the VCC that systolic blood pressure has increased/decreased.

Sympathetic Nervous System

When the VCC receives this information, it responds by sending messages via the sympathetic nervous system. Recall that when we looked at the structure of the blood vessels we learned that they have a middle layer of smooth muscle which is able to vasoconstrict or vasodilate. Importantly, arterioles are the blood vessels primarily responsible for the vascular shunt mechanism. In relation to their overall size, they have the thickest muscular layer; they are vast in number and have rings of smooth muscle called precapillary sphincters, which lie at the opening of capillaries. The arterial blood vessels are always in a state of slight contraction, known as **vasomotor tone**, but during exercise the VCC is able to control blood flow to organs and muscles in the following way.

KEY WORDS

Chemoreceptors

A sensory receptor that is selective for a chemical substance.

Baroreceptors

A sensory receptor that responds to pressure or stretch. Refers to the blood pressure receptors of the carotid artery and aorta.

pH level

A measure of acidity. A low pH = high acidity, and vice versa.

Organs (during exercise)

The VCC controls blood flow by increasing sympathetic stimulation which vasoconstricts the arterioles and precapillary sphincters which both decreases and distributes blood flow away from the non-essential capillaries of the organs.

Muscles (during exercise)

The VCC controls blood flow by decreasing sympathetic stimulation which vasodilates the arterioles and precapillary sphincters which both increases and distributes blood flow toward the capillaries of the working muscles.

HOT TIPS

In explaining the vascular shunt mechanism during exercise, there are up to four marks available. Two marks are for vasodilation (one for arterioles of muscles; one for precapillary sphincters of muscles). Two marks are for vasoconstriction (one for arterioles of organs; one for precapillary sphincters of organs).

TASK 2

Sketch a summary flow diagram to describe and explain the control of the vascular shunt mechanism. Starting from rest, include the factors affecting the VCC and how it controls the redistribution of blood flow during exercise.

Oxygen and Carbon Dioxide Transport

We have already identified that Q increases with exercise intensity and that blood carries the oxygen demanded by our working muscles. But how is oxygen and carbon dioxide carried in the blood, and does the supply of oxygen and removal of carbon dioxide limit performance? Blood consists of 45% blood cells and 55% plasma. It is within these substances that oxygen and carbon dioxide are transported.

Fig. 4.2.9 Each haemoglobin molecule can carry four molecules of oxygen.

Oxygen transport is achieved in two ways:

- (97%) transported within the protein, **haemoglobin**, packed with red blood cells, as **oxyhaemoglobin** (HbO_2)
- (3%) within blood plasma.

Having a high affinity for oxygen, haemoglobin happily combines with oxygen when it is available and just as importantly, it readily gives up oxygen to tissues where oxygen concentrations are low. Each haemoglobin molecule can carry four molecules of oxygen (see Figure 4.2.9).

Carbon dioxide transport is achieved in three ways:

- (70%) combined with water within red blood cells as **carbonic acid**
- (23%) combined with haemoglobin as **carbaminohaemoglobin** ($HbCO_2$)
- (7%) dissolved in plasma.

Recall from the introduction to Chapter 4 that the efficiency of the CV system to deliver oxygen affects performance. The actual transport of oxygen is therefore essential in that an efficient heart is very much wasted unless the blood it is pumping is carrying sufficient oxygen to meet the needs of the working muscles.

Warm-up – effects on vascular system

It has always been a recommendation for athletes to complete a warm-up before they participate in exercise, but generally on grounds of reducing the risk of injury. You will be required to explain the benefits of a warm-up specifically in regard to the vascular system, which are as follows:

- Gradual increase in blood flow/Q due to the vascular shunt mechanism via:
  - vasoconstriction of arterioles/precapillary sphincters to organs decreasing blood flow to organs and therefore increasing blood flow to working muscles
  - vasodilation of muscle arterioles/precapillary sphincters increasing blood flow delivery to working muscles.

- Increased body/muscle temperature causing a more rapid increase in transport of the **enzymes** required for energy systems and muscle contraction.

- Increase in body/muscle temperature which:
  - decreases **blood viscosity**, improving blood flow to working muscles
  - increases the dissociation of oxygen from haemoglobin in muscle tissues.

- Decrease **OBLA** (onset of blood lactic acid) due to the early onset of anaerobic work when a warm-up is not carried out.

Cool-down – effects on vascular system

It has also always been a recommendation for athletes to complete a cool-down after exercise, generally on grounds of reducing the risk of injury. We have already established that a cool-down should be active, but you will be required to explain the benefits of an active cool-down specifically in regard to the vascular system, which are as follows:

- Keeps metabolic activity elevated which gradually decreases HR and respiration.
- Maintains respiratory/muscle pumps which:
  - prevent blood pooling in veins
  - maintain venous return.
- Maintains blood flow (SV and Q) to supply oxygen maintaining blood pressure.
- Keeps capillaries dilated to flush muscles with oxygenated blood, which increases the removal of blood and muscle lacic acid and carbon dioxide.

Revise as you go! Test your knowledge and understanding

- Sketch and label a diagram to show the two circulatory systems of the vascular system and the blood vessels that blood will flow through as it travels around these two circulatory networks.
- Draw a table listing the structural characteristics of an arteriole, capillary and vein and their functions as blood vessels within the vascular system.
- Define 'venous return'. Describe the mechanics of venous return during exercise.

- Define Starling's Law of the heart.
- Sketch a diagram to summarise the redistribution of cardiac output from rest and during exercise. What is the process of blood redistribution called?
- Explain how oxygen is transported in the blood and why this affects performance during physical activity.
- Describe how the redistribution of Q is regulated during exercise.
- What are the benefits of a warm-up to the vascular system of an athlete prior to them engaging in physical activity?

Sharpen up your exam technique!

1   Why is cooling-down following exercise important for the vascular system?

(2 marks)

2   Explain how carbon dioxide is transported in the blood and why that affects performance during physical activity.   (6 marks)

3   Give two mechanisms by which a large percentage of cardiac output is distributed to the working muscles during exercise. Explain why this distribution occurs.   (4 marks)

4   Explain why a good venous return is beneficial to performance.   (3 marks)

5   Why would a warm up be of benefit to the vascular system of a swimmer?

(2 marks)

6   The heart acts as two completely separate pumps responsible for two circulatory networks of blood vessels. Draw and label a diagram to show the two circulatory networks.   (5 marks)

Chapter 5 **Respiratory System**

Learning Objectives

At the end of this chapter you will be able to:
- Review your knowledge of the respiratory structures.
- Describe and explain the mechanics of breathing at rest and the respiratory muscles, including the diaphragm and external intercostals, involved.
- Provide definitions and resting values for respiratory volumes at rest.
- Describe and explain the process of gaseous exchange in the lungs and tissues with an awareness of the role played by partial pressures.
- Identify and explain the changes in the mechanics of breathing, including the additional muscles involved and the active nature of expiration, during exercise.
- Describe and explain the subsequent changes in resting lung volumes with typical values for sub-maximal and maximal work.
- Explain the changes in gaseous exchange, including the increased diffusion gradient and accelerated dissociation of oxy-haemoglobin, in the lungs and tissue.
- Explain how the respiratory control centre regulates changes in lung volumes by both neural and chemical control during exercise.
- Describe and account for the effect of altitude on the respiratory system and how this influences performance during exercise.

Introduction

Oxygen is essential to produce the energy to fuel all our bodies' activities. Endurance performance depends on the supply of oxygen and removal of carbon dioxide from our working muscles. The primary aim of the respiratory system is to bring blood into contact with atmospheric air so that oxygen can be taken in and carbon dioxide removed.

The respiratory system performs three main processes which are linked via the heart and vascular system.

1 **Pulmonary ventilation** – the breathing of air into and out of the lungs.
2 **External respiration** – exchange of oxygen and carbon dioxide between the lungs and blood.

These processes are linked to the third by the transport of oxygen and carbon dioxide in the blood to the heart and around the systemic and pulmonary circulation.

3 **Internal respiration** – exchange of oxygen and carbon dioxide between the blood and the muscle tissues.

The respiratory processes are just as important as the heart and vascular system. It is no use having an efficient pump and transport network if the blood it carries has insufficient oxygen to produce the energy for the muscles to work.

First we will review the respiratory structures and then look at the resting mechanics of breathing, the processes of how oxygen and carbon dioxide are exchanged in the lungs and tissues, and respiratory volumes. Finally we will identify the changes in the mechanics of breathing, respiratory volumes and gaseous exchange during exercise, identify how they are regulated and consider their impact on performance, including at altitude.

Review of Respiratory Structures

You will have learned about respiratory structures in your KS4 study. However, the following section will help you review your knowledge so that you can describe and explain the efficiency of the respiratory system with reference to the mechanics of breathing and external respiration.

Pulmonary ventilation, i.e. breathing in and out, follows a common pathway through the respiratory structures before oxygen (O_2) and carbon dioxide (CO_2) is exchanged in the lungs. See figure 5.01. The action of breathing through the nose has the advantage of helping to moisten, filter and warm up air aided by the ciliated mucus lining and blood capillaries within the walls of the respiratory structure, before it enters the lungs, which improves the exchange of oxygen and carbon dioxide.

TASK 1

Put the following structures in order to show the route of atmospheric air to the site where gaseous exchange takes place: nose/trachea, mouth, alveolus, larynx, pharynx, oral cavity, alveoli sacs, left and right bronchi, nasal cavity, lungs, bronchioles.

Lobes of the Lungs

Lobes are simply divisions of each lung. Notice that in figure 5.01 the right lung has three lobes and the left two – this is to accommodate the location of the heart.

The left and right **bronchi** branch further into **bronchioles**, which branch into each lobe of the lungs. Bronchioles terminate into **alveoli ducts** leading to **alveoli sacs** or grape-like clusters of tiny air sacs. Each individual air sac is called an **alveolus** and is the actual site of gas exchange. We need to look at their structure in more detail to understand how they function to allow the exchange of oxygen and carbon dioxide.

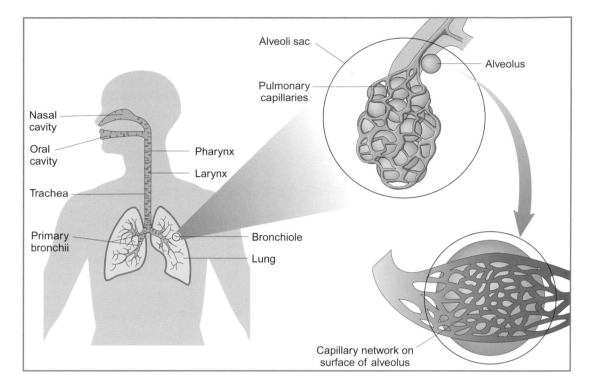

Fig. 5.01 Route of air through the respiratory structure.

Alveoli increase the efficiency of gas exchange by:

- forming a vast surface area (approximately half the size of a tennis court) for gaseous exchange to take place.
- have a single-cell layer of thin epithelial cells reducing the distance for gas exchange with:
  - an extensive network of narrow alveoli capillaries producing a short **diffusion path** due to 2 and 3
  - a moist lining/film of water helping dissolve and exchange oxygen.

Pulmonary Pleura

Like the **pericardium** of the heart, the lungs have **pulmonary pleura,** double walled sacs consisting of two membranes filled with pleural fluid, which help to reduce friction between the ribs and lungs during breathing. The outer layer attaches to the ribs and the inner layer to the lungs. This ensures the lungs move with the chest as it expands and relaxes during breathing. The inflation and deflation of the lungs, termed **inspiration** and **expiration,** result in pulmonary ventilation.

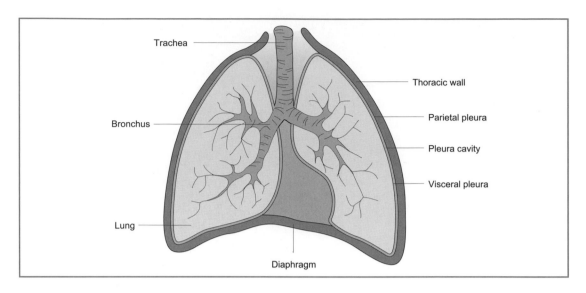

Fig. 5.02 Pleural cavity of the lungs.

Respiration at Rest
The Mechanics of Respiration

Recall that the pulmonary pleura attaches the lungs to the ribs so the lungs will inflate and deflate as the volume of the **thoracic cavity** increases and decreases. This describes the process of pulmonary respiration but what makes the ribs of the thoracic cavity expand and therefore initiate breathing? The term 'mechanics' suggests levers are involved but what applies the force for levers to move? Muscles produce the force to initiate respiration at both rest and during exercise. Figure 5.03 shows all the respiratory muscles involved in the mechanics of breathing.

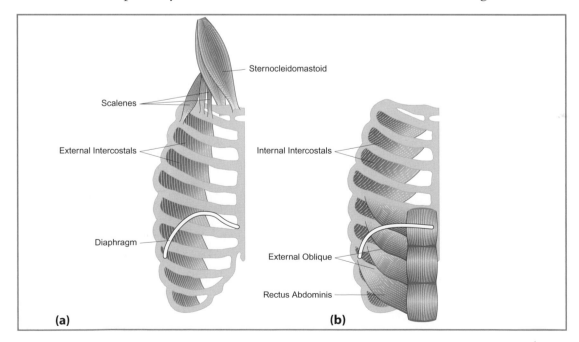

Fig. 5.03 Muscles of inspiration (a) and expiration (b) at rest.

The mechanics of respiration are easier to learn and understand by linking five steps:

1. muscles – actively contract or passively relax to cause:
2. movement – of the ribs and sternum and abdomen which causes:
3. thoracic cavity volume – to either increase or decrease which in turn causes:
4. lung air pressure – to either increase or decrease which causes:
5. inspiration or expiration – air breathed in or out.

Let us now use these steps to describe the process of inspiration and expiration. Follow these steps through inspiration and expiration in the table below and identify the active and passive muscles responsible in Figure 5.04.

Inspiration	Expiration
1 Diaphragm contracts – active External intercostals contract – active	1 Diaphragm relaxes – passive External intercostals relax – passive
2 Diaphragm flattens/pushed down Ribs/sternum move up and out	2 Diaphragm pushed upward Ribs/sternum move in and down
3 Thoracic cavity volume increases	3 Thoracic cavity volume decreases
4 Lung air pressure decreases below atmospheric air (outside)	4 Lung air pressure increases above atmospheric air (outside)
5 Air rushes into lungs	5 Air rushes out of lungs

HOT TIPS

Respiratory muscles initiate breathing by increasing and decreasing the volume of the lung cavity and therefore lung pressures. Do not make the mistake of thinking the lungs or pressure differences themselves initiate breathing.

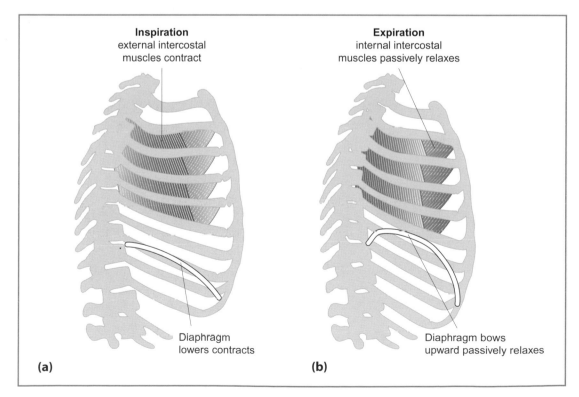

Inspiration
external intercostal
muscles contract

Expiration
internal intercostal
muscles passively relaxes

Diaphragm
lowers contracts

Diaphragm bows
upward passively relaxes

(a)

(b)

Fig. 5.04 Active inspiration (a) and passive expiration (b) at rest.

Respiratory Volumes at Rest

Recall from Chapter 4 that to calculate the efficiency of the performance of the heart we used three definitions and their average values to compare resting with exercise levels. In exactly the same manner, the respiratory system has *three* definitions and values, which help calculate the efficiency of the respiratory system. Let us look at the link between these three definitions and values at rest.

Lung Volumes

Tidal Volume (**TV**) – the volume of air inspired or expired per breath, approximately **500ml** during breathing at rest.
Frequency (**f**) – the number of breaths taken in one minute, approximately 12–15 breaths during breathing at rest.
Minute Ventilation (**VE**) – the volume of air inspired or expired in one minute. VE can be calculated by multiplying the tidal volume with the frequency of breaths in one minute.
The link between TV, f and VE is shown by the following equation:

$$VE = \qquad TV \times f$$
$$= 500ml \times 15$$
$$= 7500ml/min$$
$$= 7.5L/min$$

HOT TIPS

Remember the close similarity between these two equations and don't confuse them when answering heart/respiratory volume questions.

Remember *respiratory* refers to air and *heart* refers to blood.

TASK 2

1   Recall and write down the corresponding equation for the heart alongside the respiratory equation above.
2   If an athlete has a resting TV of 500ml and respiratory frequency of 12 per minute what would their VE be?

Inspiratory and Expiratory Reserve Volumes

Take a normal resting breath in and then immediately inspire further. Take a normal resting breath out and then immediately expire further. You should have noticed that you are able to inspire and expire above your resting TV values. These are termed your **inspiratory** and **expiratory reserve volumes** (IRV) and (ERV), approximately 3000ml and 1100ml respectively.

Residual or Reserve Volume

Try to expire all the air in your lungs. Notice you are unable to do so fully; there is always some air left in the lungs. This is called your **residual** or **reserve volume** (RV) and is approximately 1200ml.

Lung Capacities

Lung capacities are calculated by adding together two or more of the lung volumes we have considered above and are measured by breathing into apparatus that produces a graph called a **spirometer trace**. This highlights three additional lung volume capacities and definitions you are required to learn. It is easier to remember these if you actually carry them out and we will consider them in turn.

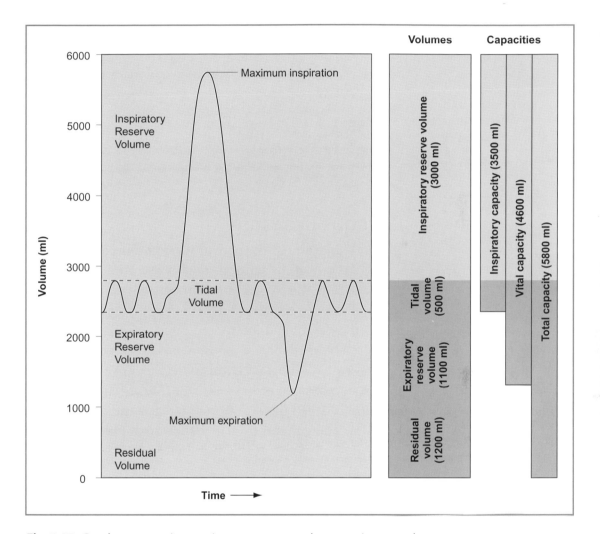

Fig. 5.05 Graph representing a spirometer trace to show respiratory volumes.

Inspiratory Capacity

Take a normal expiration, then take a maximal inspiration. This is your **inspiratory capacity** representing your total TV and IRV. The maximal volume of air that can be inspired after a normal expiration is approximately 3500ml.

Vital Capacity

Take a maximal inspiration and then forcefully maximally expire all the air from your lungs. This volume represents the total of your IRV, TV and ERV and is called your **vital capacity** (VC). The maximal volume of air that can be expired after a maximal inspiration is approximately 4600ml.

Total Lung Capacity

Take a maximal breath in. The total volume of air in the lungs at this point is called your **total lung capacity** (TLC) and represents the sum total of your ERV, IRV, TV and RV. It is approximately 5800ml.

TASK 3

Sketch a rough graph of a spirometer trace and label the lung volumes/capacities identified above.

Gaseous Exchange

We now understand the way in which pulmonary ventilation ensures the supply of air in and out of the lungs through inspiration and expiration but we need to consider how the oxygen and carbon dioxide are actually exchanged. Recall that the exchange of oxygen and carbon dioxide takes place in the lungs and tissues and is called external and internal respiration respectively. Hence, **gaseous exchange** refers to the exchange of gases, namely oxygen and carbon dioxide and relies on a process called **diffusion**. Diffusion is the movement of gases from an area of high pressure to an area of low pressure. The difference between the high and low pressure is called the **diffusion gradient** – the bigger the gradient, the greater the diffusion and gaseous exchange that takes place.

HOT TIPS

The simplest way to remember whether blood has a high or low PP of O_2 or CO_2 is to think back to the terms **oxygenated** and **deoxygenated** blood. If the blood is oxygenated it has a high PP of O_2 and low PP of CO_2 and deoxygenated blood has the opposite. Similarly the tissues/ muscles and alveoli PP of O_2 and CO_2 are the opposite to that of the PP of blood within the blood vessels of the vascular system.

Partial Pressure

Central to the understanding of diffusion is an understanding of **partial pressures** (PP). The partial pressure of a gas is the pressure it exerts within a mixture of gases. The guiding principle of PP that you need to understand is that gases always move from areas of high partial pressure to areas of low partial pressure. While it is not necessary for you to know exact pressures, you do need to understand where and when these PP are higher or lower in order for you to understand which direction gases are moving, during external and internal respiration. Let us consider external and internal respiration together to help you see where and when the PP is high or low. Refer to Figure 5.06 as you follow the table below.

	External respiration	**Internal respiration**
Where?	Alveolar-capillary membrane, between alveoli air and blood in alveolar capillaries	Tissue-capillary membrane, between the blood in the capillaries and the tissue (muscle) cell walls
Movement	O_2 in alveoli diffuses to blood; CO_2 in blood diffuses to alveoli	O_2 in blood diffuses into tissue; CO_2 in tissues diffuses into blood
Why? – O_2	PP of O_2 in alveoli higher than the PP of O_2 in the blood so O_2 diffuses into the blood	PP of O_2 in blood is higher than the PP of O_2 in the tissue so O_2 diffuses into the Myoglobin within tissues
Why? – CO_2	PP of CO_2 in the blood is higher than the PP of CO_2 in the alveoli so CO_2 diffuses into the alveoli	PP of CO_2 in the tissue is higher than the PP of CO_2 in the blood so CO_2 diffuses into the capillary blood

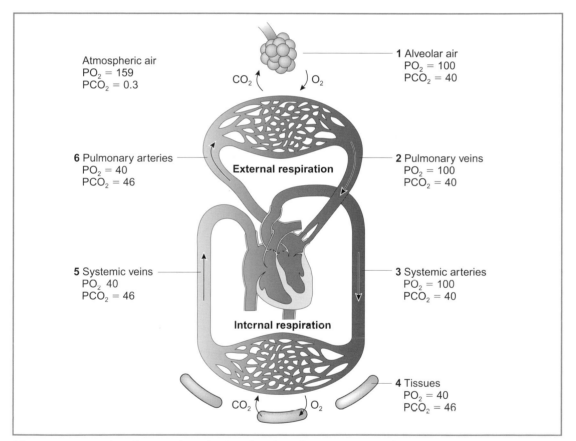

Fig. 5.06 External and internal respiration showing changes in O_2 and CO_2.

External (Alveoli) Respiration

The inspired air entering the alveoli in the lungs has a high PP of oxygen and low PP of carbon dioxide compared with the deoxygenated blood in the alveoli capillaries, which has a low PP of oxygen and high PP of carbon dioxide. These two pressure gradients cause diffusion of:

1   Oxygen from the alveoli into the blood of the capillaries to be transported back to the left atrium and

2   Carbon dioxide from the capillary blood into the alveoli of the lungs where it is expired.

Recall from Chapter 4 (see page 82) that oxygen is transported within the haemoglobin of the red blood cells (97%) and blood plasma (3%).

Internal (Tissue) Respiration

The oxygenated blood is pumped around the systemic circulation until it reaches the capillaries surrounding the body tissues/muscles. The capillary blood has a high PP of oxygen and low PP of carbon dioxide compared with the tissue/muscle cells, which have a low PP of oxygen and high PP of carbon dioxide, having used its oxygen for energy production and given off carbon dioxide as a by-product. The oxygen passed into the muscle cells is transferred from the haemoglobin in the blood capillaries to **myoglobin** within the muscle tissue, which both stores and transports the oxygen to the **mitochondria** where it is used for energy production. Recall that carbon dioxide is transported in the blood as **carbonic acid** (70%), **carbaminohaemoglobin** (20%) and **plasma** (7%) back to the right atrium of the heart.

TASK 4

Outline the changes that take place in the PP of oxygen and carbon dioxide and the subsequent movement of these gases as blood travels from the lungs to the tissues and back to the lungs.

Respiratory Response to Exercise

In relation to the respiratory response to exercise you are required to know:

1   Changes to the mechanics of breathing.
2   Changes to lung volumes.
3   Changes to gaseous exchange during:
    (a) external respiration – at the alveoli-capillary membrane
    (b) internal respiration – at the tissue-capillary membrane.
4   How these changes are regulated by the respiratory centre (neural and chemical).
5   The effect of exercising at altitude on the respiratory system.

Mechanics of Respiration during Exercise

As you begin to exercise, the demand for oxygen by the working muscles increases and respiration similarly needs to increase in both rate and depth of breathing. We have already identified that the respiratory muscles initiate breathing. It is therefore no surprise that to increase the rate/depth of breathing during exercise, additional muscles to those of the diaphragm and external intercostals used at rest are required. The additional muscles for both inspiration and expiration are shown in figure 5.03 and bold in the table below.

Inspiration	Expiration
1 Diaphragm contracts External intercostals contract **Sternocleidomastoid** contracts **Scalenes** contract **Pectoralis minor** contracts	1 Diaphragm relaxes External intercostals relax **Internal intercostals** contract (active) **Rectus abdominus/Obliques** contract (active)
2 Diaphragm flattens with more force Increased lifting of ribs and sternum	2 Diaphragm pushed up harder with more force Ribs/sternum pulled in and down
3 Increased thoracic cavity volume	3 Greater decrease in thoracic cavity volume
4 Lower air pressure in lungs	4 Higher air pressure in lungs
5 More air rushes into lungs	5 More air pushed out of the lungs

The net effect of these additional respiratory muscles is to increase both the depth and rate of breathing to increase the supply of air containing oxygen to the site of gaseous exchange in the alveoli.

Lung Volume/Capacity Changes during Exercise

Like the heart, respiration increases in line with exercise intensity in order to supply the increased oxygen demands of our working muscles. The table below summarises these changes. Both the rate (f) and depth (TV) of breathing increase, which in turn increase VE from resting values of 6 L/min up to maximal values of 160–180L/min in trained aerobic athletes. Notice that TV increases while the ERV and IRV decrease. TV uses up some of these two reserve volumes in order for TV to increase. It is thought that primarily TV increases at lower intensities of workload to increase VE but during maximal work it is a further increase in the rate of breathing that increases VE further. It is not efficient to increase TV towards the maximal VC value due to the time/effort it takes. Try running while taking a maximal inspiration and expiration and see why this is not feasible.

Lung volume	Definition	Resting volume	Change due to exercise
Tidal volume X	Volume of air inhaled/exhaled per breath during rest	500ml per breath	Increases: up to around 3–4 litres
Frequency	Number of breaths in one minute	12–15	Increase: 40–60
= VE Minute ventilation	Volume of air inspired/expired in one minute	6–7.5L/min	Increase: values up to 120L/min in smaller individuals and up to 180+L/min in larger aerobic trained athletes
Inspiratory reserve volume	Volume of air that can be forcefully inspired after normal TV inspiration	3100ml	Decreases
Expiratory reserve volume	Volume of air that can be forcefully exhaled after normal resting TV expiration	1200ml	Slightly decreases

Lung capacities similarly change during exercise and are summarised in the following table.

Lung volume	Definition	Resting volume	Change due to exercise
Vital capacity	Maximal volume of air that can be expired after maximal inspiration: VC = TV + IRV + ERV	4800ml	Slight decrease
Residual volume	Volume of air remaining in the lungs after a forced expiration	1200ml	Slight increase
Total lung capacity	Maximal volume of air contained in the lungs after a maximal inspiration: TLC = TV + IRV + ERV + RV	6000ml	Slight decrease

TASK 5

A TV of 500ml and frequency of 12 produces a VE of 6L/min. Explain why increasing the frequency to 24 and a TV of 4000ml per breath during exercise would be beneficial to an aerobic athlete.

Ventilatory Response to Light, Moderate and Heavy Exercise

Figure 5.07 shows the pulmonary ventilation response to sub-maximal and maximal exercise intensities. You will be required to describe and explain the changes in VE from resting to sub-maximal and maximal workloads.

Fig. 5.07 Ventilatory response to sub-maximal (light/moderate) and maximal (heavy) exercise.

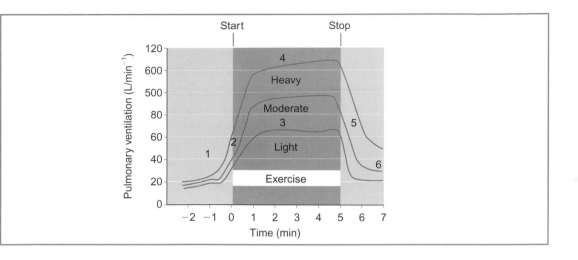

Ventilatory response to exercise mirrors that of the heart except that it is the Respiratory Control Centre (RCC), controlling the respiratory muscles, which increases or decreases breathing. Let us look at the VE response in steps which correspond to the stages on Figure 5.07 to make this process easier to understand.

1   **Anticipatory rise** prior to exercise in all three work intensities due to the release of hormones (adrenalin), which stimulate the RCC.

2   **Rapid rise** in VE at the start of exercise due to neural stimulation of RCC by muscle/joint proprioreceptors.

3   **Slower increase/plateau** in sub-maximal exercise due to continued stimulation of RCC by proprioreceptors, but with additional stimulation from temperature and chemoreceptors due to an increase in temperature, CO_2 and lactic acid levels and a decrease in oxygen in the blood. **Plateau** represents a **steady state** where the demands for oxygen by the muscles are being met by oxygen supply.

4   **Continued but slower increase** in VE towards maximal values during maximal work due to continued stimulation from the receptors above and increasing chemoreceptor stimulation due to increasing CO_2 and lactic acid accumulation.

5   **Rapid decrease** in VE in all three intensities once exercise stops due to the cessation of proprioreceptor and decreasing chemoreceptor stimulation.

6   **Slower decrease** towards resting VE values. The more intense the exercise period the longer the elevated level of respiration required to help remove the increased by-products of exercise, e.g. lactic acid.

Exercise Changes to Gaseous Exchange

We have already covered gaseous exchange within both external and internal respiration, but you now need to consider the changes in gaseous exchange that occur during exercise. Both external and internal respiration increase during exercise in order to increase the supply of oxygen to the working muscles but to understand how, we need to have a basic understanding of an oxygen-haemoglobin dissociation curve.

Oxygen-Haemoglobin Dissociation Curve

An oxygen-haemoglobin dissociation curve informs us of the amount of haemoglobin saturated with oxygen. Haemoglobin that is fully bound or loaded with oxygen is termed **saturated** or **associated**, whereas oxygen unloading from haemoglobin is called **dissociation**. Figure 5.08 shows the curve at rest.

Fig. 5.08 O_2 dissociation curve in resting conditions: body temp of 37/38°, blood pH 7.4 and PP O_2 100 in lungs and 40 in tissues.

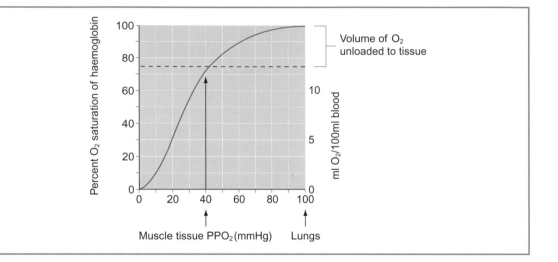

TASK 6

1   Look at the PP oxygen (mmHg) on the bottom 'x' axis in Figure 5.8 and familiarise yourself with what this curve is showing.

2   At rest, the PP of oxygen in the lungs is 100mmHg. Follow this line up from 100mmHg and see where it intersects the curve. Draw a line across to the side 'y' axis and record the value. If you have followed these steps correctly you should have a figure around 98%. This represents the percentage of saturation of oxygen associated with haemoglobin in the alveoli capillary blood.

3   At rest the PP of oxygen in the tissues/muscles is around 40mmHg. Repeat the steps above and calculate the percentage saturation of oxygen and haemoglobin in the tissues/muscles capillary blood.

4   What has happened to approximately 25% of the oxygen associated with haemoglobin?

If you have completed the task above correctly you should have a basic understanding of what the oxygen-haemoglobin dissociation curve is showing. Task 6 illustrates an important principle: the higher the PP oxygen, the higher the percentage of oxygen saturation to haemoglobin (Hb). Hence, a higher PP oxygen of 100mmHg in the lungs results in almost 100% saturation, compared with a lower PP oxygen of 40mmHg in the tissues which results in only 75% saturation. Approximately 25% of the oxygen has dissociated from haemoglobin into the tissues/muscles. Where do you think we need the association and dissociation of oxygen and haemoglobin to take place in order to maintain an efficient supply of oxygen to the working muscles during exercise?

The answer is of course association in the lungs, so the blood can carry the oxygen to the muscle capillaries where it can dissociate and unload the oxygen to the muscle tissue to provide energy for work.

TASK 7

1   Look at the oxygen–haemoglobin dissociation curves shown in Figure 5.9.
2   The curve on the left represents the normal curve we have already looked at. Read off the values for the percentage saturation of oxygen and haemoglobin in the tissues/muscles using the curve on the right.
3   What effect does moving the curve to the right have on the saturation of haemoglobin if we assume the PP of oxygen remains the same in the tissues?
4   What are the benefits of the curve shifting to the right for an athlete?

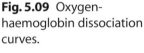

Fig. 5.09 Oxygen-haemoglobin dissociation curves.

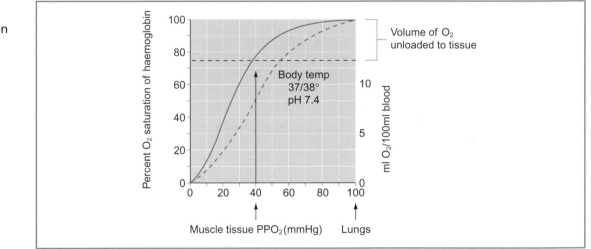

Task 7 demonstrates that a shift of the oxygen-haemoglobin dissociation curve to the right represents a greater dissociation of oxygen, hence, more oxygen unloading from the haemoglobin in the blood to the muscle tissue. Now that you have an understanding of the oxygen dissociation curve, let us look at the changes taking place within external and internal respiration during exercise.

External Respiration

During exercise, skeletal muscles are using a greater amount of oxygen to provide energy and consequently are producing greater amounts of carbon dioxide as a by-product. Hence, venous blood returning to the lungs from the right ventricle has a higher PP of carbon dioxide and lower PP of oxygen. In contrast alveolar air has a high PP of oxygen and low PP of carbon dioxide. This has the effect of increasing the **diffusion gradient** for both oxygen and carbon dioxide between the alveoli-capillary membrane resulting in both a quicker and greater amount of gaseous exchange. The high PP of oxygen in the alveoli and low PP of oxygen in the capillaries ensures haemoglobin is almost fully saturated with oxygen.

Partial pressure	Alveolar air	Direction of diffusion (High to low PP)	Alveoli capillary blood	Diffusion gradient
O_2	100 (high)	⟶	40 (low)	60
CO_2	40 (low)	⟵	46 (high)	6

Although you are not required to provide actual partial pressures, they do help to explain how the diffusion gradient works. The oxygen and carbon dioxide will diffuse across until the partial pressures are equal, hence, the greater the diffusion gradient the greater the amount of oxygen and carbon dioxide exchanged.

Internal Respiration

You should already understand that a greater oxygen dissociation in the muscle tissues during exercise is required in order to increase the supply of oxygen to the working muscles. Four factors all have the effect of shifting the dissociation curve to the right or, more simply, increasing the dissociation of oxygen from Hb in the blood capillaries to the muscle tissue. These four factors are:

1 increase in blood and muscle temperature
2 decrease in PP oxygen within muscle increasing the oxygen diffusion gradient
3 increase in PP of carbon dioxide increasing the carbon dioxide diffusion gradient
4 **Bohr effect** – increase in acidity (lower pH).

Interestingly all of these factors increase during exercise. The effect is that the working muscles:
* generate more heat when working
* use more oxygen to provide energy, lowering the PP oxygen
* produce greater carbon dioxide as a by-product
* increase lactic acid levels which increase muscle/blood acidity (lower the pH).
Collectively all four of these factors increase the dissociation of oxygen from haemoglobin that increases the supply of oxygen to the working muscles and therefore delays fatigue and increases the possible intensity/duration of performance. See Figure 5.10 and the table below.

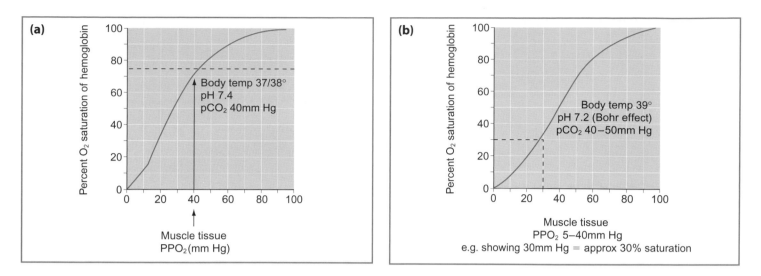

Fig. 5.10 Comparison of oxygen – haemoglobin dissociation curve at rest (a) and exercise conditions (b).

Partial pressure	Capillary blood	Direction of diffusion (High to low PP)	Muscle tissue	Diffusion gradient
O_2 resting	100	→	40	60
O_2 during exercise	100	→	<5	95
CO_2 resting	40	←	45	6
CO_2 during exercise	40	←	80	40

Comparison of the differences in PP from rest and exercise during internal respiration

Control of Breathing

The **respiratory control centre** (RCC) regulates pulmonary respiration (breathing). As with all the cardio-respiratory systems, the RCC is located in the **medulla oblongata** of the brain and responds in conjunction with the CCC and the VCC. Recall from the mechanics of breathing that the respiratory muscles actually initiate breathing. Let us now consider how the RCC controls these respiratory muscles to regulate pulmonary ventilation.

Nervous/Neural Control

The respiratory muscles are under **involuntary neural control**. Although we can voluntarily change our rate and depth of breathing with conscious thought, we may be more concerned with concentrating on where the ball or opponent is than on breathing during exercise!

The respiratory control centre has two areas, **the inspiratory** and **expiratory centres**, which are responsible for the stimulation of the respiratory muscles, at rest and during exercise.

At Rest

1   The inspiratory centre is responsible for the rhythmic cycle of inspiration and expiration to produce a respiratory rate of 12–15 breaths a minute.
    (a)   The inspiratory centre sends impulses to the respiratory muscles via:
          • **phrenic** nerves to the diaphragm
          • **intercostal** nerves to the external intercostals.
    (b)   When stimulated these muscles contract, increasing the volume of the thoracic cavity, causing inspiration (active).
    (c)   When their stimulation stops, the muscles relax, decreasing the volume of the thoracic cavity, causing expiration (passive).
2   The expiratory centre is inactive during quiet/resting breathing. Expiration is passive as a result of the relaxation of the diaphragm and external intercostals.

During Exercise

Pulmonary ventilation increases during exercise, which increases both the depth and rate of breathing. This is regulated by:

1   the inspiratory centre which:
    (a)   increases the stimulation of the diaphragm and external intercostals
    (b)   stimulates additional inspiratory muscles for inspiration, the **sterno-cleidmastoids**, **scalenes** and **pectoralis minor**, which increase the force of contraction and therefore the depth of inspiration.
2   the expiratory centre which:
    (a)   stimulates the expiratory muscles, **internal intercostals**, **rectus abdominus** and **obliques**, causing a forced expiration which **reduces** the duration of inspiration.
    (b)   The inspiratory centre immediately stimulates the inspiratory muscles to inspire, which results in an increase in the rate of breathing.

Hering-Breuer Reflex

The action of the expiratory centre also acts as a safety mechanism in the lungs to ensure they are never over-inflated. Stretch receptors in the lungs detect when the depth of breathing increases and stimulate the RCC to inhibit the inspiratory centre and stimulate the expiratory muscles. During exercise this has the result of decreasing the depth and increasing the rate of breathing.

Factors Influencing the Neural Control of Breathing

Emotions, pain, Hering-Breuer reflex, respiratory irritants are all factors that affect breathing. However, we need to identify those factors more concerned with the primary purpose of respiration – to maintain appropriate levels of blood and tissue gases (oxygen and carbon dioxide) and pH levels in order for athletes to continue exercising. The factors affecting the activity of the RCC are summarised in Figure 5.11 and linked to the regulation of breathing. The main receptors and the information they send to the RCC during exercise that you need to know are:

1 **Chemoreceptors** from within the medulla and carotid arteries send information to the inspiratory centre on:
   (a) increase in PP carbon dioxide – thought to be the primary factor
   (b) decrease in PP oxygen
   (c) decrease in pH (increasing acidity).
2 **Proprioreceptors** located in the muscles and joints send information to the inspiratory centre on motor movement of the active/working muscles.
3 **Thermoreceptors** send information to the inspiratory centre on increase in blood temperature.
4 **Baroreceptors** or stretch receptors located in the lungs send information to the expiratory centre on the extent of lung inflation during inspiration.

Receptors 1–3 above all stimulate the inspiratory centre to increase the force/depth of breathing. Baroreceptors stimulate the expiratory centre to actively expire, reducing the duration of inspiration, and thereby increasing the rate of breathing.

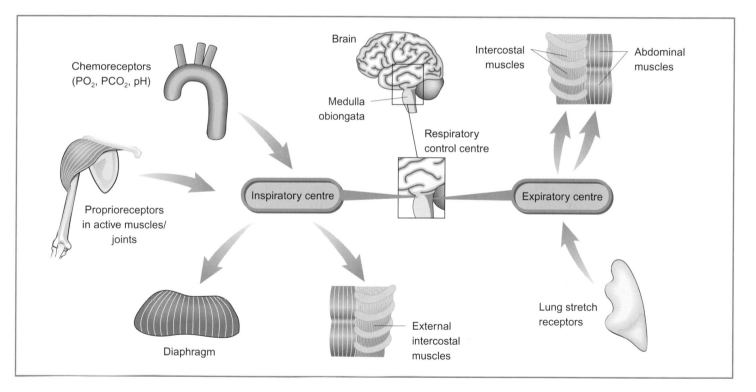

Fig. 5.11 Factors affecting the activity of the inspiratory and expiratory centres in the RCC.

TASK 8

1 Follow the steps in figure 5.12.
2 Which area of the RCC is responsible for increasing the depth of breathing?
3 Which area of the RCC is responsible for increasing the rate of breathing?

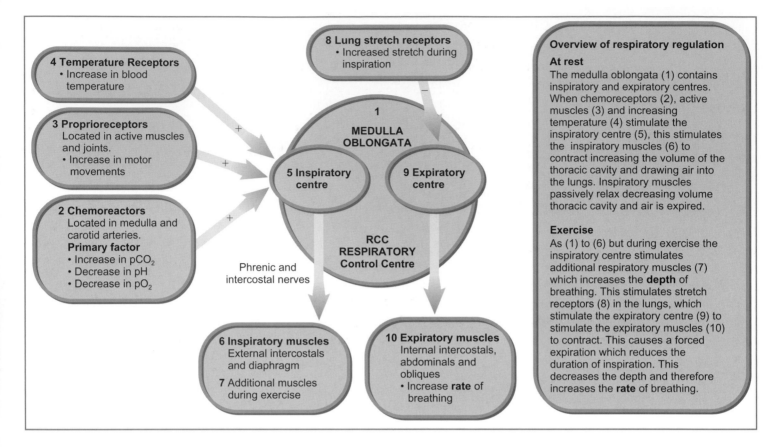

Fig. 5.12 Summary of respiratory control at rest and during exercise.

Effects of Altitude on the Respiratory System

We have already identified that an adequate supply of oxygen to the working muscles is essential for performance. Exposure to high altitude has a significant effect upon performance by affecting the normal processes of respiration. At high altitude (above 1500 metres) the PP of oxygen in the atmospheric air is significantly reduced and it is primarily this reduction in PP that causes a sequence of knock-on effects, which decrease the efficiency of the respiratory processes. Figure 5.13 summarises the effects of altitude on the respiratory system.

The course specification requires you to understand how the respiratory system responds to the effects of altitude and not how it adapts to altitude. However you should still understand and acknowledge that during continued or long-term periods at altitude, the body adapts by increasing the levels of haemoglobin or red blood cells. Although this is primarily a vascular adaptation, the respiratory muscles will have also adapted and become more efficient.

TASK 9
What are the benefits of the body's adaptation to altitude when an athlete then runs at sea level?

Fig. 5.13

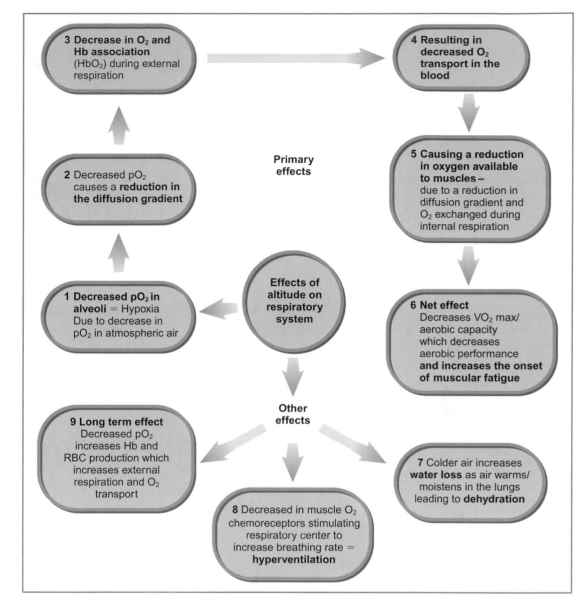

3 Decrease in O_2 and Hb association (HbO_2) during external respiration

4 Resulting in decreased O_2 transport in the blood

2 Decreased pO_2 causes a **reduction in the diffusion gradient**

5 Causing a reduction in oxygen available to muscles – due to a reduction in diffusion gradient and O_2 exchanged during internal respiration

Primary effects

Effects of altitude on respiratory system

1 **Decreased pO_2 in alveoli** = Hypoxia Due to decrease in pO_2 in atmospheric air

6 **Net effect** Decreases VO_2 max/ aerobic capacity which decreases aerobic performance **and increases the onset of muscular fatigue**

Other effects

9 **Long term effect** Decreased pO_2 increases Hb and RBC production which increases external respiration and O_2 transport

8 Decreased in muscle O_2 chemoreceptors stimulating respiratory center to increase breathing rate = **hyperventilation**

7 Colder air increases **water loss** as air warms/ moistens in the lungs leading to **dehydration**

Cardio-respiratory control

It is much easier to understand the control mechanisms of the heart, vascular and respiratory system as one. Many of the factors affecting the activity of the CCC, VCC and RCC are the same and stimulate the control centres to respond at exactly the same time. Figure 5.14 shows the overlap between the heart, vascular and respiratory systems.

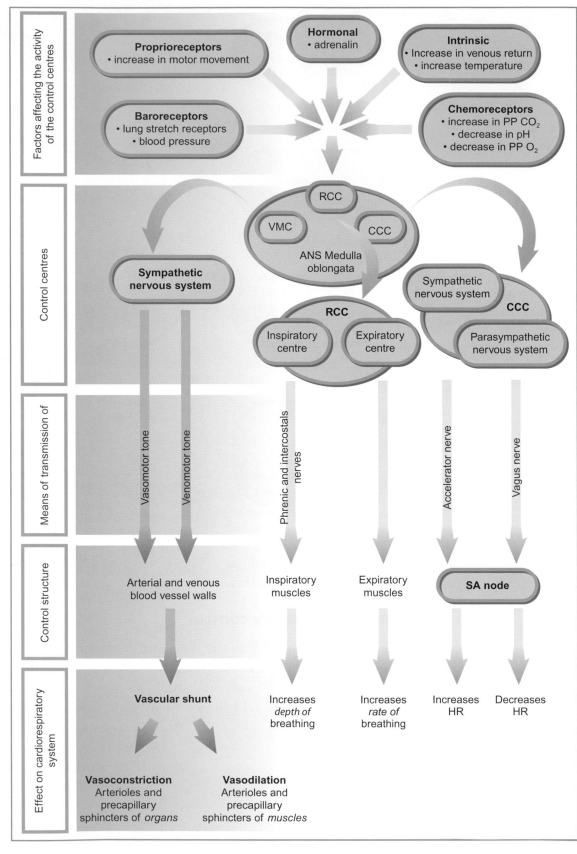

Fig. 5.14 Control and regulation of cardiorespiratory control during exercise.

Revise as you go! Test your knowledge and understanding

- List the respiratory structures atmospheric air travels through on route to the alveoli in the lungs.
- How does the structure of the lungs enable the efficient exchange of O_2 and CO_2?
- What are the benefits to performance of an efficient gaseous exchange in the lungs?
- Describe the mechanics of breathing at rest and during exercise.
- Define the terms minute ventilation, tidal volume and respiratory frequency.
- Give average values for minute ventilation during rest, sub maximal and maximal exercise.
- Explain how gas is exchanged between the alveoli and the alveoli capillaries during exercise.
- Explain how gas is exchanged between the capillaries and muscle cells during exercise.
- Explain the main factors affecting the association of oxygen with haemoglobin.
- What is the net effect of these factors on the association of oxygen and haemoglobin within muscle tissues during exercise and how does this affect performance?
- Where and how is respiration controlled?
- Describe and explain the factors that effect the activity of the RCC.
- Describe the effects of altitude on the respiratory system.
- How would altitude affect the performance of a marathon runner?

Sharpen up your exam technique!

1   At rest and during physical activity the performer varies the volume of gas exchanged in the lungs. Give typical minute ventilation values (L/min or ml/min for a fit 20-year-old athlete at rest and during maximal exercise.   (2 marks)

2   Describe how neural control enables the athlete to increase lung volumes. Why is this beneficial to performance?   (3 marks)

3   An endurance performer increases the volume of gases exchanged during prolonged exercise. Explain why the structure of the lungs enables efficient exchange of gases.   (3 marks)

4   Describe the changes in the mechanics of breathing which allow the performer to exchange larger volumes of gas during exercise.   (3 marks)

5   Explain how gas is exchanged between the blood and the muscles tissues during exercise. Why is this beneficial to performance?   (5 marks)

6   Peak performance in certain activities may be affected by altitude. Describe the effect of altitude on the exchange of gases at the alveoli and why this may influence performance.   (4 marks)

7   Explain how the respiratory control centre in the medulla oblongata responds to the increased demand for oxygen during exercise.   (4 marks)

Chapter 6 Defining, Developing and Classifying Skills in Physical Education

Learning Objectives

At the end of this chapter you should be able to:
- Identify the characteristics of skilful performance.
- Define and identify the characteristics of motor skills, including perceptual, cognitive and psychomotor skills.
- Classify movement skills by placing them on a variety of continua.
- Define and identify the characteristics of gross motor abilities and psychomotor abilities.
- Understand the progression from motor abilities to fundamental motor skills to sport specific skills.

Introduction

In our everyday lives we all utilise millions of skills which we have mastered and which enable us to take part in social, thinking and performing situations. Whilst all these skills are important, in PE we focus on motor skills which are essential in sport.

In this section we are particularly concerned with understanding the meaning of the term 'skill' and the factors which underpin skilful performance. Examining the classification of skills enables us to embark on their analysis which is important to our understanding of how we should best learn and teach skills. Distinguishing between the terms 'skill' and 'ability' helps us to understand how individuals differ in the way they master skills and how some are able to perform at a higher level than others. Finally, we will gain an insight into the way, particularly as young children, we develop our abilities into fundamental motor skills which we then take further and fine tune to become the motor skills that we will use in particular sports. We must also ensure that we can show our understanding by being able to apply the concepts to the practical activities that we are involved in.

Fig. 6.01 Skill as a special task – the Fosbury flop.

Developing and Classifying Skills in PE
What is Skill?

We can use the term 'skill' in different ways. Firstly, we can use it to refer to specific tasks or acts which we perform, e.g. a short serve in badminton or a Fosbury flop.

Secondly, we use the term to refer to a series of movements that have a clearly defined objective. This use is typified by games such as basketball and netball where not only does the performer have to have good techniques but also has to be able to interpret situations correctly.

Thirdly, we use the term in a qualitative manner to describe how consistent, successful and technically correct a performer is.

TASK 1

1   Choose an activity that you have taken part in and identify the skill (tasks or acts) of that activity.

2   In that activity name a performer who you consider to be skilful (consistent, successful, technically correct).

Characteristics

Fig. 6.02 How would you describe this performance?

TASK 2

Look at this picture or view a video clip of an elite performer. Write down a list of words that you think would best describe this performance.

There are many words that can be used to describe a skilful performance. You may have used some of them in the task above.

Efficient – the skill is well co-ordinated and appears effortless. The unskilled performer will appear much slower and more clumsy and will also tire much more quickly.

Fluent – the skill is well co-ordinated, well timed and precise. The performer is in control of the movement. The movements of the unskilled performer will appear jerky and uncontrolled.

Aesthetic – the skill is pleasing to the eye; the performer looks very competent. The unskilled performer will look clumsy, unco-ordinated and awkward.

Learned – the skill has had to be practised over a period of time. Learning means that it is more or less a permanent change in behaviour indicating that the skill can be performed consistently, time after time. The unskilled performer may occasionally perform the skill successfully due more to luck than practice or learning.

Goal directed – the skill will be aimed at achieving a set result. Prior to performing the skill, the end result will be clearly identified and understood by the performer. The unskilled performer may not appreciate what they are attempting to achieve or why.

Follows a technical model – we usually judge how good/skilful a performance is by comparing it to the model of how the perfect skill should be performed, e.g. we know what the perfect forehand tennis drive should look like. The skilful performance will mirror this model. In some situations this model has to be adapted to suit that situation. The unskilled performance will have many discrepancies when compared to the perfect model.

Having identified the key characteristics, they can be the focus of a definition of skilful performance. Knapp's definition is a popular one and states:

> *skill is the learned ability to bring about predetermined results with maximum certainty, often with the minimum outlay of time or energy or both.*

You should be able to link this definition to many of the characteristics that we have identified.

HOT TIPS

Make sure that you can apply all the theories that you learn to a practical example. Questions in the exam will usually ask you to do this.

TASK 3

1   Watch a partner performing a skill that they are very good at. List the characteristics of skill you can see.
2   Watch a partner performing a skill that they have not done before. List the characteristics of skill you can see.
3   Compare your two lists.

Types of Skill

We each have to have a very large skill base to successfully exist in our complicated lives. Psychologists who study skills tend to group them together into different types. We have to learn all these different types of skill to be able to perform the many different tasks which we have to do in our daily lives.

TASK 4

Think of a typical day in your life. List all the skills that you perform in that day. Group similar skills together into different types of skill.

You will have identified several different groups of skills in Task 4, e.g. social skills when you queue for the bus and when you eat your lunch; thinking skills when you have to work out the cost of your lunch or answer a question in class; a 'doing' or motor skill when you run for the bus or walk between classes. Some of these types of skill, whilst being very important to us, are not very relevant to our area of study. In this study of PE we need to focus on specific types of skill.

KEY WORDS

Cognitive skill

A skill which involves the mental/intellectual ability of the performer.

Perceptual skill

A skill which involves the detection and interpretation of information.

Motor skill

A skill which involves movement and muscular control.

Cognitive Skills

Cognitive skills are sometimes referred to as intellectual skills as they involve the thought processes. Examples are working out tactics to use against your opponents in a game of hockey/basketball or in a 1500 metres race.

Perceptual Skills

These skills involve the detection and interpretation of information. Sometimes we can receive the same piece of information but interpret it in different ways (see Figure 6.03). We sometimes wonder how referees can look at the same piece of play but interpret it completely differently from us!

We use perceptual skills a lot in sport particularly in individual and team games. Examples are when we have to detect and interpret information to decide where, when and how to play or pass the ball. Good perceptual skills are essential if we are to make effective decisions.

Motor Skills

Motor skills involve controlled muscular movement with a set goal. Examples are running, jumping and swimming.

Fig. 6.04 Perceptual skills are essential in team games.

Fig. 6.05 Swimming is a motor skill.

Fig. 6.03 Who do you see – an old lady or a young woman?

TASK 5

Use the practical activities that you have taken part in and give examples of cognitive skills, perceptual skills and motor skills.

In doing Task 5 you may have noticed that it is difficult to be definite as many activities have elements of more than one type of skill. This leads us to consider another type of skill that is very important in the study of PE and Sport.

Perceptual Motor or Psychomotor Skills

Skills that we use in PE have elements of cognitive, perceptual and motor skills. They involve thinking, detecting and interpreting information as well as performing muscular movement. These skills are referred to as **perceptual motor/psychomotor** skills or sometimes simply as movement skills.

Analysing Movement Skills

Just as we looked at analysing the general skills that we use in terms of their characteristics, we can also analyse movement skills. Psychologists have identified a range of characteristics or classifications to use.

The classification of movement skills is not simple, nor is it an exact science. It is difficult to be specific about the characteristics of a skill because many of them can change depending on the situation in which the skill is performed. Many skills also have elements of all characteristics. Because of this, skill classification uses **continua** that allow us to illustrate that skills have characteristics to a greater or lesser extent dependent on the situation that they are being performed in. The most commonly used classification continua are detailed below.

Muscular Involvement (Gross–Fine) Continuum

GROSS_____FINE

Running   Wrist/finger action of a spin bowler in cricket.

Swimming

Hammer throwing

In this classification we look at the precision of the movement.

Gross skills involve large muscle movements where there is little concern for precision. Examples are running, swimming and hammer throwing.

Fine skills involve more intricate movements using small muscle groups. They usually involve accuracy and emphasise hand-eye co-ordination. An example of a fine movement skill is the wrist/finger action of a spin bowler in cricket.

Fig. 6.06 Hammer throwing is a gross skill.

Fig. 6.07 The wrist and finger action of a spin bowler is a fine skill.

Environmental Influence (Open–Closed) Continuum

OPEN	CLOSED
Pass in rugby/netball	Tennis serve
Hammer throwing	Gymnastics through vault

HOT TIPS

Always explain/justify why you have placed a particular skill at that point on the continuum.

In this classification we are concerned with how environmental conditions affect the movement skill. In referring to the environment we take into account all the factors that affect the performance, e.g. team mates, opponents, playing surface. Additionally, if performed outdoors, the weather may also be a factor.

Open skills involve movement skills that are affected by the environment. They are predominantly perceptual and involve decision making. Movements have to be adapted to suit the situation. They are generally externally placed in an environment that is unpredictable. Examples of open skills would be a pass in a rugby or netball game.

Closed skills are movement skills that are not affected by the environment. In these skills we aim to do the same set technical model at each performance and they are therefore habitual. They are usually self paced, with the performer knowing exactly what they have to do. Examples of closed skills are the tennis serve or gymnastics through vault.

Fig. 6.08 Shooting in netball is an open skill.

Fig. 6.09 A gymnastics vault is a closed skill.

Continuity (Discrete – Serial – Continuous) Continuum

DISCRETE	SERIAL	CONTINUOUS
Catching a ball	Gymnastics/trampolining sequence	Running/cycling
Penalty in soccer/hockey	Triple jump	Swimming

In this classification we are concerned with how clearly defined the beginning and end of the movement skill are.

Discrete skills are movement skills that have a clear beginning and a clear end. If this single skill is to be repeated it must start again. Examples of discrete skills are catching a ball in cricket or rounders, a penalty in soccer or hockey, or a high serve in badminton.

Serial skills are movement skills that have a number of discrete elements that are put together in a definite order to make a movement or sequence. Examples of serial skills are a gymnastic or trampolining sequence and a triple jump.

Continuous skills are movement skills that have no definite beginning or end. The end of one cycle of the movement is the start of the next. The movement skill usually has to be repeated several times for the skill to be meaningful. Examples of continuous skills are running, cycling and swimming.

Fig. 6.10 A penalty in football is a discrete skill.

Fig. 6.11 A trampolining sequence is a serial skill.

Fig. 6.12 Cycling is a continuous skill.

Pacing (Self-paced–Externally Paced) Continuum

SELF PACED	EXTERNALLY PACED
High jump	Receiving a pass
Tennis serve	Windsurfing

In this classification we are concerned with the level of control that the performer has over the timing of the movement skill. This control can relate to both when the movement is started as well as the rate at which it is performed.

Self (internally) paced – the performer determines when the movement skill starts together with the rate at which it proceeds. Self-paced skills are normally closed skills. Examples of self-paced skills are high jump and tennis serve.

Externally paced – the control of the movement skill is *not* determined by the performer but by the environment. In many cases this involves opponents to whom the performer has to react. They are normally open skills. Examples of externally-paced skills are receiving a pass in soccer or hockey and windsurfing.

Difficulty (Simple–Complex) Continuum

SIMPLE	COMPLEX
Swimming	Tennis serve
Sprinting	Somersault

In this classification we are concerned with how complex the movement skill is, which is determined by analysing the following aspects:

- perceptual load together with the degree of decision making
- time available to carry out the perceptual and decision-making tasks
- quantity of sub-routines together with their speed and timing
- use of feedback.

Simple skills would have very low levels of some of the aspects identified above. Performers would have little information to process and few decisions to make, as well as a small number of sub-routines in which the speed and timing would not be critical. The use of feedback would not be significant. Whilst such movement skills are simple they may still be difficult to learn and perform. Examples of simple skills are swimming and sprinting.

Complex skills would have high levels of most of the aspects identified above. Performers will have a high perceptual load leading to many decisions which have to be made. The skill will have many sub-routines where speed and timing are critical, together with significant use of feedback. Examples of complex skills are tennis serve and somersault.

Fig. 6.13 Sprinting is a simple skill.

Fig. 6.14 The tennis serve is a complex skill.

Organisational (Low–High) Continuum

KEY WORDS

Sub-routine

Movement skills are usually comprised of several parts that are referred to as sub-routines, e.g. breast stroke consists of the following: body position, arm action, leg action, breathing. These sub-routines together make up the movement skill.

LOW	HIGH
Swimming strokes	Cartwheel
Trampolining sequence	Golf swing

In this classification we are concerned with how closely linked the sub-routines of the movement skill are.

Low organisation skills are made up of sub-routines that are easily separated and practised by themselves. Having been practised separately the sub-routines can be put back together into the whole skill quite easily. Examples of low organisation skills are swimming strokes, trampolining or gymnastics sequences.

High organisation skills are movement skills where sub-routines are very closely linked together and very difficult to separate without disrupting the skill. Consequently highly organised skills are usually practised as a whole. Examples of highly organised skills are cartwheels and the golf swing.

Fig. 6.15 The golf swing is a highly organised skill.

KEY WORDS

Positive transfer

The process of one skill helping the learning and performance of a separate but similar skill.

> ### TASK 6
> Select three skills from practical activities in which you have taken part and classify them on the six continua above. Identify the situation in which each skill is being performed and explain your reasons for its position on the continua.

It is important for us to be able to analyse movement skills in order to appreciate and understand the requirements of the skill and adopt the best approaches to teach, practise and improve it. Placing a skill on each of the continua and justifying this positioning will be very helpful in deciding how the skill can be practised and improved. This will be helpful to you when you focus on developing your skills in your PPP.

Application of Classification in determining Practice Types

Practice conditions are the type and style of practice administered by the teacher or coach. The appropriate type of practice will ensure the opportunity for performance to be improved. The conditions in which a skill is learned and practised should, as far as possible, replicate the circumstances of the real performance. It is important that environmental conditions and the movements involved in practice transfer positively to the situation in which the skill is performed. Practice conditions are determined by the nature of the skill. Therefore before deciding on the practice type, the teacher should consider the following:

Classification

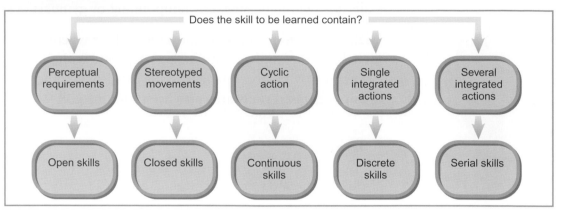

Organisation

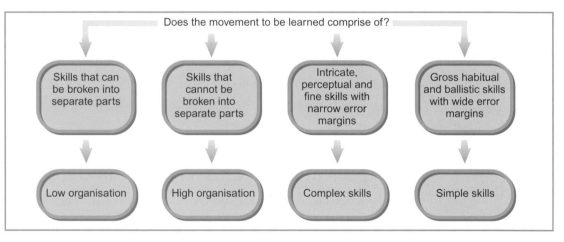

Practice types

Varied Practice

Open skills are best practised in an environment which is constantly changing or variable. An example of a varied practice would be a 3 versus 2 offensive drill in basketball. This will improve positional play and passing technique in a situation which directly reflects the game. A varied practice will provide opportunity for decision making and develop perceptual skills. The player will also learn to adapt technique and body shape to respond to the changing environment. Adaptations are stored and therefore the experience or schema of the novice is expanded. Furthermore, the nature of this practice improves **selective attention** and the skill of detecting **warning signals** making **information processing** faster and more efficient.

Before introducing varied practices the novice should build a motor programme in a fixed environment. The repetitive action in this situation will cause the learner to 'groove' or 'over-learn' the skill, which can later be adapted.

Fixed Practice

Closed skills require fixed practice conditions because such skills need to be over-learned. For example, when learning the skill of long jump, skill drills or repetitive practices can be used because the environment in which a closed skill is performed remains the same and the movement pattern once perfected never changes. Unchanging body movements are known as **stereotyped actions** and should be grooved to the point of being habitual.

Part Practice

Skills that are low in organisation can be broken down into separate sub-routines. Part practice involves working on an isolated sub-routine with the intention of perfecting it. For example, the throwing phase in shot putt would be the focus of teaching, allowing the learner to concentrate on just one area. Part teaching reduces the possibility of overload and is good if the task is complex or dangerous.

Some skills can be taught by reversing the order of part presentation, for example the discus throw in. The order of teaching would be:

1 throw and release   3 initial preparation   5 grip.
2 travel and trunk position   4 stance

Fig. 6.16 Throw and release in discus.

This teaching technique is called **backward chaining**.

Whole Practice

Skills that are high in organisation need to be taught as a whole. Examples of such skills include sprinting and dribbling which, because of their cyclic or continuous nature, will not break down into separate sub-routines. Ideally, all movements should be taught as a whole as this method allows the learner to experience the feel of the skill. This 'feeling tone' is termed kinaesthesis.

TASK 7

1 Discuss the advantages of teaching a skill by using backward chaining.
2 List five benefits of learning an open skill through varied practice.
3 Consider why a varied practice may decrease reaction time.
4 The model below is an illustration of progressive part practice and assumes that a movement has three clear and separate sub-routines.

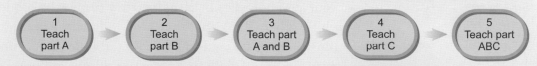

| 1 Teach part A | → | 2 Teach part B | → | 3 Teach part A and B | → | 4 Teach part C | → | 5 Teach part ABC |

(a) Think of a skill that could be taught using progressive part presentation.
(b) Discuss the advantages of this type of practice.

Whole–Part–Whole

This type of practice involves the presentation of the whole motor programme, for example the entire swimming stroke. By introducing a float as a mechanical aid the practice could then focus on part of the skill, for example the leg action. To conclude, the whole stroke would be reintroduced incorporating the improved leg kick.

Simplification of Skill

If a task is high in organisation and also complex, the skill should be made easier. This is called **task simplification**. For example, a bicycle could be fitted with stabilisers, short tennis would be introduced before progression to the major game and tackle bags in rugby practice would be a good mechanical aid to help the teaching of a potentially dangerous task.

Identifying the Differences between Skills and Abilities

We now understand what we mean by the term 'skill'. Often we use the term 'ability' instead of 'skill' but we will now examine the term 'ability' to show that the two are in fact different.

The characteristics of skill are that it is learned, goal-directed and follows a technical model. If we are to learn a particular skill we must have certain abilities that the skill relies on. For example, to be able to perform a handstand you must have the strength in your arms to support your body weight as well as the balance to keep your legs above your hands.

Fig. 6.17 Performing a handstand needs strength and balance.

Characteristics of Abilities

Below are the words that can be used to describe abilities.

Innate/genetically determined – we are born with abilities determined by the genes we inherit from our parents.
Stable and enduring – abilities tend to remain unchanged but can be affected by our experiences and are developed by maturation.
Support skills – each skill usually needs us to have several supporting or underpinning abilities if we are going to be able to learn the skill effectively.

Abilities are thought to be the foundation blocks that we possess and build on, helping us to learn and perform skills. We inherit our abilities from our parents and some psychologists believe that they cannot be modified or improved by practice, whilst others think that they are modified by maturation and experience. However, all psychologists tend to agree that abilities determine your learning and performance of skills and activities. If you are born with a lot of slow twitch muscle fibres you could become a good endurance athlete but will never excel in sprinting. Similarly, if you are born with low levels of flexibility it is unlikely that you will ever be a top class gymnast.

Having identified these characteristics of ability they can be the focus of a definition. Schmidt says that ability is:

> ❛ *an inherited, relatively enduring trait that underlies or supports various kinds of motor and cognitive activities or skills. Abilities are thought of as being largely genetically determined.* ❜

Bull stated:

> ❛ *Abilities are usually thought of as stable and enduring traits that underpin skills and contribute to the speed with which individuals learn psychomotor skills and to the quality of their performance.* ❜

Types of Ability

Research into types of ability is as yet inconclusive and different psychologists use different methods to identify them. Fleishman identified two types.

KEY WORDS

Gross motor ability

Usually involves movement and is related to physical fitness.

Gross motor abilities also referred to as **physical proficiency abilities**, usually involve movement and are related to physical fitness. Fleishman identified nine of them.

Dynamic strength – exerting muscular force repeatedly over a period of time, e.g. press ups.
Static strength – the maximum strength that can be exerted against an external object.
Explosive strength – energy used effectively for a short burst of muscular effort, e.g. vertical jump.
Stamina – the capacity to sustain maximum effort involving the cardiovascular system, e.g. a marathon.
Extent flexibility – flexing or stretching the trunk and back muscles.
Dynamic flexibility – being able to make several rapid flexing movements.
Gross body co-ordination – the organisation of the actions of several parts of the body whilst the body is moving.
Gross body equilibrium – being able to maintain balance using the internal senses.
Trunk strength – the strength of the abdominal muscles.

There are also other gross motor abilities besides the nine that Fleishman identified, such as static balance, dynamic balance, eye-hand co-ordination and eye-foot co-ordination.

Fig. 6.18 Explosive strength.

Fig. 6.19 Gross body co-ordination.

TASK 8

For each of the gross motor abilities above, identify a skill/activity that you do that it underpins/supports.

KEY WORDS

Percepual motor abiliities

Usually involves the processing of information, making decisions and putting these decisions into action. These actions are usually movements.

Perceptual motor abilities – Fleishman identified eleven of these, including:

Multi-limb co-ordination – being able to organise the movement of several limbs at the same time.

Response orientation – choosing quickly the position in which an action should be made (as in choice reaction time).

Reaction time – being able to respond quickly to a stimulus.

Speed of movement – being able to make gross rapid movements.

Finger dexterity – being able to work with tiny objects using the fingers.

Manual dexterity – being able to make accurate arm/hand movements involving objects at speed.

Rate control – being able to change the speed and direction of responses accurately.

Aiming – being able to aim accurately at a small object.

Fig. 6.20 Reaction time.   **Fig. 6.21** Aiming.

Psychologists have devised tests which aim to measure some of these abilities.

A skill will rely on several abilities to support or underpin it. That does not mean that the performer who has high levels of those abilities is automatically guaranteed success. The performer has to learn to apply and co-ordinate those abilities through practice if they are to be effective and successful in the skill.

Coaches and teachers often refer to performers being 'natural' athletes or games players in that they are successful in most sports. This implies that there is one ability that supports or underpins all these activities. Present research evidence does not support this idea, instead indicating that specific skills/activities require particular abilities. Some skills/activities require very similar combinations of abilities to support them and by developing and practising these abilities they may well transfer to other similar skills.

Research has also shown that skills are sometimes underpinned by different abilities at different stages, such as learning and mastering a skill. In the early stages of learning a complex skill, many perceptual abilities will be important, whereas when you are more proficient kinaesthesis is an essential ability.

Fig. 6.22 A stork stand is used to measure gross body equilibrium.

TASK 9

1 Measure gross body equilibrium (static balance). You will need to use the gym or sports hall floor and wear your trainers. Work with a partner who will time you with a stopwatch. Stand on your preferred leg with your foot flat on the floor. Place the sole of your other foot flat against the inside of your straight knee. Place your hands on your hips. Your partner will commence timing when you close your eyes. They will stop the watch when you: open your eyes, take your hands off your hips, or move either of your feet.

2 Measure your performance against the figures in the table below.

Men		Women	
Best time(s)	Points	Best time(s)	Points
60	20	35	20
55	18	30	17
50	16	25	14
45	14	20	11
40	12	15	8
35	10	10	4
30	8	5	2
25	6		
20	4		
15	3		
10	2		

TASK 10

Identify the abilities that underpin the activity you have chosen for your PPP. For each one, explain how they underpin your activity.

HOT TIPS

You should know how abilities are developed, particularly those applicable to your activity, as well as how they influence fundamental motor skills.

How are Abilities developed?

Some psychologists believe that abilities can be developed and, this being the case, how does the teacher do this? It is generally thought that abilities can be developed during early childhood and it is important that during this period children are exposed to a wide range of experiences and the opportunity to practise. Children should also receive expert teaching and coaching, as well as have access to the necessary facilities and equipment. Children who have the support of their family and friends, who may also be suitable role models, tend to enhance their abilities.

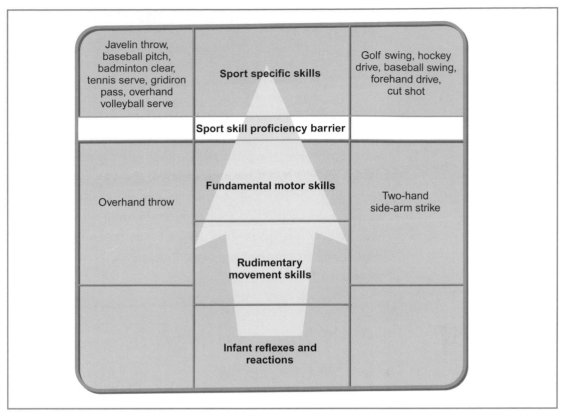

Fig. 6.23 Development stages of skills.

Motor Skill Development

In the last section we looked at abilities and how they support a variety of skills. Generally it is accepted that these abilities are improved through maturation and experience. Abilities are seen as building blocks upon which we develop skills. Children develop skills in an ordered manner that follows set stages.

They first use their abilities to learn basic or rudimentary movement skills such as walking, running, skipping, pushing, stretching and balancing. These basic movement skills will form the foundation on which further development takes place.

During the early years of primary school education (4–9 years old) children are physically and mentally capable of learning skills and are also highly motivated and enthusiastic about it. At this stage expert teaching is needed to develop the child's rudimentary movement skills further into **fundamental motor skills** (FMS). Each FMS has a series of sub-routines against which successful mastery of the skills can be measured.

These FMS have definite coaching points that can be identified and by which teachers and coaches can ensure that children are learning correctly. Examples of FMS are catching, kicking, running, dodging, over arm throwing, vertical jumping and the two-handed side arm strike, ball bounce, leap and forehand strike.

KEY WORDS

Fundamental motor skills (FMS)

These are common motor skills with specific observable patterns.

TASK 11
Identify the FMS in your PPP practical activity.

Once learned correctly and mastered, these FMS will be developed into sports-specific skills by adapting and practising each one so that it matches the requirements of the particular sport. For example, the FMS of catching is adapted and practised by children in order that it can be used in rounders, cricket, netball and rugby. By looking at each of these sports you can see that most have different adaptations of the FMS. In rounders and cricket it will be adapted to catch a small hard ball, whilst in netball the ball is bigger and softer, and in rugby the ball is an oval shape. It can be seen how sports-specific skills are developed from their respective FMS.

| Softball | Cricket | Volleyball | Badminton | Netball | Baseball | Javelin | Tennis |

Fig. 6.24 The FMS of overarm throwing can be developed into many sports-specific skills.

Research has been carried out into the sporting achievements of children in the State of Victoria, Australia. Findings indicated that children need to learn the appropriate FMS at an early age if they are to successfully learn the sports-specific skills. The research indicated that those children who did not master the FMS were less willing to try when faced with learning difficult sports-specific skills and often dropped out of those sports.

TASK 12
Identify the sports-specific skills that develop from the FMS you have identified in your PPP activity.

Revise as you go! Test your knowledge and understanding

- Identify three different ways in which we can use the term 'skill'.
- Identify five characteristics of skilful performance.
- State Knapp's definition of skill.
- Give a sporting example of each of the following types of skill:
    - cognitive
    - perceptual
    - motor
    - perceptual motor.
- Describe what is meant by the term 'continuum.'
- Why do we use continua?
- Name the six continua used to classify skills. Classify a skill from your PPP activity on all six continua.
- What factors concerning the skill should the teacher consider before deciding on the type of practice?
- Describe what is meant by a *varied practice*.
- List the benefits of a varied practice to the performer of open skills.
- What is the meaning of the term *fixed practice*?
- Describe the term *part practice* and list the advantages of this practice type.
- Explain the term *whole practice* and list the advantages of this practice type.
- Under which circumstances would the teacher choose to simplify the task?
- Identify the characteristics of abilities.
- Identify two different types of abilities and give examples of them both.
- Identify the abilities which underpin your PPP activity.
- Name a skill from your PPP activity and identify the FMS from which it developed.

Sharpen up your exam technique!

1   Describe four key characteristics of skilful performance.   (4 marks)

2   Describe the differences between a *motor skill* and a *perceptual skill* using examples from your practical activities.   (4 marks)

3   Why is a continuum often used for classifying movement skills?   (2 marks)

4   Why is it important in skill classification to view skills on a continuum?   (2 marks)

5   Draw a continuum showing the position of discrete skills, serial skills and continuous skills. Place an example of each type of skill on your continuum.   (3 marks)

6   (a) Define what is meant by the Open/Closed skill continuum in skill classification.   (3 marks)
    (b) Classify a named skill on this continuum and give two points to justify its classification.   (3 marks)

7   By using practical examples illustrate when it would be best to use the whole mode of presentation as a teaching method.   (4 marks)

8   Ability is important in the acquisition and improvement of practical skills.
    (a) Describe the main characteristics of ability.   (2 marks)
    (b) Explain the terms *gross motor* ability and *psychomotor* ability. Apply these terms to a basketball or netball player attempting to receive a pass whilst being closely guarded.   (4 marks)

9   Describe the main characteristics of *skilful movement* and *ability*, identifying the differences between the two.   (6 marks)

10 The figure below shows the development of motor skills.

Motor Abilities_____Motor skills_____ Sport-specific skills

Using the figure and a practical example explain how a named sport-specific skill can be developed.   (3 marks)

Chapter 7 **Information Processing**

Learning Objectives

At the end of this chapter you should be able to:
- Understand the key components of information processing.
- Identify and draw the information processing models of Whiting and Welford.
- Understand the components of memory and the roles they play in information processing.
- Define reaction time, movement time and response time, together with choice reaction time and the factors that affect them.
- Identify the different types of feedback and their importance.
- Analyse the information processing requirements of movement skills in your practical activities.

Introduction

Information processing focuses on how we deal with the vast amount of information that is available to us when we are performing skills. Information processing theories compare our systems to those of a computer in order to help us understand the various procedures that we apply to the information, which is important to our performing our skills successfully. These procedures include the detection and interpretation of the information and the use of it to make decisions and put them into action. We also need to have an understanding of the way in which we make decisions and the factors that influence the speed at which we make them. Information processing theories also help us to understand the important part that our memories play as well as the role that feedback, both from ourselves and teachers/coaches, has in performing skills. We have to understand the theories and ensure that we know how to apply them to our practical activities.

Basic Models of Information Processing
What is Information Processing?

The theories of information processing attempt to explain how we take in the vast amount of information in our surroundings, interpret it and make decisions about courses of action we should take. They compare us to computers but also take into account the more personalised nature of our interpretation and decision-making processes. If we were to identify three key processes in the working of a computer, we would say: inputting information; processing information; outputting information. In humans this is the same as: sensory input; central mechanisms (brain); effector mechanisms (muscles).

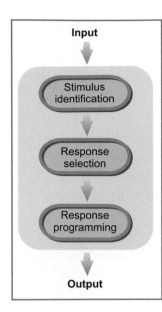

Fig. 7.01 Stages in information processing.

KEY WORDS

Stimulus

Information that stands out from the background and to which the performer pays attention.

We are, therefore, looking at how information enters our system, how we interpret it and make decisions, how we put those decisions into action, together with what we do with the new information our actions generate. This can be explained as follows:

Stimulus identification – we first have to decide if a **stimulus** has occurred and this is done by our sensory systems receiving information. Patterns of movement are also detected and interpreted, for example, we would interpret the information to decide the direction and speed that a ball was travelling. It can be seen that this stage involves the perceptual processes.

Response selection – this stage acts on the information received from stimulus identification stage and is concerned with deciding which movement to make, e.g. the ball is high and to my left so I must move to my left and catch it.

Response programming – this next stage receives the decision about which movement to make and is responsible for organising our motor system (nerves and muscles) to carry out the appropriate movement.

There are numerous information processing models but we will focus on two.

Whiting's Model

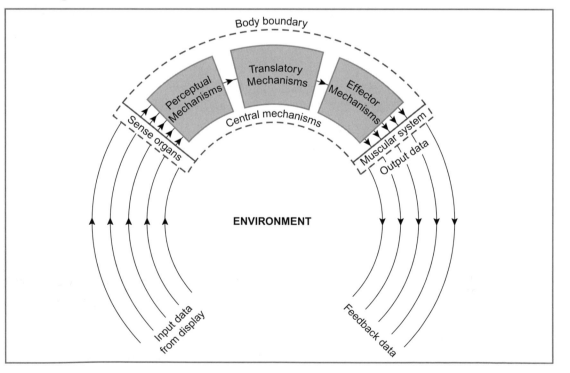

Fig. 7.02 Whiting's Model for perceptual motor performance.

Whiting emphasised that we should realise that, although we show these models as static diagrams, not only is our environment constantly changing but the components of the models, whilst retaining the same basic structure, are constantly changing and becoming more sophisticated. The models, therefore, should be seen as being dynamic.

Welford's Model

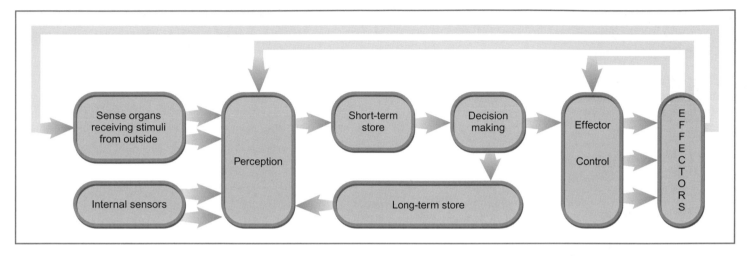

Fig. 7.03 Welford's model of information processing.

Welford's model is a little more complicated than Whiting's. Both have the same basic processes of information processing, but we need to look in a little more detail at the elements of the models if we are to have a better understanding of the process.

Display – the surroundings or environment that the performer is in. For a netball player it would include the ball, team mates, opponents, spectators and the noise they make, the umpires and the coach/teacher. Some of the information generated by the display will be noticed by the performer and will stimulate the sensory systems.

Sensory input – we use the senses of vision, hearing and **proprioception** to be aware of what is happening around us. These senses detect information that stimulates their sensory receptors.

Touch – allows us to feel pressure and pain so we know how hard we have kicked a ball or are gripping a racket. Awareness of pain helps us avoid serious injury.

Kinaesthesis – gives us information relating to the contractions of muscles, joints and tendons. When you have mastered a skill you are able to 'feel' how it is to perform using kinaesthetic information.

Equilibrium – tells you whether you are balanced, and turning or falling. It also enables you to know your body position. Information is generated from the inner ear.

Perception

The process which involves the interpretation of information. This is the process by which we make sense of the stimuli we receive.

Motor programme

A series of movements stored in the long-term memory. They specify the movements the skill consists of and the order they occur. They can be retrieved by one decision.

Perception – the process which interprets and makes sense of the information received. It consists of three elements: *detection* – the brain identifies that a stimulus is present; *comparison* – having identified the stimulus it is now compared to similar stimuli that we have stored in our memory; and *recognition* – when the stimulus is matched to one stored in the memory it is identified or recognised.

Memory – this plays an important role in both the perceptual and decision-making processes. It consists of three parts: short-term sensory stores, short-term memory and the long-term memory.

Decision making (translatory mechanism) – once the information has been interpreted the correct response has to be put into action. This correct action will be in the form of a **motor programme** which identifies the movements the action is made up of, the order they are in and where they take place.

Effector mechanism – the motor programme is put into action by sending impulses via the nervous system to the appropriate muscles so that they can carry out the appropriate actions.

Feedback – when the motor programme has been put into action by the effector mechanism the display changes and creates new information. This new information is known as feedback and can be internal as well as external.

Serial and Parallel Processing

Most information which we process is done sequentially or in stages. These stages are different and have an effect on each other and are known as serial processes. Serial processing would occur in a trampolining routine when the performer processes the information relating to each movement of the routine stage by stage.

However, some processes occur at the same time and are referred to as parallel processes. These do not have an effect on each other. An example would be in a team game when you will be processing information about the speed, height and direction of the ball coming towards you and also about the positions of team mates and opponents.

HOT TIPS

Make sure that you are able to draw and explain Whiting's and Welford's information processing models as well as being able to apply them to a practical activity.

Within the models we have identified it can be seen that generally the same processes are involved but sometimes with different names.

TASK 1

Choose one of the two models identified (Whiting's or Welford's). Use a skill or a number of skills in your chosen PPP activity to explain and illustrate how each component of the model works in that activity.

Memory

Memory plays an important role in information processing, particularly in interpretation of information when we rely on our previous experiences. It is also important in determining the motor programme we are going to use to send the appropriate information to the muscles. This importance can be seen in the way memory links with other processes in Welford's information processing model. Memory can be split into three components: short-term sensory stores, short-term and long-term memory.

Short-term Sensory Stores

All stimuli entering the information processing system are held for a very short time (0.25–1 second). These stores have a very large capacity. The perceptual mechanism determines which of the information is important to us and we direct our attention to this. This is the recognition aspect of perception. Other irrelevant information is quickly lost from the sensory stores to be replaced by new information. This filtering process is known as **selective attention**.

KEY WORDS

Selective attention

The process of picking out and focusing on the relevant parts of the display. This filtering out is also important because irrelevant information is ignored.

Selective Attention

By focusing our attention on relevant information we filter this information through into the short-term memory. Selective attention enables the information important to our performance to be filtered and concentrated on. Information unimportant to the performance and therefore not attended to is filtered out. The importance of this process is highlighted by theories that suggest that there is a limited amount of information we can process. The process of focusing on the important and ignoring the irrelevant also helps us to react quickly. For example, sprinters will focus their attention on the track and the gun, ignoring fellow competitors and the crowd.

TASK 2
What is the information you focus on and what do you ignore in your chosen PPP activity?

Fig. 7.04 The sprinter selectively attends to the starter's gun.

Short-term Memory

This aspect of memory is often referred to as the ' work place'. It is here that the incoming information is compared to that previously learned and stored in the long-term memory. This is the comparison aspect of perception.

The short-term memory has a limited capacity, both in terms of the quantity of information it can store and the length of time it can be stored for. Generally, these limits are thought to be between 5 and 9 pieces of information for up to 30 seconds. The number can be increased by linking or 'chunking' bits of information

Fig. 7.05 Rugby players remember lineout strategies by chunking information.

together and remembering them as one piece of information. The period of time can also be extended if you rehearse or repeat the information.

A good non-sporting example of this is when you look up a phone number before dialing it. You group the numbers together and repeat them to yourself until you dial the number. In rugby, lineout strategies are remembered by the players referring to them with a number or name.

Information in the short-term memory considered to be important is rehearsed or practised and by this process passes into the long-term memory for future use. This process is referred to as encoding.

Long-term Memory

The long-term memory holds the information that has been well learned and practised. Its capacity is thought to be limitless and the information is held for a long period of time, perhaps permanently.

Fig. 7.06 Motor programmes are stored in long-term memory and you never forget them.

Motor programmes are stored in the long-term memory as a result of us practising them many times. You will no doubt realise that you never forget how to ride a bike or swim even when you have not done them for some time.

The long-term memory is the recognition part of the perceptual process when the stored information in the long-term memory is retrieved and compared to the new information which is then recognised.

Strategies to improve Retention and Retrieval

Now we realise how important the memory is to our performance it would help us if we were able to improve our ability to store information and to be able to remember it. Psychologists think that we can do this by the following methods.

Rehearsal/Practice

When learning we need to practise or rehearse the skill as much as possible. Expert performers do a lot of skill practice until they have 'over learned' the skill and it has become automatic. It is thought that practice carries the skills image 'to and fro' between the short and long-term memories establishing a memory trace. This helps both retention and retrieval.

Association/Linking

Coaches and teachers should always try to link new information to that which the performer already knows. Specific-sports skills can be linked to fundamental motor skills, for example, throwing the javelin can be linked to the overarm throw. This helps the learner mentally organise the skill. Linking parts of serial skills together both physically and mentally is also important. For example, parts of a basketball lay-up shot or parts of a gymnastics sequence.

Remember the limitation of the short-term memory. Teachers and coaches should give learners three coaching points to remember when they go to practise. When they have mastered these three, more can be given.

Simplicity

Learners should be given time to take in new information, which should be kept simple. More complex information can be added later. It is also important that similar information/skills should not be presented close together as they may interfere with each other. For example, beginners learning to swim should not be introduced to two different strokes in the same session.

Organisation

Information is more easily remembered if it is organised in a meaningful way. It is suggested that gymnastics and trampolining sequences will be remembered more easily if the individual movements are practised together in order that the performer links the end of one movement to the beginning of the next.

Imagery

Information can be remembered better by having a mental image. Demonstrations are really important in order that learners are able to create an image of the skill in their mind. Some coaches link images to words. For example 'chin, knee, toe' gives the learner the picture of the correct body position in the shot putt.

Meaningful

If the learner is made aware that the information being learned is relevant to them and their performance it becomes meaningful and is more likely to be remembered.

Chunking

Information can be grouped together allowing more to be dealt with at one time. Experienced performers use chunking to look at the whole field of play, recognize developing patterns and anticipate what will happen.

Uniqueness

If the teacher or coach presents information in an unusual or different way then it is more likely to be remembered.

Enjoyment

If the teacher can ensure that the learner enjoys the experience this will increase the possibility of it being remembered.

Positive Reinforcement

Praise and encouragement when learning a skill will aid retention.

Reaction Time

Reaction time is the speed at which we are able to process information and make decisions. Being able to respond quickly is very important in many sports and often determines if we are successful. The speed at which we make decisions involves a complicated process which can be illustrated by the following information processing model.

Fig. 7.07 The information processing components each take time

Put simply, there are four parts to reaction time, made up of the time it takes for:

1   the stimulus to activate the particular sensory system
2   the stimulus to travel from the sensory system to the brain
3   the brain(central mechanisms) to process the stimulus
4   the relevant commands to be sent from the central mechanisms to the relevant muscle or group of muscles.

KEY WORDS

Reaction time

The time between the onset of the stimulus and the start of the movement in response to it.

Movement time

The time it takes from starting the movement to completing it.

Reaction time is defined as the time between the onset of the stimulus and the start of the movement in response to it. In the sprint start, **reaction time** is the time from the gun going off to the sprinter putting pressure on their starting blocks. You will remember from Chapter 6 that reaction time is an ability.

There are two other components connected with performing movements quickly – movement time and response time.

Movement Time

Movement time is the time it takes from first starting the movement to completing it. In the sprint start it is represented by the time from the sprinter first pressing on their blocks to when they cross the finish line and hopefully finish first!

Response Time

This is the time from the onset of the stimulus to the completion of the movement. It is the total time, adding reaction time to movement time. For example, it is the time from the gun going off to the sprinter crossing the finishing line.

◄—Reaction time—► ◄————————Movement time————————►
◄————————————————Response time————————————————►

Fig. 7.08 Components of response time.

Factors which affect Reaction Time

There are several factors that affect reaction time, which is an ability that varies between individuals, according to the following criteria.

Age – reaction time gets quicker until you are about 20 and then gets slower as you get older.

Gender – males generally have quicker reaction times than females but as we get older the difference becomes less.

> ### TASK 3
> Using a reaction time ruler, get each member in your group to have 10 trials with their preferred hand. Find the mean reaction time for the males and females.

Limb used – the further the information has to travel in the nervous system the slower the reaction will be. Normally the reaction of feet is slower than hands.

Personality – extroverts tend to have quicker reaction than introverts.

Alertness/arousal/motivation – levels of these will affect our reaction time. Optimum levels are needed to react quickly.

Body temperature – if we are cold, our reactions are slower.

Sensory system receiving the stimulus – reaction time will vary depending on the sense that is being used.

Fig. 7.09 The sensory system used affects reaction time.

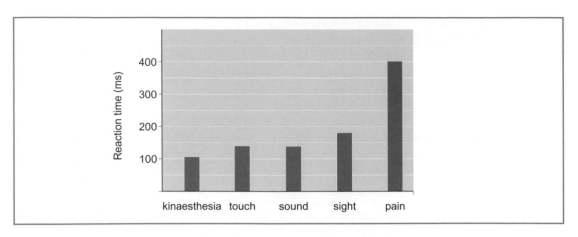

There are also external factors which affect reaction time, which are:

If a warning is given – if you are expecting the stimulus your reaction will be quicker. In the sprint start the starter says 'set' to warn the sprinter that the gun is about to go off.
Stimulus intensity – loud sounds or bright colours stimulate quicker reactions. We use an orange football in the snow and a white cricket ball for night matches.
The likelihood of the stimulus occurring – if the stimulus has a good chance of occurring you will react quicker than to one that occurs infrequently.

Choice Reaction Time

In our previous examination of reaction time we have looked at the performer's reaction when there is just one stimulus, for example, the sprinter reacting to the gun. This is **simple reaction time**. In many sporting situations performers are faced with more than one stimulus and more than one response. This is known as **choice reaction time**. For example, a badminton player having the stimuli of the different shots their opponent may play and the responses of which shot to select to return the shuttle.

TASK 4

Work with a partner. You will need a stopwatch and a pack of playing cards. Your partner will time you for each of the tasks below.

1. Simply turn the cards, one at a time, onto one pile face up.
2. After shuffling the cards turn the cards over one at a time separating the cards into a red pile and a black pile.
3. After shuffling the cards turn them over one at a time now piling them into four suits.
4. After shuffling the cards turn them over one at a time now putting them into eight piles: the face cards and the number cards for hearts, clubs, diamonds and spades.

What do you notice about the times for each task?

You should see from Task 4 that the greater the number of piles, the more choices you have and the slower your time becomes. The greater the number of choices you have, the more information you have to process to make your decisions and this slows down your reaction time.

KEY WORDS

Hick's Law

Choice reaction time increases linearly as the number of stimulus/choice alternatives increases.

Hick's Law has important implications for us within sport. If we are trying to outwit our opponent we should aim to disguise our intentions. For example, our short and long serves in badminton should have exactly the same preparation. Our opponent then has to choose from a number of possibilities and therefore their reaction time is increased. If, however, we are receiving, we should attempt to pick up clues about which serve it is going to be thus reducing our choice of response and therefore our reaction time.

Fig. 7.10 Reaction time increases as the number of stimulus/response alternatives increase.

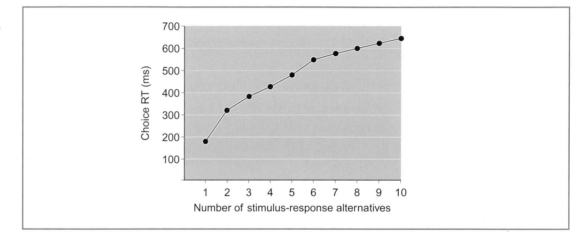

How do Teachers/coaches Attempt to Improve the Performer's Response Time?

Practice – the more often a stimulus is responded to the shorter the reaction time becomes. If enough practice is done the response becomes automatic and requires little attention.

KEY WORDS

Mental rehearsal

This is the picturing of the performance in the mind and does not involve physical movement. It consists of mental imagery, viewing videos of the performance, reading or listening to instructions.

Mental rehearsal – this practice can be done in the form of **mental rehearsal**. This enables the performer to ensure that they attend to the correct cues and expect and respond to the correct stimuli. It also activates the neuromuscular system acting like physical training. It is also thought to have an effect on the control of arousal levels. Mental rehearsal works better with complex tasks which require a lot of information processing.

Experience – playing the activity enhances the performer's awareness of the probability of particular stimuli occurring.

Stimulus–response compatibility – if the response you are expected to make to the stimulus is the one you would normally make you will react quicker than with a different response.

Cue detection – analysing an opponent's play to anticipate what they are going to do. For example, analysing a badminton player's shots so that you are able to detect the difference between their overhead clear and drop shot.

Improve the performer's physical fitness – this will influence response time. The fitter you are, the quicker you will be.

Concentration/selective attention – in simple reaction time situations you focus on the relevant stimulus and ignore everything else. This limits the information you process. For example, during a sprint start, focusing on the gun.

Level of arousal/motivation – the teacher/coach has to ensure that the performer is at the appropriate level of arousal/motivation for the activity.

Warm-up – ensuring physical and mental preparation for the activity.

Anticipation – we have left this to last because it is a very important strategy in reducing both types of reaction time. There are two main forms of anticipation:

- *Spatial* – predicting what *will* happen. The cricket batsman who has detected the difference in the fast bowler's action is able to pick out the slower ball.
- *Temporal* – predicting *when* it will happen. The sprinter who has identified the period between the 'set' command and the gun will be able to move as the gun goes off.

Anticipation has very important implications for teachers and coaches. They should encourage their performers to look for relevant cues in their opponents' actions in order that they will then be able to predict what they will do and disguise their own actions to prevent opponents anticipating. They should also ensure that their performers do not become too predictable in what they do.

TASK 5

Look at the ways to improve response time and identify those which your teacher/coach has used with you in your PPP activity.

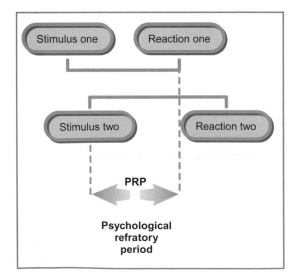

Fig. 7.11 The PRP is the delay caused by being able to process only one piece of information at a time.

Psychological Refractory Period

Anticipation has many benefits but we should also be aware of the drawbacks. If we anticipate incorrectly about what our opponents are about to do or when they will do it, our reaction time will be slowed down. If we have detected a stimulus and are processing that information when a second stimulus comes along, we are unable to attend to and process the second stimulus until we have finished processing the first one, making our reaction time longer. This extra reaction time is known as the **psychological refractory period (PRR)**.

This is why it is so important that we both disguise our actions or deliberately try to make our opponents take a wrong decision, e.g. sell them a dummy, making them go one way when we are really going the other. The psychologists explain this by saying that we have a single channel for processing information and that it will only process one piece of information at any one time.

TASK 6

Think of situations, deliberate and accidental, in your activity when the PRP operates, for example, the ball hitting the top of the net in tennis.

Feedback

KEY WORDS

Feedback

The information received by the performer during the course of the movement and as a result of it.

In our information processing models, **feedback** was the link between the output and input. Feedback occurs as a result of the movements we make and it is used to compare our performance with what we actually intended to do.

TASK 7

Describe the ways in which you get feedback about your performances in your chosen activity.

There are several different types of feedback.

Intrinsic – feedback from the internal proprioceptors about the feel of the movement. Kinaesthesis is also involved. For example, the feel of whether or not you have hit the ball in the middle of the bat in a cricket shot. It is important to experienced performers who may be able to use it during a movement in order to control it. Beginners should be made aware of this feedback in order that they pay attention to experiencing the movement's feel.
Extrinsic – feedback from external sources such as the teacher/coach or team mates. It is received by the visual and auditory systems and is used to augment intrinsic feedback. It is important for beginners, as they are limited in their use of intrinsic feedback.

Intrinsic and extrinsic feedback can come in different forms.

Terminal – feedback received after the movement has been completed. It is sometimes given immediately the movement is completed but it can be given later, for example, at the next training session. It is a form of extrinsic feedback.
Concurrent (continuous) – intrinsic feedback received during the movement, usually from the proprioceptors and kinaesthesis, for example, a batsman finding the middle of the bat, but can be from the teacher/coach giving instructions.
Positive – feedback received when the movement is successful and reinforces learning. For example, in badminton a teacher/coach praises the learner when they perform the short serve correctly. It can be either intrinsic or extrinsic.
Negative – feedback received when the movement was incorrect. It is then used to correct the movement to make it successful the next time. It can be intrinsic or extrinsic.

Feedback is very often referred to in the following two forms.

Fig. 7.12 Extrinsic feedback from teachers/coaches is important for beginners.

Knowledge of results – this feedback is about the outcome of our movements and is extrinsic. It will come from teachers and coaches, actually seeing the result (did the shot go in the basket?) or watching the movement on a video recording. It is essential in skill learning, particularly in the early stages. Knowledge of results can be both positive and negative. It is seen as being important in improving the next performance of the movement.

Knowledge of performance – this type of feedback concerns the movement itself and the quality of it. It is normally from external sources but can be internal arising from our kinaesthetic awareness. The teacher or coach will talk to the performer and give them information about their success and why they were successful, as well as the aspects of the performance which were not good and why. Knowledge of performance can also come from a video recording of the performance or the feeling the performer has about how the movement went.

TASK 8

Look at your answers from the previous task and identify the forms of feedback you receive in your chosen activity.

Feedback is important in order that:
- the performer knows what to do to improve their performance
- good actions are reinforced and the stimulus–response bond is strengthened (see pages 152–4)
- bad habits are prevented and incorrect actions stopped
- the performer is motivated and their confidence boosted. It will also help them avoid drive-reduction (see pages 164–5).

It is important that feedback is:
- compared to previous performances
- specific to the activity/skill being performed and to the performer
- easily understood by the performer
- in manageable amounts for the performer to take in
- linked to goals if it is to be most effective.

Revise as you go! Test your knowledge and understanding

- Name the two information processing models you have studied and draw one of them.
- Identify the following information processing terms: display; sensory input; kinaesthesis; proprioception; effector mechanism.
- Explain the difference between serial and parallel processing.
- Identify the three components of memory.
- Identify two characteristics of the short-term memory.
- Explain what the term 'selective attention' means and give a practical example of its use.
- Identify four strategies you could use to improve the retention and retrieval of information in your memory.

HOT TIPS

Ensure that you know the appropriate uses of feedback, particularly in relation to the different stages of learning which the performer goes through.

- Define reaction time, movement time and response time.
- Name four factors which affect reaction time.
- State Hick's Law and draw a diagram or graph to illustrate it.
- What is the PRP?
- Identify four types of feedback.
- What is the difference between knowledge of results and knowledge of performance?

Sharpen up your exam technique!

1   Define the terms short-term and long-term memory and show the relationship that is thought to occur between them.   (4 marks)

2   Some pieces of information stored in the long-term memory are more easily retrieved than others. How can a PE teacher help a performer to retain information in the long-term memory?   (3 marks)

3   How might you improve the *reaction time* of a performer in your chosen activity?   (4 marks)

4   Describe the Psychological Refractory Period (PRP). Use an example to show how it could be used to increase the reaction time of an opponent.   (3 marks)

5   Explain the differences between knowledge of results and knowledge of performance in the context of skill learning and state when you would use each of these types of feedback.   (4 marks)

6   Give three reasons why feedback is important to the novice.   (3 marks)

7   Feedback can affect motivation. What type of feedback is appropriate to motivate the novice and how might this change for the skilled player? (3 marks)

Chapter 8 **Control of Motor Skill in Physical Education**

Learning Objectives

At the end of this chapter you should be able to:
- Understand the make up of a motor programme.
- Describe motor programmes through the use of practical examples.
- Demonstrate how Open and Closed Loop Theory explains how skills are controlled.
- Understand Schema Theory and compare it to Open and Closed Loop Theory.
- Apply your knowledge to your PPP.

KEY WORDS

Motor skills

Physical actions.

Control

Control involves the manipulation and adjustment of the movement to produce the required skill.

Executive motor programme

The overall plan of the whole skill.

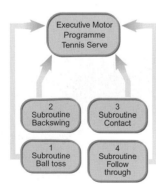

Introduction

In this chapter we will focus on the control of motor skills during performance. This will lead on to how sports skills are learned and improved.

Motor Programmes

A motor programme (MP) or **executive motor programme** (EMP) is a plan of the whole skill or pattern of movement. This plan is stored in the long-term memory. It is adjusted or modified each time the skill is performed and is therefore continually updated in the long-term memory. Every skill performed in sport is the product of a motor programme and so there are countless examples. The one given (left) is a tennis serve. Although classified as a closed skill, new adjustments are needed each time the ball is served.

Sub-routines

Motor programmes are made up of **sub-routines** and so a movement plan has a hierarchy of importance. Sub-routines are the building blocks of the motor programme. They are often described as mini skills and are usually performed in a particular order. Therefore, sub-routines usually occur in sequence.

As a novice player develops into an expert, the sub-routines are performed almost without thought and the execution of the skill will be fluent and appear to be automatic. If this standard of control is achieved the skill is said to have been grooved or **overlearned**.

Some skills have very clear sub-routines, which can be taken out of the motor programme and practised individually. These skills are said to be **low organisation** and tend to be classified as serial tasks. The javelin throw is a good example of a skill which is low in organisation.

Isolating a sub-routine enables the teacher to focus on a particular weakness in the skill. The possibility of breaking the skill down influences how it can be taught. For example, the javelin throw could be learned one part at a time until the whole skill has been covered. Alternatively, the throw and release sub-routines could be presented first and the skill taught in reverse order. This method is known as **backward chaining** and is explained in more detail on page 119.

Skills considered to be **high organisation** will not divide into sub-routines and therefore cannot be broken down. These tend to be continuous tasks like running, skiing and dribbling in basketball or hockey.

Fig. 8.01 The javelin throw is an example of executive motor programme: grip, stance, preparation, travel and trunk position, throw and release.

Fig. 8.02 Running is one example of a skill that is both high in organisation and continuous.

These motor programmes are taught as a whole. Both methods of presentation are covered in more detail in other chapters.

TASK 1

Complete the following tasks by relating as far as possible to the activity chosen for your PPP.

1. Whilst observing a group practice session, select two motor programmes, one low organisation and one high. Discuss your choice with a partner and justify the reasons for your selection.
2. Draw a model of a motor programme from your chosen activity showing the **hierarchical structure** and **sequential organisation** of sub-routines.
3. Investigate the advantages of presenting the skill to a novice (a) in parts and (b) as a whole.

Fig. 8.03 Control is about adjusting and manipulating the body and limbs to bring about the desired response.

Motor Control

Now the make up of a motor programme is known, the next stage of investigation is to find out how a sports person can adjust their movements whilst performing. For example, there is a precise time when the gymnast will open out during a somersault and in cricket, quick adjustments are made by the hands in order to catch. These learned and intended movements do not happen by chance – they are the products of motor control. One explanation of motor skill control is given by **Open Loop and Closed Loop Theory**.

Open Loop and Closed Loop Theory (Adams)

This theory extends to three levels.

Level One

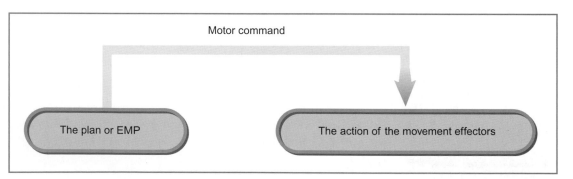

Fig. 8.04 Open loop does not engage feedback.

The plan of the action is stored in the long-term memory and comprises the EMP. When the situation demands, the plan is quickly sent to the working muscles known as the **movement effectors** or **muscle spindles** for action. This open loop is termed the **memory trace** and is responsible for starting the action. This initial

146

movement is produced without reference to **feedback**. This is because some skills happen so quickly that feedback cannot be used to correct or adjust the action. For example, when a golf drive has been started, the movement is so rapid that it is impossible to deviate from the plan. The operation of open loop occurs without thought and no attention is given to the plan after the action has begun.

Level Two

Fig. 8.05 The movement in a golf drive is so rapid feedback cannot operate once the swing has started.

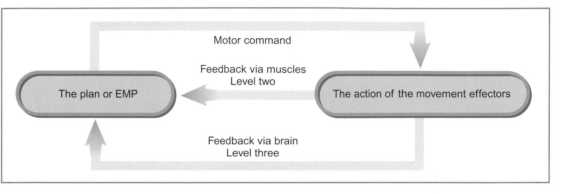

Fig. 8.07 Levels two and three involve feedback, which either completes or closes the loop.

Fig. 8.06 Level two feedback operates via the muscle spindles. Rapid adjustments can be made without thought.

Level two operates by way of a short feedback loop, which passes through the muscle spindles. It enables the performer to make rapid adjustments without thinking. For example, the skier will constantly adjust position to retain balance. Although changes are produced without thought and careful attention to the plan, the brain is told of an adjustment and this is stored for future reference. The job of the short feedback loop is to complete the skill.

Level Three

Fig. 8.08 Level three feedback loop operates at the associative stage of learning as all information regarding performance is processed cognitively.

At this level the feedback loop is longer because information on the performance is relayed back to the brain. The brain in turn controls the modification of the movement by passing corrective messages back to the working muscle. Therefore, this loop involves conscious thought and great attention to the plan. Novices at the associative stage of learning use this loop, as a high degree of concentration is required to execute the skill. As a consequence the skill appears jerky and ill-timed.

The feedback loops form a perceptual trace which is responsible for adjusting or correcting a skill if required during its execution. The perceptual trace operates by comparing the current performance of action with the plan already stored in long-term memory. If the plan matches, the skill proceeds. However, if there is fault, the skill is adjusted and this change is stored as a new motor programme. Therefore, whilst control has been gained learning has also taken place.

Fig. 8.09 Open loop (memory trace) stores the plan and starts or initiates the skill. Closed loop (perceptual trace) provides feedback and makes adjustment if required. The perceptual trace completes the skill.

Fig. 8.10 A 'novel response' is spontaneous and often creative. Such a response cannot be pre-programmed.

 KEY WORDS

Schema

A store of information and experience.

Generalised movement

Adaptations and modifications of movements which transfer the influence of one skill on the learning and performance of another.

Summary

- Open loop (level one): without feedback; unconscious control – control without thought; skill is started via the memory trace.
- Closed loop (level two): short feedback loop operates; subconscious control; smooth execution; comparison via perceptual trace.
- Closed loop (level three): longer feedback loop operates; jerky execution; perceptual trace operates at a cognitive level.

Most skills are controlled by both the open loop and closed loop systems.

Although the work of Adams on open and closed loop systems has helped the understanding of how skills are controlled and learned, there are a number of drawbacks with his theory.

1. It is not possible to store the large number of motor programmes as separate plans or memory traces for every movement in long-term memory. Therefore there is an information retention problem.
2. If it were possible to retain an infinite number of motor programmes it would be difficult for the memory trace to retrieve or recall the required plan in sufficient time to execute the skill.
3. In sport, many actions appear unusual and spontaneous. These are creative actions often seen in open skills and are called 'novel responses'. If the relevant motor programme has not been set up in long-term memory, the action of the novel response cannot be explained by his theory.

Schema Theory (Schmidt)

Whilst explaining how the novel response is made possible, **Schema Theory** answers the problems relating to storage and retrieval of information.

Schema is a build up of experiences, which the theory states can be adapted and used to meet the demands of new situations. The process of applying previous experiences to new situations is called **transfer**. Schema Theory is based on the idea that plans are not stored as separate items presented by closed loop theory. Instead they are retained in long-term memory as relationships with motor programmes. These relationships are termed **generalised movements** and they allow the performer to adapt quickly in response to a given situation.

Experience is accumulated by gathering information from four areas. These areas are termed **memory items** and represent an important basis of Schema Theory. They are explained below in terms of two attackers approaching one defender in rugby. The example focuses on the ball carrier.

Knowledge of initial conditions. This relates to whether the player in possession has previously experienced a similar situation or environment in practice or in a game. *Knowledge of response specifications.* This involves knowing what to do in this situation. Options open to the carrier would be to pass, dodge, dummy or kick.

The first and second memory items are called **Recall schema**, which has two functions:

1   to store information about the production of the movement in a generalised form
2   to start or initiate the movement.

Knowledge of sensory consequences. Every successful action has a particular touch or feel. This is referred to as the **feeling tone**. In this case the player would need to estimate how hard to pass the ball and again previous experience is the guide. Acquiring the correct feel or **kinaesthesis** is a major factor in controlling and learning motor skills.

Knowledge of outcome. This memory item involves knowing what is likely to happen once the movement has been completed. For example, the dummy pass would send the defender in the wrong direction.

The third and fourth memory items are called **Recognition schema**, which has two functions.

1   to control the movement throughout production
2   to form an evaluation regarding the effectiveness of the response after performance. This feedback of information enables the player to store additional motor programme relationships, which in turn are adapted in response to novel situations. The schema of the performer is now said to have expanded and learning has taken place.

TASK 2

1   Observe a live or videoed performance of your chosen practical activity and select one skill from the performance. By applying the theories covered in this unit, discuss with a partner how the skill might be controlled during execution.

2   Consider the strategies that a teacher or coach could use to expand the schema of a performer in your chosen activity.

3   Design and deliver a practice session for a small group which will broaden schema.

4   Classify a skill from your chosen activity and analyse the practice requirements which would help the performer to acquire the skill of control.

Revise as you go! Test your knowledge and understanding

- What is meaning of the term 'motor programme'?
- Describe a sub-routine.
- Explain the meaning of hierarchical and sequential organisation of a motor programme.
- Identify the meaning of high and low organisation of skill.

- In what ways does the organisation of the skill influence the presentation of the skill during a practice session?
- Describe open loop control.
- Explain the function of the memory trace.
- What is the meaning of the term 'feedback'?
- Outline how feedback operates in level two and three of the closed loop model.
- Explain the purpose of the perceptual trace.
- What is the meaning of the term 'schema'?
- List the four memory items of Schema Theory.
- Describe the function of recall and recognition schema.
- Why is Schema Theory considered to be an explanation as to how skills are learned and controlled?
- What measures would a good coach take during practice sessions to ensure that the schema of a performer was expanded?
- List the reasons why a broad schema gives an advantage to a performer in sport.

Sharpen up your exam technique!

1 What is a motor programme?   (1 mark)

2 How is a motor programme created and operated?   (4 marks)

Chapter 9 **Learning Skills in Physical Education**

Learning Objectives

By the end of this chapter you will be able to:
- Understand the theories of learning.
- Apply the theories of learning to practical situations.
- Demonstrate knowledge of motivation theories and show how they relate to learning.

Connectionist or Association Theories

Connectionist or Association Theories rely on the learner linking or connecting a stimulus from the environment with a movement response. The stimulus may take the form of a problem. For example, in badminton the shuttle may be hit high and deep into the opponent's court. In response the receiver could play an overhead clear shot. If successful, this response becomes connected or associated with the stimulus and stored in the long-term memory. Connections are called 'learning bonds' which can be recalled and repeated in similar environmental conditions.

Reinforcement

The process causing behaviour to reoccur by strengthening the S/R learning bond.

Positive reinforcement

The presentation of approval, which increases the probability of behaviour reoccurring. Approval may be praise or some form of 'satisfier'.

Negative reinforcement

The withdrawal of disapproval when desired behaviour prevails. Disapproval may have taken the form of criticism or some form of 'annoyer'. Positive and negative reinforcement strengthen the learning bond.

Learning bonds are strengthened through repetition, for example, practising the same response to the same stimulus repeatedly. Strengthening is also brought about through a process called **reinforcement** which increases the probability of behaviour reoccurring.

A psychologist named Thorndyke believed that learning takes place when a stimulus is connected with a response to form a learning bond. He applied three rules to this theory.

1 *Law of Effect* – positive reinforcement increases the chances of behaviour reoccurring.
2 *Law of Exercise* – the more often a response is reinforced the stronger the learning bond will become.
3 *Law of Readiness* – learning by connecting can only take place when the nervous system has reached an appropriate stage of maturation.

Operant Conditioning

Operant Conditioning is a major connectionist theory and is concerned with changing the response in a given situation. Skinner presented this theory after

Fig. 9.01 A skill drill is a repetitive practice designed to strengthen a learning bond. The teacher would constantly reinforce the skills as they occur.

TASK 1

1   What is a skill drill?
2   By applying the laws of Thorndyke, explain how a skill drill strengthens the learning bond.

experimenting with the behaviour of rats in a maze. To understand how it relates to PE, four points need to be remembered and applied to a practical situation.

1   It is necessary to structure a situation to bring about a desired response. This involves arranging the practice environment so it is a copy of the game situation.
2   This structure allows 'behaviour shaping' to take place. Behaviour shaping enables complex forms of behaviour to be learned in parts or small steps.
3   Performance will take the form of trial and error. This means the player will attempt the structured practice. Sometimes the wrong response will emerge but at other times the response will be correct.
4   Apply reinforcement to the response made by the player.

Practical Application of Operant Conditioning

For example, teaching a badminton smash:

1   Structure the environment to bring about the desired response. The coach would repeatedly serve the shuttle high and deep.
2   Behaviour shaping. The nature of the serve will induce the smash shot.

3 Trial and error. The player can attempt the skill but the result may not always be correct.

4 Reinforcement. Positive reinforcement or approval should be given to the correct response.

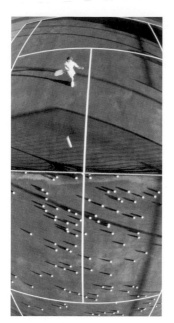

Fig. 9.02 Operant Conditioning involves structuring the practice to bring about the correct or desired response.

TASK 2

1 Design a practice session using Operant Conditioning to enhance the skills of catching and passing in netball.

2 Select a skill from an activity of your choice and say how you would coach that skill using Operant Conditioning.

3 Give reasons to suggest why a good coach would avoid using punishment.

Cognitive Learning Theory

The major **cognitive** learning theory is the **Gestalt Theory**. Gestalt theorists believe that skills are best presented to the learner as whole problems. The learner will solve the problem by drawing on previous experience and by developing a **perception** of what is required to answer the task successfully. The learner must be motivated and have a positive self-image in order to reach a solution. When it is reached, insight is developed and this marks a permanent stage in learning.

The main differences between connectionist theories and Cognitive Learning Theory are as follows:

KEY WORDS

Perception

The interpretation of sensation. It is influenced by many factors, e.g. age, expectation, arousal level, intelligence, ability and previous experience. It is vital to the process of decision making.

Cognitive

A cognitive process is a thinking process and focuses on brain activity.

Mechanical guidance

The use of an aid or object to give the learner a 'feel' for the skill, e.g. a float, cone or tumbling harness.

Connectionist – skills are best delivered in parts. The development of the learning bond by connecting the stimulus with the response explains how we learn. *Cognitive* – skills are best delivered as a whole. The development of insight occurring when the whole problem is solved explains how we learn.

An example of the cognitive theory at work could be related to swimming. Gestalt theorists would argue that stroke action is best taught as a whole and at no time should leg and arm action be practised in isolation. This gives opportunity to the individual to 'work out' the most effective action for him or herself. However, for the non-swimmer, buoyancy aids would need to be used. This is a form of **mechanical guidance** and would serve to simplify the whole task. Gestalt theorists believe part learning to be inefficient because it does not present all the information necessary for the learner to develop total understanding or insight.

Observational Learning

Observational learning is a form of visual guidance usually associated with demonstration. The aim of a demonstration is to present the learner with a visual model which can be copied and matched. Learning by imitation is a very powerful principle being both time saving and more interesting than a lengthy verbal explanation. Demonstrations are important at all stages of learning. During the

Fig. 9.03 Creating, conditioning or adapting games rather than perfecting techniques in isolation best accomplishes learning. This is the view of the Cognitive Learning Theorists.

Fig. 9.04 Learning through demonstration is effective only if pupils are attentive, motivated and have the basic ability to reproduce the skill.

cognitive phase the novice will be able to grasp the general idea of what is required and be motivated by the exhibition. At the autonomous stage a demonstration is useful in highlighting detailed and specific points in performance.

Learning by demonstration is not a fail-safe method. A psychologist named Bandura indicates that observational learning takes place only if the learner can put four elements into place.

1   *Attention.* The learner must focus directly on the model. The teacher can help this process by telling the learner to watch for or attend to specific items in the demonstration such as the hip turn before the discus is released. This instruction is called verbal guidance. To hold the attention of the learner, the model of performance must be brief, attractive and meaningful.

2   *Retention.* The image of the demonstration must be stored or retained by the learner if it is to be copied successfully. Verbal guidance will prevent information overload and help to hold the picture in the short-term memory, but the demonstration should be repeated several times as insurance. The observer should be encouraged to picture the image in the mind's eye. This process is called mental rehearsal. A good teaching technique to aid retention is to connect a second image to the demonstration. For example, to be told to 'put the ball onto the shelf' helps to achieve the correct trajectory of the set shot. This technique is called symbolic rehearsal.

3   *Motor reproduction.* The learner must have the maturation, confidence and physical ability to copy or replicate the skill being modelled.

4   *Motivation.* A key element in learning and performance is motivation. In order to reproduce the model the observer must have the drive or motivation to learn.

TASK 3

1   With a partner, identify and explain how the observer would respond to a demonstration in order to learn effectively.

2   Demonstrate a new skill to one group and use a verbal explanation to convey the skill to another. Identify the more successful method and give reasons why it was more effective.

Phases of Movement Skill Learning

Fitts and Posner (1967) were amongst the first psychologists to examine how motor skills in sport were learned. They were concerned to know how long a novice needed to practise before it could be claimed a skill had been truly learned and what was the most difficult period of learning. They concluded that three stages existed in learning and although the boundaries between each stage remain unclear there are considerable implications for both teaching and learning. These stages can determine how difficult the practice should be, the nature of feedback given by the teacher and when to progress to a more advanced skill.

Cognitive Stage

During this initial phase the learner is thinking about the skill in order to formulate a mental picture of the whole plan or motor programme involving all the linking sub-routines. This stage may occur directly after demonstration (see section on observational learning) and although no physical action is taking place the learner is immersed fully in the process of mental rehearsal.

Associative Stage

This is the practice phase. Performers may remain in this phase for many years and some never progress. During this stage progress takes place as the learner begins to eliminate mistakes. Concentration is intense as the skill is regarded as an executive motor programme requiring level three information processing control (see closed loop theory of control on page 148). The timing of the action improves as the performer learns to attend only to specific and relevant cues. Demonstration, mental rehearsal and positive reinforcement are vital at this stage if learning is to continue.

Most importantly, the learner will begin to make use of internal feedback (see kinaesthetic feedback, level two of closed loop theory on page 149). The 'feel' of successful execution will enhance learning and improve the fluency and consistency of the action.

Autonomous Stage

This is the phase of expertise and is the stage of automatic control. The performer can now execute the skill with the minimum of conscious thought and concentration can be directed to peripheral factors in the environmental display. The teacher can now focus on the fine detail of the skill and make use of specific and negative feedback to ensure perfection.

In order to guarantee that the performer remains at the autonomous stage of learning it will be necessary to return to the associative or even the cognitive stage. Once again, mental rehearsal is an important process even at this stage. Going 'back to basics' will endorse learning and prevent bad habits emerging in performance.

Furthermore, because the skill has become so well learned (over-learned or grooved) it is relegated to the status of a sub-routine and becomes part of a new programme. The implication for the teacher is that new learning can take place to incorporate the previous skill. For example, the now well-grooved skill of dribbling a basketball becomes a sub-routine of a lay-up shot.

On attaining the autonomous stage the expert can be encouraged to contribute to their own learning by way of self-analysis, mental rehearsal and personal motivation through goal setting.

Fig. 9.05 The expert player no longer needs to look at the ball.

The child relies heavily on external feedback. Hence there is great concentration on the ball because the correct 'feeling tone' has yet to be learned. Feedback should be positive and general. Demonstration and mental rehearsal are important at this stage.

Methods of Guidance

There are four methods of guidance that can be used by the teacher or coach to help the learning process:

1   visual guidance
2   verbal guidance

3   manual guidance
4   mechanical guidance.

Visual Guidance

The benefits of demonstration at every phase of learning have been considered previously. There are other forms of visual guidance such as wall charts, pictures, diagrams and models. All are good in the early stages of learning for highlighting technical points in complex skills. However, static displays quickly lose their impact as the learner enters the associative stage or practice phase of learning.

An alternative way of using visual guidance to enhance a particular skill would involve changing or modifying the visual display in the learning environment. For example, a badminton court could be reduced in width to focus the learner on playing deep shots. Similarly, a basketball court may be chalked as an indication of the take off point for a lay-up shot. In this context visual guidance is used to reduce information overload. This would be useful for a novice as the full environmental display is often confusing.

Verbal Guidance

Giving verbal instruction is at the centre of most teaching environments. Even in Discovery style initial verbal instruction is required. It provides information about the very first aspects of skill and is used to direct attention to the key points during demonstration.

KEY WORDS

Concurrent feedback

Feedback given by the coach during the skill.

This form of guidance is used to best effect in open skills when quick decisions and rapid body adaptations are needed. Furthermore, it is easier to tell players about complicated tactics rather than to show them. In closed skills of a continuous nature advice can be given quickly to improve form. For example, the instruction 'high knees' will remind the sprinter to emphasise leg action. This **concurrent feedback** is given by the coach/teacher while the skill is actually being performed.

This kind of verbal prompting is best used at the autonomous stage of learning. An expert in shot putt, for example, would understand the instruction to 'widen the base' but this advice would be meaningless to a novice.

Verbal guidance can also create an image of the skill. If the long jumper is told to make a body shape like a long bow after take off this will help to achieve the desired hip extension necessary for flight. This image formation was referred to earlier as **symbolic rehearsal**.

Manual Guidance

Manual guidance methods involve the coach holding and physically manipulating the body of the learner to induce the correct pattern of movement. For example guiding the arm through a forehand shot in tennis.

Mechanical Guidance

Mechanical guidance makes use of an object or piece of apparatus to shape the skill. A tumbling harness in gymnastics is an example of mechanical aids.

Fig. 9.06 An example of manual guidance.

Both forms of physical guidance are useful in the early phases of learning as they develop confidence and help to establish a kinaesthetic feel of the new skill. However, there are drawbacks. The learner may become reliant on such aids and never progress. The expert would receive limited value, as the constraint does not replicate the true feel of the skill. Finally, mechanical guidance is used to eliminate error and gives no opportunity to the learner to correct their own mistakes.

Fig. 9.07 An example of mechanical guidance.

TASK 4
1   What are the advantages and disadvantages of both manual and mechanical guidance?
2   Using your chosen skill as a focus, think of some verbal guidance strategies and test their effectiveness in a practical lesson.

Transfer of Learning

In the context of PE, transfer means the influence that one skill has on the learning and performance of another. The process is extremely important to the acquisition of movement skills because practically all learning is based on some form of transfer.

The term 'transfer' has been mentioned already and understanding the link between transfer and Schema Theory is a key issue. It is thought that we rarely learn a totally new skill after the early years of childhood and new patterns of movement arise out of previous experiences. This idea also connects with the cognitive theory of learning. It is now important to directly address the process of transfer.

Positive Transfer

Often performers who are good at one sport tend to be proficient in a number of activities. This may be because they have obvious natural abilities such as balance, co-ordination and explosive strength. Skills in a number of sports may also be explained in that patterns of movement relate positively across different activities. This relationship is **positive transfer**.

In the primary school the emphasis should be placed on the teaching of very basic skills called fundamental movement patterns. The Australians present these basic patterns very successfully. The State of Victoria has established a 'Fundamental Skills Programme' in which skills such as kicking, catching and overarm throwing are taught and tested. Children develop a 'pool of experience' or a movement schema, which will transfer to more difficult motor programmes later on.

Fig. 9.08 The overarm throw must be taught in the early years as it transfers positively to many skills. Some of which are shown in the pictures.

Negative Transfer

Transfer can also be negative in that one skill can impede the learning and performance of another. An obvious example of this would be the flexible wrist action required in a badminton or squash shot which conflicts with the firm wrist action required in a tennis cross-court stroke. Therefore, the teacher should not have winter tennis sessions operating whilst badminton is being taught.

Transfer Appropriate Processing

Even if the physical performance of the motor skill transfers negatively, the cognitive information processing requirements may be similar. For example, in order to rally in both badminton and tennis, the cognitive information processing requirements are similar. Shots need to be timed and directed over a net. The relevant term in this case is 'transfer appropriate processing'. Therefore, a new skill may be different from any pattern performed before but if the information processing requirements are similar then positive transfer could occur.

TASK 5
Identify the positive and negative elements of transfer that may exist between the following pairs of activities.

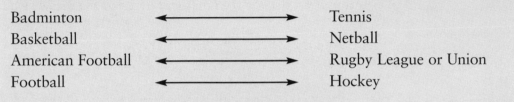

Badminton	←——————————→	Tennis
Basketball	←——————————→	Netball
American Football	←——————————→	Rugby League or Union
Football	←——————————→	Hockey

The teacher would consider other elements of transfer.

Proactive transfer. This occurs when previously learned skills influence the learning of new skills. For example, an overarm throw must be taught before teaching tennis serving.

Retroactive transfer. This takes place when newly learned skills influence skills already learned. A goalkeeper changing his sport to rugby union may learn how to jump in the line. Upon reverting to football his previously learned catching skills could show improvement.

Bilateral transfer. Skills can be transferred from one side of the body to another. There is great advantage in using both hands and both feet to equal effect in sport. For example, the dominantly right-handed basketball player would be an asset if the lay-up shot could be executed with equal proficiency with the left hand.

To acquire this skill the player will need to analyse how the skill is performed right-handedly and work out how to reproduce it through the left hand. This requires transfer from theory to practice.

Principle to skill. The ideas and strategies of one game may relate positively to another. For example, possession is retained in hockey and football by passing in triangles and in both games the pass can be made to space or to a player.

Near transfer. Tasks given in practice are very similar to the game situation, for example, in unopposed rugby.

Far transfer. The practice tasks are different from those experienced in the actual game but give experiences which could be adapted and used in a variety of situations. An example is five-a-side rugby permitting forward passing.

Ability to skill. Some people have natural abilities from which specific skills can be nurtured. Someone who is fast and powerful has the potential to acquire the skill of sprinting whilst balance and co-ordination are the prerequisites of the games player.

Practice to performance. Match and competition conditions must be replicated precisely in practice to ensure a link is made between 'rehearsal and reality'. For example, a team may practise set moves in training against active opposition.

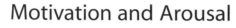

Motivation and Arousal

The term **motivation** implies drive and energy. It shows itself in determination and perseverance during practice and without it learning would not be possible.

Teachers, coaches and performers must be aware of the importance of motivation and understand the two major sources of the drive to succeed.

1 *Intrinsic motivation* occurs when an individual participates in an activity for its own sake. For example, a skier may learn to snowboard because success will bring personal satisfaction.
2 *Extrinsic motivation* occurs when people perform and learn in order to receive material gain. Perfecting fundamental gymnastic movements to gain certification or to win a trophy are examples of rewards, which generate extrinsic motivation.

Extrinsic reward is an effective agent to increase the motivation of the first time performer, but it must be given sparingly. Tangible reward can eventually be a drawback to the learning process. Those who are intrinsically motivated are more likely to continue in participation than those who seek reward.

Motivation has two components:

1 **Intensity of behaviour** refers to the amount of emotional energy shown by the individual. To understand this idea think of a continuum with one extreme being deep sleep while the other extreme is high or frenetic energy.

Deep sleep ⟵————————————————⟶ Frenetic energy

2 **Direction of behaviour** refers to the way arousal is used to achieve an ambition or goal.

The level of **arousal** greatly affects our capacity to learn and later to control psychomotor skill in the context of a sports situation. To understand the extent to which levels of arousal are influencing factors it is essential to be aware of the theories of arousal.

Fig. 9.09 Learning to snowboard for its own sake and personal satisfaction is an example of intrinsic motivation.

Drive Theory

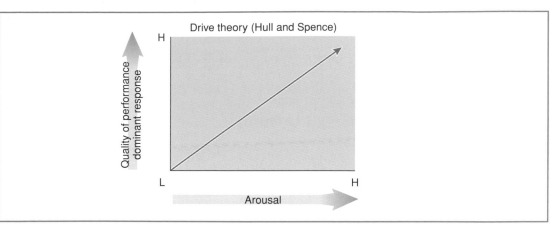

Fig. 9.10

Drive Theory indicates a relationship between arousal and performance. An increase in arousal is proportional to an increase in the quality of physical performance. However, the quality of performance depends on how well a skill has been learned.

KEY WORDS

Dominant response

The behaviour most likely to occur.

Actions that have already been learned, termed 'learned behaviours', tend to be our **dominant responses**. A dominant response is the behaviour most likely to occur when we are pressured to respond. Hull suggested that as arousal increases, as would happen in a competitive situation or when a novice feels they are being assessed, there is a greater likelihood of our dominant response occurring.

High arousal would be beneficial at the expert stage (autonomous phase of learning) because our dominant behaviour would tend towards the correct response. However, at the novice stage of performance (associative stage of learning) our dominant behaviour is likely to exhibit mistakes.

Drive Theory indicates that arousal level has a serious influence on learning. The novice would learn and perform more effectively in conditions of low arousal. A calm emotional state would enable full concentration to be given to external feedback and the sequential execution of sub-routines. Sub-routines cannot be 'run off' automatically as they require thought and attention in the early stages of learning (see closed loop theory of control and phases of motor skill learning on pages 148–50).

Fig. 9.11 Performing for certificates, medals and social reinforcement is an example of extrinsic motivation.

TASK 6

Look again at the illustration of the snowboarders, left and on page 160.
1   Referring to Drive Theory, discuss the reasons why the novice would learn more effectively in conditions of low arousal whilst the expert would perform best when experiencing high arousal.

continued

2   Consider the measures that you would take to ensure that the novice was in a calm emotional state during the snowboarding lesson.

3   How could the arousal level of the expert be increased to ensure that top performance potential was achieved?

Inverted U Theory

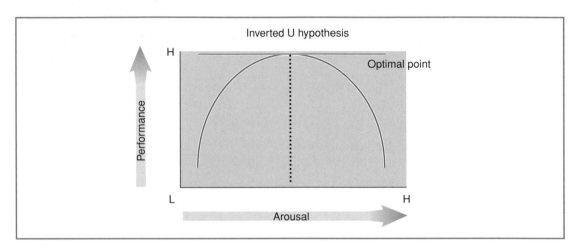

Fig. 9.12

The Inverted U Theory indicates or predicts that as arousal increases so does the quality of performance. This improvement continues up to a point mid-way along the arousal axis. This point is called the optimum point or threshold of arousal and indicates that the best performance occurs at moderate levels of arousal. After this optimal point, if arousal continues to increase, the capacity to both learn and perform a motor skill will deteriorate.

It will be evident later on that every individual has a different optimal point and this has significant meaning for all who are involved in sport. Conditions of both under-arousal and over-arousal severely limit learning potential. However, a person at the optimal state will learn more effectively. The reasons for this are given below.

KEY WORDS

Attention field

Awareness of the environment.

Under-arousal. In these conditions it is difficult for the performer to direct and focus attention on the display. Review the work on observational learning and remember how important it was for the learner to attend carefully to the demonstration. When focus is lost the attention field of the performer or learner widens excessively. This means that attention is given to many items in the immediate environment but is not directed sufficiently to the most important cues. This condition seriously limits concentration and the potential to learn. The learner will appear to be in a daydream and would be lacking in concentration. In these circumstances the process of selective attention does not operate and information overload will prevent accurate decision making.

KEY WORDS

Hypervigilance

Panic or extreme anxiety.

Selective attention

The process of directing the focus of attention.

Cue utilisation

Focusing on the most important information from the environment.

Variability in practice

A teaching technique in which the drill or practice to attain a goal is changed at regular intervals.

Over-arousal. With this condition the novice will be in a state of high anxiety and, as with under-arousal, the effectiveness of learning is severely limited. In this case the field of attention narrows excessively and as a result the appropriate environmental cues are missed and not detected. The condition of over-arousal can be described as a highly energised state, recognised as panic. The technical term for this feeling of nervousness is **hypervigilance**. At this point **selective attention** cannot operate, concentration is impeded and decisions are illogical.

Optimal arousal. This is the perfect state in which the potential for learning can be maximised. The attention field of the individual adjusts to the ideal width and as a result the learner or performer is able to concentrate fully. The increased capacity to concentrate means the most important information can be detected from the environment and logical decisions can be made. The process of selecting the most important information is called **Cue Utilisation Hypothesis**. Optimal arousal levels differ in accordance with the individual's stage of learning.

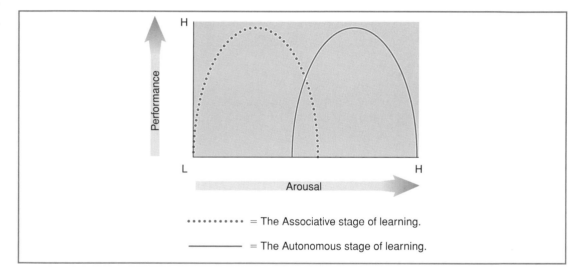

Fig. 9.13

Drive Reduction Theory

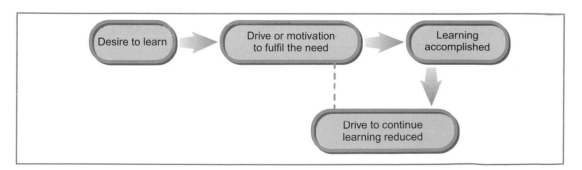

Fig. 9.14 When the learning goal has been achieved the desire to continue to learn increases. The dotted line implies that a new goal should be introduced.

Fig. 9.15 Setting short-term targets and long-term goals will improve the effectiveness of learning.

This theory predicts that an individual is initially highly motivated to learn a new skill, for example, a parallel turn in skiing. Once the skill has been mastered and the need to learn is established, the drive to continue learning is reduced. This reduction in motivation is likely to cause a deterioration in performance. The performer at the autonomous stage of learning may suffer from reduced drive. Measures taken to prevent a drop in motivation would centre upon the issuing of new challenges in the form of higher targets or goals. In addition, the coach must take care to vary the practices in training sessions even in closed tasks. Repetition of the same practice drills will result in boredom and bring about drive reduction or inhibition. This technique of changing the approach during practice is called 'variability in practice'.

Practice Conditions

Massed and Distributed Practice

Massed practice involves short sessions with no breaks within the time given for practice. This type of practice is good when a skill is simple and it appears to suit discrete tasks. A set shot in basketball would be an example of such a skill. For this type of presentation to succeed the motivation to learn must be high and pupils should have the ability to cope with the mastery of the whole skill.

Fig. 9.16 Continuous skills are taught most effectively through distributed practice.

Distributed practice involves the inclusion of breaks into practice and is suited to continuous tasks which may become tiring. For example, rowing would best be taught through distributed practice. The breaks would allow the learner to engage in mental practice, which is a process where the performer would 'run through' the task at a cognitive level. Research has proved distributed practice to be more effective than massed practice in the learning of movement skills.

Mental Rehearsal

Mental rehearsal, often referred to as mental practice or imagery, contributes to the effective learning and performance of movement skills in sport. It is a cognitive process in which the performer will picture the execution of a skill, bringing to mind the kinaesthesis of the movement and the desired outcome.

Mental practice has a place as a pre-event strategy for expert performers. For example, an accomplished long jumper would visualise the approach, take off, flight and landing techniques prior to performance. More significantly to this section of this book, mental practice plays an important part in the learning process having been proven to be almost as good as physical practice.

Some studies indicate that mental practice has a direct physical influence on performance by stimulating tiny muscle movements that will be used in the skill. However, the major role of mental rehearsal is to serve a perceptual function. A period of mental imagery during a break in physical practice can help the learner to

Fig. 9.17 Mental rehearsal creates a picture in the mind of the athlete to help learning and performance of movement skills.

solve a problem, which may have arisen during practice. This could be one reason why the quality of performance increases after a rest period. Furthermore, mental rehearsal enables the learner to understand the sequencing of the movement more clearly and how best to concentrate attention on the most relevant stimuli. Imagery will also help to groove the correct response so that a clear picture of the skill can be retained in the long-term memory.

Revise as you go! Test your knowledge and understanding

- In relation to Connectionist Theory, explain the meaning of the term 'learning bond'.
- Define the process known as reinforcement.
- Identify the four key elements that make up Operant Conditioning.
- Explain how the Cognitive Theory of Learning works.
- Name and explain four forms of guidance.
- What is the meaning of the term 'transfer of learning'?
- Explain why demonstration is an effective teaching method.
- Identify and explain the four sub-processes of Observational Learning Theory.
- Define the terms 'motivation' and 'arousal'.
- Draw and label a diagram of Drive Theory.
- Draw and label a diagram of the Inverted U Theory.
- Explain why learning is most effective at the optimal level of arousal.
- Explain the terms 'massed practice' and 'distributed practice'.

Sharpen up your exam technique!

1   What is a stimulus–response bond? How can a PE teacher ensure that it is strengthened when teaching swimming or athletics?   (5 marks)

2   What is meant by the *cognitive theory* of skill learning? Give a practical example from your activity experience where the application of this theory led to improvement.   (4 marks)

3   Explain four methods of guidance and show how they could be used to develop swimming skills.   (5 marks)

4   Name and explain three different types of transfer. Provide an explanation for each type in the context of a sporting example.   (6 marks)

5   Define *motivation* and use practical examples from PE to describe two methods available to motivate performers.   (3 marks)

Chapter 10 **Physical Education and Sport in Schools**

Learning Objectives

At the end of this chapter you should be able to:
- Understand that PE and sport make a field of study.
- Describe our field of study as play, physical recreation, sport and PE (with the sub-categories of outdoor recreation and outdoor education).
- Identify both shared and differing characteristics of each concept.
- Understand the broad concept of leisure.
- Analyse school PE as a subject and as a valuable lifetime experience.
- Explain outdoor education with reference to pollution, appreciation of the environment and both real and perceived risk.

Introduction

In this section we will be looking at and investigating the contemporary scene in the UK – that is, some of the issues and aspects of sport and PE that are relevant to us today. The Contemporary Studies module is divided into two sections, which will be covered over the next four chapters, as follows:

Specification Section 1) PE in Schools

Chapter 10: PE and sport in schools

Specification Section 2) Sport in Society

Chapter 11: Concepts of sport in society

Chapter 12: Sport and culture

Chapter 13: Sporting issues analysis

The conceptual area relates to both PE in schools and sport in society, so will be covered in Chapters 10 and 11. Most people at some time in their lives have played games. People also watch and perhaps take part in sport, have experienced PE from a young age, and may regularly use the local leisure centre or recreation centre. But have you ever thought about what each of these words, along with the linked concepts of outdoor education and outdoor recreation actually mean? That will be our task. It is important that the true meaning of each of these concepts is teased out so that similarities, differences and overlaps between them are clear and exceptions to rules can be identified and explained.

In Chapter 12 the link between sport and culture will be identified. A global view will be taken and analysis made of sports and physical activities in some other societies. We will try to judge why particular sports and pastimes are pursued and how they reflect the cultures in which they exist. The most dominant and popular sports and activities in the commercial setting of the United States, for example, contrast greatly with those existing in remote Pacific islands and tribal cultures of Africa. The task is to analyse the differences.

Chapter 13 is issues-based and is dominated by the two central themes of **mass participation** and sporting **excellence** in the UK. Factors affecting both people's likelihood of taking part in sport on a regular basis and their chance of making it to a level of excellence and success in international competition will be the focus. The pursuit of mass participation and sporting excellence in the UK is not an isolated concept but is affected by and has an effect upon society and the people within it. Every day, information about sport and physical performance is presented in the newspapers and on television – in fact, via every aspect of the multi-faceted and vast media machine. Sport has become part of the entertainment industry, rather than just something that a minority of people do. This shift in emphasis over the last 20 or 30 years has clearly changed the nature of sport in this country. Today we have problems associated with bad behaviour by some performers and some spectators; huge multinational and small local companies invest millions of pounds in sponsorship; the influence of the media is profound.

In order to study concepts and sporting issues, the work of agencies involved in the administration of sport in the UK needs to be explained – organizations like UK Sport, Sports Coach UK and individual National Governing Bodies (NGBs) of Sport, not forgetting of course the massive impact of the National Lottery since 1995. These influences must therefore be assessed, with particular reference to their contributions to mass participation and sporting excellence.

KEY WORDS

Concept

An idea, thought, view or theory about something.

Field of study

Our focus area which includes different types of physical performance.

PE and Sport in Schools

All of the concepts below make up our **field of study**. Anyone playing tennis, for example, may be pursuing the activity in a number of different ways.

Play

Tennis (or a form of it) can be played in the garden by children or by parents with their children. The level of skill is likely to be quite low and of secondary importance to the experience of playing; the level of organisation is also likely to be quite low. Organisation in this context refers to the structure of the game, which includes timings, boundaries and how strictly any agreed or imposed rules are adhered to. The equipment being used may be plastic, too big, old or improvised.

Recreation

Tennis may also be played as a form of physical recreation. The term 'recreation' implies enjoyment, which is likely to be a key motive. The game would certainly be

Fig. 10.01 Defining the field of study. Is this 'play', 'physical recreation', 'sport' or 'PE'?

recognised as tennis, yet would be different in some respects to that played at a major tournament such as Wimbledon. What would be the differences? The skill level and outcome (or result) will probably be of secondary importance to the experience or process of taking part, as would be the reasons for being there in the first place. Physical recreation would be more structured than play, but with plenty of scope or flexibility for the changing of rules, and taking breaks for drinks, rest or chats!

Physical Education

Let's now consider a tennis experience you may have had in a PE situation in your school or college. It probably involved your PE teacher demonstrating and explaining certain skills and tactics to do with the game, followed by practice within a small group or team game situation (depending on the numbers in the group and the facilities available), with the possibility of a full game towards the end of the lesson. Depending on your interest, skill level and commitment, you might also have had an opportunity to play tennis during lunchtime or break time 'clubs' or even to represent your school in a tennis team. Irrespective of the specific time (lesson time, lunch time or after school), and the skills taught by your PE teacher, the need for appropriate behaviour and attitudes both on and off the court would have been stressed. It seems then, that PE is about more than just physical skills. There are several dimensions or aspects to physical activity within the scope of PE in a school situation. These issues will be explored in greater depth later in the chapter.

Sport

Finally, tennis as sport needs to be explored. The annual Wimbledon Lawn Tennis Championships are the obvious example here, as are league and cup competitions at club level or inter-school fixtures. Some internal school competitions could also be classified as sport. So what are the characteristics of tennis in a sporting context? The level of skill is likely to have increased significantly from the previous situations, along with the level of organisation. There will now be strict adherence to Governing Body rules, timings and boundaries. The outcome or result is also of increased significance, perhaps even at the loss of enjoyment or personal satisfaction.

The Four 'W' Questions

So far we have looked at physical performance as it falls within the four activity categories of play, physical recreation, PE and sport. It has already become apparent that things seem to change as we move from one to the other. In clarifying these changes it can be useful to focus attention on what can be called the 'W' questions.

1 **Who** is taking part?   3 **Where** is it taking place?
2 **When** is it happening?   4 **Why** are they taking part?

We could also add the question 'how?' to this list and assess the level of organisation and commitment involved as well as the attitude of the performer (what is going on in the performer's head). Clear and detailed answers to these questions will probably tell you everything you need to know. The clarification and detail can be added by expanding the questions:

1 Who? – Adults or children?
2 When? – Strict time or more flexible time?
3 Where? – Purpose built high-tech facility or the back garden?
4 Why? – **Intrinsic** or **extrinsic** reasons? (self-satisfaction or for prizes or prestige?)
5 How? – In a highly organised and structured situation or a more flexible one?
   With an attitude of fun or one of serious commitment to the outcome?

TASK 1

Using answers from the 'W' questions, write your own slogan or definition for each of the four central concepts of:

- play
- physical recreation
- PE
- sport.

You may have noticed that the language used so far has been fairly safe. Definites have been avoided, and phrases such as 'is likely to be', 'could be' and 'would often be' have been used. Such is the nature of philosophical study and debate, within which this conceptual area of study falls. Be prepared then, to be open minded and flexible in your own attitudes and opinions.

TASK 2

Local facilities may be called sports centres, leisure centres, or recreation centres. Based on your knowledge so far identify any differences in approach that you might expect from each.

(a) Who would be attracted to each centre?
(b) What would be the main aim/focus of each centre?

Leisure, Recreation, Outdoor Recreation and Outdoor Education

Leisure is a broader concept and can be described as an umbrella term. Figure 10.02 illustrates that people play, do physical recreation and might pursue sport in their leisure time. PE is different in that it is a compulsory school subject. In this context therefore, PE is not pursued in leisure time. It is placed under the leisure umbrella though, because school PE programmes have the potential to 'educate for leisure' and become 'lifetime sports'. Children may try a range of activities, some or even one of which are then pursued in leisure time after the school day, or after school age and into adulthood.

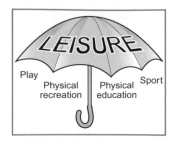

Fig. 10.02 Field of study.

KEY WORDS

Leisure

Free time in which the individual has freedom to choose.

Leisure

'*Leisure is a time when there is an opportunity for choice.*'

We come across the term '**leisure**' all the time. Leisure management and leisure and recreation courses are now commonplace at various levels of study. Leisure centres can be found in most areas. We are bombarded with advertisements for labour saving devices that will supposedly increase our leisure time and those in the leisure industry compete ferociously for our time (and money). So what exactly is leisure?

It can be explained as the time that an individual has (or sets aside) when they are not working or doing things that are essential for life (like sleeping) or considered absolutely necessary (like some household tasks and responsibilities).

TASK 3

1 In pairs, suggest reasons for the growth of leisure time in the last 50 years.
2 Build up a spider diagram of possible leisure activities. Include your own favourite activities and those of people of different ages, abilities and interest groups.

Leisure activities are pursued in free time. As each individual has their own interests and decides on their own leisure pursuits, the range of things that can be done in free time is enormous. The activities may be:

• active (e.g. going to the gym or cycling) or passive (e.g. cooking or reading)
• pursued inside or outside the home
• at a cheap natural facility such as the countryside or a more expensive purpose built facility such as a theme park or an ice rink.

The fun starts when you argue that the person is:

• going to the gym, but doesn't really enjoy it and is there purely for health reasons
• cycling to work as a necessity because the car has broken down
• cooking in a hurry to feed the family before they all rush off to their own leisure activities – the cook is simply providing food necessary for life not a social or culinary experience
• reading a long and boring document connected with household administration or work.

Hopefully we would agree that in these specific cases, the activities should not be classed as leisure. The person cycling to work has not freely chosen to do so, the person at the gym is not enjoying it, the cook is fulfilling a responsibility and the reader would probably prefer to be reading something different.

It is important to consider the state of mind with which an individual approaches an activity. This is central to whether it can be classified as leisure. For one person, gardening might be a passionate hobby giving relaxation, whereas for another it could be a dreaded and resented chore. It seems that we cannot easily define leisure in terms of the actual activity.

It would be better to define it in less definite terms, focusing on the 'W' questions and on outcome – what the chosen activity does for the individual.

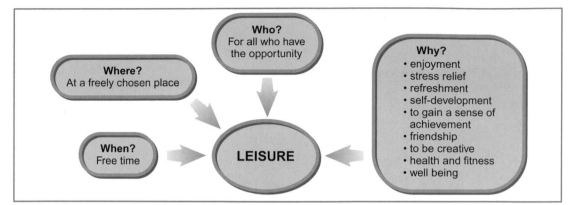

Fig. 10.03

TASK 4

In groups of four, each identify three leisure activities and analyse your reasons for doing them. What do they do for you? Draw a chart of your group's findings.

HOT TIPS

Remember that leisure is an experience as well as an activity.

It seems that leisure is a bit more complicated that we first thought. It is more than just free time and more than just an activity. The freely chosen activity is simply the vehicle, which allows you to experience and benefit from leisure.

So what about outdoor education and outdoor recreation? The word 'outdoor' implies the direct use of the natural environment for either recreation or education. So, by walking in the hills, canoeing down rivers, camping in forests or abseiling down a rock face, we are experiencing either recreation or education in the great outdoors. In other words, the outcome may be enjoyment orientated (with any learning being welcome but incidental), or learning orientated with learning as the primary objective. These two concepts will be studied in greater detail later.

Different Views of the Whole Picture

In addition to the umbrella model suggested earlier (Fig. 10.02), each of the concepts may be illustrated on a continuum – an imaginary scale between two extremes. The scale measures an increase or decrease in a number of aspects such as level of organisation, level of skilfulness and so on.

TASK 5

What increases as you move from play to physical recreation and on to sport on the continuum shown in Figure 10.04? Try to think of at least five different features that might change.

It may also be helpful to visualise the transition or movement as a narrowing process, as shown below.

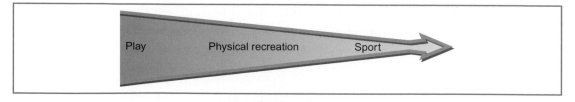

Fig. 10.04

Here, play is the broadest concept in that it is theoretically available to the greatest number of people – it is inclusive. Sport, especially when pursued at a high level, is not available to everyone – it is exclusive. Sport may exclude people in terms of:

- ability – not all people are skilful enough to perform at a high level
- time – not everyone is dedicated enough to give the time needed to perform at top level
- opportunity – other factors might also stand in the way of performing at a sporting level, for example, availability of transport, facilities or finance.

Later in this section we will be looking at the two main sporting issues of **mass participation** and **sporting excellence** and how each of these may be achieved in our society. At this stage it is sufficient to introduce them as concepts, which range from the inclusive idea of mass participation or sport for all, to the more exclusive or narrower idea of excellence. We can now look at each of the concepts in more detail.

KEY WORDS

Mass participation

An inclusive idea that sport and physical activity is for everyone irrespective of skill level or commitment.

Sporting excellence

A more exclusive notion in that not everyone has got or can get what it takes to get to the top in sport.

Play

According to one theory, 'If it's fun, it's play'. The word *play* has many uses such as:

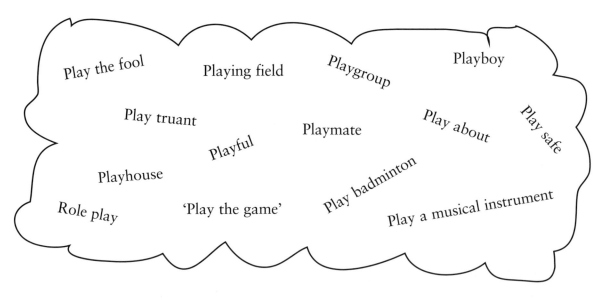

TASK 6

1 Look at the pictures in Fig. 10.05 with a partner. Try to decide on the main characteristics of play. Is everyone playing? Do they have to? Who are they playing with? Are they having fun? If so, why? What choices can they make? How much freedom do they have? How spontaneous does it look? Does play have to be physical? Are they learning anything?

2 In groups of 5 or 6, play for five minutes (toy cars, cuddly toys, Twister, hide and seek, skipping, etc.). One person from each group should observe each group at play and note down interesting behaviour, incidents, comments or body language for later discussion!

Our task is to clarify the nature of play in its purest form. The best way to start is to observe children at play.

Remember we are analysing the concept of play, deciding on its characteristics, motives and outcomes, and seeing if we can identify these elements in our play observations and experiences. The more play elements you can find, the more likely it is that you can classify a particular activity as play.

Play is for everyone, but children seem to play more than adults, probably because they have more time, but perhaps for other sociological reasons too. Play is a temporary experience which makes us feel good and which is experienced either alone or in groups. Its purpose is for immediate enjoyment. Generally, there are no predetermined rules for play and it is engaged in for its own sake (it is, therefore, intrinsically rather than extrinsically valuable). Because nothing tangible comes

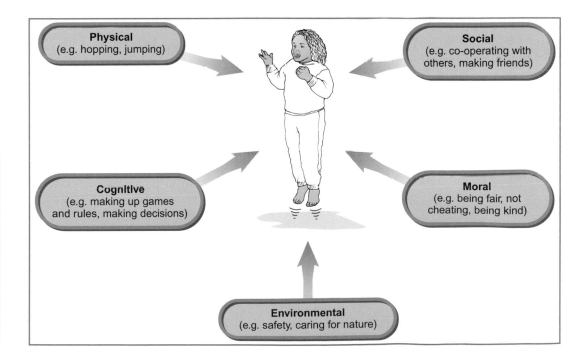

Fig. 10.05 Children playing

Fig. 10.06 Values of play.

Fig. 10.07 Adults at a party – is this play?

Fig. 10.08 Adult play – what is the motive?

TASK 7
How many characteristics of play can you identify in each of the photographs (Figs. 10.07 and 10.08)?

from pure play, it can be classed as non-serious. Freedom to choose when and where to play are also important characteristics of play in its purest form.

In play (as in leisure), meaning, purpose and attitude of mind are all more important than the activity itself. It is also true that play is more than an activity – it is a valuable experience. After all, the philosophy of nursery education is that children learn through play. They can learn to solve problems, make decisions, make moral choices and judgements, and to co-operate and make friends with others. Physical skills can also be acquired. Crucially, children learn more about themselves through play.

Now, what about adults at play?

The key feature of adult play is motive. It is pursued to escape from the realities of real life, such as commuting, doing housework or other stressful rather than pleasurable situations. When adults play it does not necessarily mean that they have to play the fool or act like children.

We can now create a framework for play using the 'W' questions:

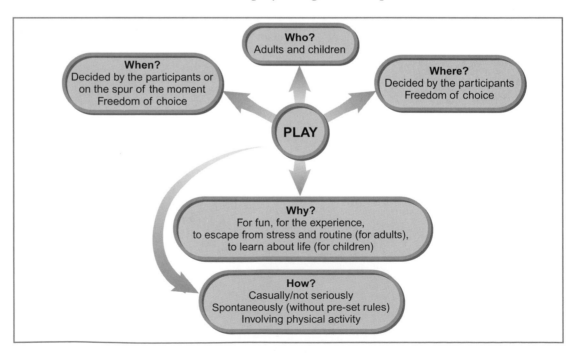

Fig. 10.09 The concept of play.

It is important that we understand that the above characteristics are not always evident. If we watched children playing we may find the following:
• The fun and enjoyment stops if they argue or when someone is hurt.

Play

A spontaneous, enjoyable, child-like activity.

- Where play takes place is sometimes structured. Certain areas of the playground might be out of bounds or they might be forbidden to go near the road or the neighbours' flowerbeds.
- Play is not always spontaneous. It can be both pre-arranged in terms of time and pre-arranged in terms of rule structure, for example, a regularly played playground game will probably have some established and agreed rules (which can be changed by agreement).
- Play is not always physically active.
- The participants do not always have a free choice of when to play. After all, the bell at the end of playtime might stop them or they could be called in to tea.

Physical Education

HOT TIPS

Be aware of the characteristics of play, but also of situations when these characteristics may not be evident.

Fig. 10.10 Different aspects of PE.

PE is something that all children in this country experience as a compulsory school subject as part of the National Curriculum. You may have studied PE at GCSE level and now you are furthering your study of both theoretical and practical aspects of the subject at AS level. But have you ever stopped to think about PE as a concept? We need to:

- define it
- identify its characteristics
- establish what is valuable about it
- analyse the various opportunities for physical activity in schools.

What is Physical Education?

This is what others have said about PE:

An area of educational activity in which the main concern is with bodily movement.

Leeds Study Group (1970)

The formal inculcation of knowledge and values through physical activity experiences.

Schools Council working party (1972)

. . . to develop within individuals a range of personal, social and scholastic qualities.

Alderson (1990)

that aspect of education which specifically employs psycho motor activities and the related moral and social experiences in the development of mature, disciplined and well integrated people.

BAALPE (1970)

PE is about pupils learning about themselves; their capabilities, their potential and their limitations. It is the foundation of all sports participation, but it goes beyond the individual and understanding themselves – it's learning how to work with and to respect others.

Lucy Pearson (England cricketer and teacher)

It seems that, although PE is fundamentally a physical experience, it is also concerned with personal, social, health and moral development. It is not only a subject, but a process of education. PE can be described as 'education of and through the physical.' We can learn:

- physical skills – enabling us to take part in a variety of sporting activities
- personal skills – useful lessons, qualities or values such as cooperation, self-confidence and leadership.

Analysis of your own experience and of others' opinions has probably helped you to identify characteristics of PE.

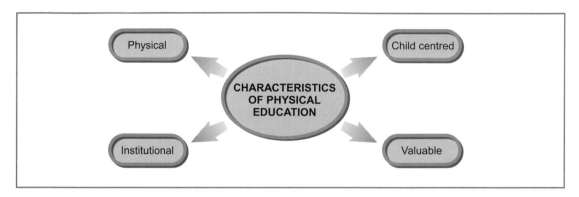

Fig. 10.11

What is Valuable about PE?

Kane identified nine objectives for PE.

1 Emotional stability – development of self-discipline.
2 Self-realisation – to make the most of the individual's unique abilities and potential.
3 Leisure-time activities – to learn skills that can be used for a lifetime during leisure.
4 Social competence – development of social skills.
5 Moral development – development of desirable behaviour.
6 Organic development – cardiovascular fitness.
7 Motor abilities – for example co-ordination, agility and balance, which can be developed into sport specific skills.
8 Aesthetic awareness – appreciation of quality of movement.
9 Cognitive development – development of thinking and reasoning powers.

Our specification requires us to recognise four broad groups of values:

HOT TIPS

Be sure that you understand and can give examples of the values of PE.

1 Those that improve health and motor skill – physical values.
2 Those that prepare for active leisure or a career – preparation values.
3 Those that develop personal and social skills – personal values.
4 Those that improve the quality of life – qualitative values.

What Different Opportunities are there for Physical Activity within Schools?

In addition to PE experienced in lesson time, children can be physically active during break, lunch times and after school. They might take part in:

- informal playground activities at break time
- lunch-time clubs for all abilities, or inter-house or inter-form competitions
- after-school matches against other schools, or in leagues, cups or other competitions.

This is beginning to sound like the difference between play, physical recreation and sport. This idea can be illustrated in Fig. 10.12.

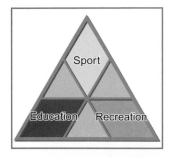

Fig. 10.12 Dimensions of physical activity in school.

This model to the left shows the inter-relationship between PE, recreation and competitive sport within a school. The outer triangle represents the boundary of the institution while the three inner triangles represent curriculum PE, extra-curricular sport and recreational activities. Each small pyramid can exist as a separate entity but the triangles overlap to illustrate the ideal. In each unit there can be sporting, educational and recreational elements, which together give a broad, balanced and varied programme. The broad base of the main triangle illustrates the necessity for mass participation which is needed to support and feed into the narrower, perhaps more exclusive experience of sport at the top.

Theory does not always make it into practice. There are many constraints on PE teachers and departments, which mean that they cannot always produce the ideal broad and balanced programme. The constraints are varied. There could be inadequate facilities, equipment or curriculum time. Staff numbers could be low and specialist expertise unavailable. In addition, some pupils may lack interest, ability or effort. Strategies are needed to successfully overcome these constraints so that the ideal model can operate and thrive in any school.

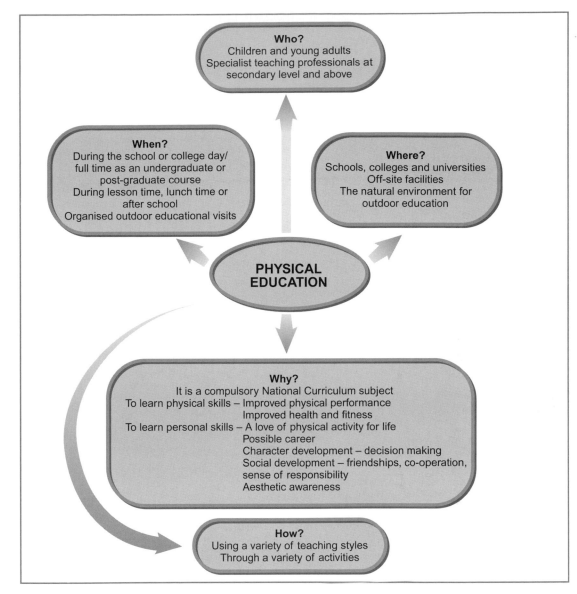

Fig. 10.13 The concepts of physical education.

HOT TIPS

Remember that outdoor pursuits can give personal challenge, develop awareness and respect for the countryside, teach people to work effectively with and depend on each other and provide a sense of adventure or excitement.

Outdoor Education

Outdoor and adventurous education can be described as learning in and about the outdoors. Just as for outdoor recreation, the essence of outdoor education is the use of the natural environment for outdoor pursuits. Outdoor recreation takes place during leisure time and can result in the informal acquisition of valuable lessons and life skills as a consequence of the experience. Outdoor education on the other hand is part of a structured school or college programme in which positive and useful values are formally sought and taught. According to Prince Philip, outdoor education experiences are an '*aid to navigation through life*'.

Outdoor education belongs under the umbrella of PE, and so has the same potential sets of values:

- physical health and skill learning
- preparation for active leisure
- personal and social development
- enhancement of quality of life.

Outdoor education is compulsory under the National Curriculum at secondary level, but sadly, various factors limit regular participation in a broad range of outdoor adventurous activities. Firstly, there is the problem of funding. Voluntary contributions from pupils may be insufficient to cover costs. Secondly, teachers need specialist, time-consuming and expensive training for outdoor education. They may not get funding or be willing or able to give the required time. There is also the very real concern of health and safety, with some teachers being increasingly reluctant to take the responsibility for organising and managing trips. Also, of course, suitable facilities may be too far away and sufficient time may not be available.

The Outward Bound Trust

'It's a buzz because your body senses a risk. It feels great to overcome a fear, to feel that you've done it!'

Over 50 years ago, Kurt Hahn, a progressive educationalist, and Lawrence Holt, a wealthy industrialist, founded the Outward Bound Trust. It was the first organisation in the world dedicated to personal development using the natural environment. Outward Bound works in partnership with the Duke of Edinburgh's Award Scheme and provides a variety of courses such as physical expeditions, skill courses and a city challenge course in urban areas.

What distinguishes outdoor education from the rest of PE is the element of risk and unpredictability which results from the natural environment.

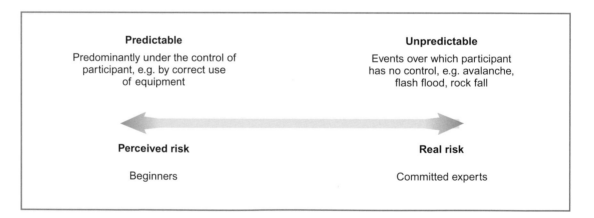

Predictable	**Unpredictable**
Predominantly under the control of participant, e.g. by correct use of equipment	Events over which participant has no control, e.g. avalanche, flash flood, rock fall

Perceived risk → **Real risk**

Beginners — Committed experts

Fig. 10.14 It looks risky, but it's completely safe!

Perceived risk is actively sought by teachers in order to give beginners the opportunity to learn and challenge themselves in a situation that appears dangerous and gives a real sense of adventure. In reality, the risk is imagined and students are kept completely safe within staff leader risk assessment guidelines. For example, abseiling for a beginner certainly feels risky, but correct procedures and safety equipment ensure complete safety.

The potential outcome of real risk is a natural disaster such as a flash flood. It is avoided at all costs by qualified and experienced staff, by thorough planning, attention to weather reports and by the use of appropriate kit and equipment. A qualified and experienced group leader will never be afraid to abandon an expedition for safety reasons – the alternative could be injury or even death caused by hypothermia, avalanche, blizzard or flood. Only the highly experienced and skilled should venture into unpredictable situations, which become part of the challenge.

The Use of Artificial Facilities

Artificial facilities are increasingly used to simulate the natural environment. Swimming baths are used for canoeing, sophisticated watersports centres and artificial ski centres continue to be built and climbing walls are common.

TASK 11

Writing in the role of the Head of a school PE department, prepare a short presentation for parents to advertise a proposed Year 10 outdoor activity week. Include:

- activities on offer
- valuable experiences that their children are likely to gain
- likely costs

- qualifications of staff
- safety procedures in place.

Sport in Schools

Having established that school PE can include sporting experiences, let's now look at how sport in schools is currently being encouraged and promoted. At primary level we will focus on TOP Sport (one of the TOP Programmes), and at secondary level on Sports Colleges and the School Sport Co-ordinator programme. The work of Sports Development Officers will also be reviewed. The Youth Sports Trust (YST) is involved in each of these initiatives.

The Youth Sport Trust

The Youth Sport Trust is a registered charity established in 1994 to 'build a brighter future for young people through sport'. Its mission is to work with other organisations in order to develop and implement quality PE and sport programmes for children and young people.

The YST believes that all young people have the right to:

- experience and enjoy PE and sport
- a quality introduction to PE and sport suited to their own level of development
- progress along a structured pathway of sporting opportunities
- the best teaching, the best coaching and the best resources
- experience and benefit from positive competition

Fig. 10.15

- develop a healthy lifestyle
- a sound foundation for lifelong physical activity.

Recent YST research projects include the Nike 'Girls in Sport' Project, which sought to find out why so many teenage girls drop out of physical education and sport, and to suggest ways of changing this. The Youth Sport Trust is grant-aided by the Department for Education and Skills (DfES) to provide advice and help for schools applying for Sports College status, and to give ongoing support as they implement their development plans.

The TOPS Programmes

The YST has developed the following series of linked and progressive schemes for young people aged 18 months to 18 years called the TOPS programmes.

TOP Tots	Helping children aged 18 months to 3 years to experience physical activities and games.
TOP Start	Encouraging 3 to 5 year olds to learn through physical activity.
TOP Play	Supporting 4 to 9 year olds as they acquire and develop core skills.

TOP Sport	Providing 7 to 11 year olds with opportunities to develop skills in a range of sports. Other programmes for this age group include: TOP Athletics, TOP Dance, Fit for TOPs, TOP Gymnastics, TOP Outdoors and TOP Swimming.

TOP Skill	Challenging 11 to 14 year olds to extend their sporting skills and knowledge.
TOP Link	Enabling 14 to 19 year olds to take a lead in the organisation of sport.
TOP Sportsability	Creating opportunities for young disabled people to enjoy, participate, and perform in PE and sport.

Key features of the TOPS Programmes include:

- resource cards
- child-friendly equipment
- quality training for teachers and deliverers.

TASK 12

Contact a local Junior or Primary School and try to find out whether they have been involved in the TOP Sport programme. What was good about it? Were there any negative aspects?

TOP Play and TOP Sport are being delivered extensively in England, Scotland and Northern Ireland with 20,000 schools now involved. To get involved schools contact their TOP Programme scheme manager who is often the Local Education Authority (LEA) PE Adviser. Meanwhile the Sports Council for Wales has developed the Dragon sport initiative.

Fig. 10.16

Dragon Sport

This scheme is based on New Zealand's Kiwi Sport scheme and focuses on the recruitment of volunteers to provide extra-curricular sports sessions for children. Dragon Sport is supported by the YST and resources and training are based on TOP Sport.

The main aims of Dragon Sport are to:

- give 7–11 year olds regular, well-organised and enjoyable sporting experiences
- develop strong school – club links
- support clubs in developing junior sections
- encourage parents, teachers and other to take up roles in sports leadership.

> *Dragon Sport is boosting extra-curricular sport for primary school children right across Wales . . . we're focusing on the recruitment of mums, dads and teachers to help out in sport sessions, whether it is coaching, refereeing, washing kit or taking the register. We want parents to take an active role in their children's sport.*

Sports Colleges

> *Specialist sports colleges will play an important role in helping to deliver the Government's Plan for Sport. They will become important hub sites for school and community sport providing high-quality opportunities for all young people in their neighbourhood.*
>
> Richard Caborn MP, Minister for Sport, DCMS (March 2001)

Sports Colleges became part of the specialist schools programme in 1997. The aim is to have a network of 250 specialist institutions by 2005. Sports colleges receive an initial grant to improve sporting facilities, and additional funding each year to carry out development plans.

Their mission statement is to:

> *raise standards of achievement in physical education and sport for all their students across the ability range. They will be regional focal points for excellence in physical education (PE) and community sport, extending links between families of schools, sports bodies and communities, sharing resources and developing and spreading good practice, helping to provide a structure through which young people can progress to careers in sport and physical*

education. Sports Colleges will increase participation in PE and sport for pre- and post-16 year olds, and develop the potential of talented performers. **'**

In short, the five key aims of Sports Colleges are to provide:

1 high quality teaching in PE and sport
2 increased opportunities for gifted and talented performers
3 access to sports specific qualifications such as GCSE, AS and A Level physical education
4 links with local primary schools, other secondary schools and special schools
5 improved sporting facilities and opportunities for the local community.

Most initiatives attract some criticism and Sports Colleges have already received their share. Applying for Sports College status is a complicated and time-consuming process. Schools have to raise £50,000 in private sector sponsorship and write a detailed three-year development plan, which may deter some schools. It has also been cynically suggested that some Head teachers seek specialised status for the 'wrong reasons,' perhaps to raise the perceived status of their school, rather than from a genuine desire to improve sporting opportunities and standards in the school or the wider community. Others have criticised the fact that some geographical areas may be left without a 'local' sports college and that a non-local school will then poach the most gifted performers. Further, due to ongoing staffing constraints, some sports colleges have so far been unable to fulfil their obligation to serve primary, secondary and community duties and therefore may become 'ivory towers' for the elite rather than sporting beacons for all.

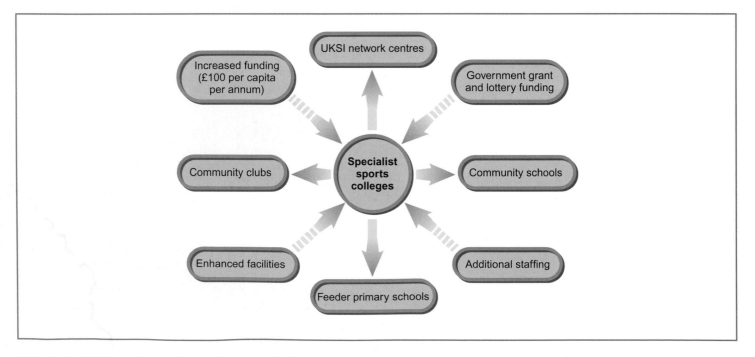

Fig. 10.17 The ins and outs of specialist sports colleges.

TASK 13

1   Use the DfES or Youth Sport Trust website to find out how many Sports Colleges there are in England and identify the one nearest to you.

2   With reference to your identified Sports college:
   • What strategies and/or initiatives have been developed to successfully achieve the five Sports College aims.
   • What are the school's focus sports?
   • Has it received lottery funding?
   • Do the PE teachers work with the local primary school?
   • Does it attract many students from out of its normal catchment area?
   • To what extent have facilities improved since status was achieved?
   • Does it have any links with a United Kingdom Sports Institute network centre?

School Sport Co-ordinators

Many Sports Colleges are hub sites for School Sport Co-ordinator partnerships, another key initiative aimed at shaping PE and sport in schools. By 2004 there will be 1000 School Sport Co-ordinators (SSCos) working to improve the quality and quantity of after-school sport and inter-school competition across their 'families' of schools.

The School Sport Co-ordinator programme is a joint initiative of Sport England, the Department for Education and Skills (DfES), the Department of Culture, Media and Sport (DCMS), the New Opportunities Fund (NOF) and the Youth Sport Trust (YST).

The programme is based around groups of four or five partner secondary schools – each group being managed by a partnership development manager (PDM) who is often based at a Sports College. Each secondary school has a SSCo who works with up to five primary and/or special schools. In turn, each of these schools has a primary link teacher (PLT).

This team works together to improve opportunities for young people across the family of schools. Specifically it aims to:

• give a variety of sporting access to disadvantaged young people
• encourage participation by young people who are currently under represented in PE and sport, including disabled people, girls and those from ethnic minorities
• improve young people's self-esteem and confidence through PE and sport
• provide PE and sport courses to teachers and other adults for ongoing professional development.

Fig. 10.18 A local network of sports development.

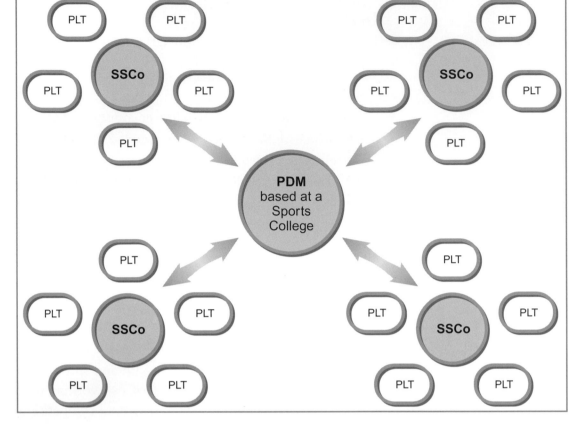

Key

PDM – Partnership Development Manager
SSCo – School Sport Co-ordinator
PLT – Primary Link Teacher

Sports Development Officers

Who are they?

Sports Development Officers (SDOs) are employed by local authorities and are part of a county Sports Development Unit. They usually work with all sports, but are sometimes sports specific (SSDOs). Their responsibilities include:

- working to increase community access to sport and leisure
- working to increase opportunity and provision
- providing advice, support and resources to performers, coaches and clubs
- promoting Sport England's Active Sports Programme
- developing 'Coaching for Teachers'
- organising sports festivals and courses
- helping set up clubs
- advising on lottery and specialist sports college applications.

They work with:

- county, borough and district leisure services departments
- schools, colleges and universities

- county and NGBs of Sport
- Sport England
- Sports Coach UK.

Revise As You Go! Test Your Knowledge and Understanding

- Explain the idea that leisure is an umbrella term.
- What, other than physical skills and values, can children learn through play?
- What are the differences between children and adults at play?
- What are the characteristics of PE?
- Identify different types of values associated with PE.
- What part of a school day is most likely to be recreational?
- How might a mountain walk develop you as a person and influence your relationships with others?
- What are some likely benefits of attending a specialist sports college?
- Can you think of any possible negative effects of specialist sports colleges?
- How does the Youth Sport Trust help to improve sporting provision for children in the UK?
- Identify two features of either TOP Sport or Dragon Sport.

Sharpen up your exam technique!

1   It has been suggested that all sports have their origins in play.
    (a) What are the main characteristics of play?   (3 marks)
    (b) How does play sometimes fail to fit each of your chosen characteristics?
                                                                                      (3 marks)

2   'PE is about pupils learning about themselves.' Explain the view that Physical Education is a process of educating the whole person.   (3 marks)

3   Outdoor adventurous education consists of activities such as canoeing or rock climbing, which take place in the natural environment. Explain real and perceived risk in an outdoor adventurous situation.   (3 marks)

4   Not all schools have access to the natural environment for outdoor adventurous education. What are the advantages and disadvantages of using artificial facilities for outdoor adventurous education?   (4 marks)

5   How do state schools support and encourage:
    (a) mass participation?
    (b) sporting excellence?   (6 marks)

Chapter 11 **Concepts of Sport in Society**

Learning Objectives

At the end of this chapter you should be able to:
- Understand the concepts of physical recreation, outdoor recreation and sport.
- Give examples of physical recreation, outdoor recreation and sporting activities.
- Explain why people take part in physical recreation activities.
- Describe how physical recreation activities differ from sporting activities.
- Understand the values associated with outdoor recreation.
- Understand how amateurism differs from professionalism.
- Analyse the various relationships between coaches and performers.

Introduction

In this chapter we are continuing our conceptual investigations, but now move from schools and into society to look at the ideas of physical recreation, outdoor recreation and sport. We also investigate the various roles of a sports coach.

Physical Recreation

To physically recreate is to take part in a game or activity for its own sake – not for any extrinsic reward. It may be an activity such as swimming, skiing or running, which occurs at the Olympic Games, but the emphasis is on:

- participation, not standard of performance
- taking part, not winning
- enjoyment and satisfaction, not record breaking.

So, a game of badminton played recreatively is more playful than competitive. It will probably also be played at a relatively unsophisticated level where skills are quite low or inconsistent and where National Governing Body rules and scoring systems are not strictly adhered to. There will only be few if any requirements about type of kit and equipment. Interestingly, with the booming leisure and recreation industry now also a fashion industry, people are dressed in the trendiest sporting clothes irrespective of commitment, level of ability or even intention to be active at all!

Fig. 11.01

TASK 1

What features in the photographs in Fig. 11.01 suggest that the activities are being pursued recreatively?

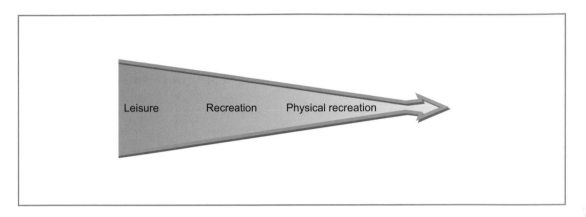

Fig. 11.02 Our field of study as a narrowing process.

KEY WORDS

Opportunity

The chance or probability of an individual taking part based on time, money, etc.

Provision

The supply of facilities, which allow you to participate.

Esteem

Society's view of the individual, which may lead to a lack of self- confidence.

Figure 11.02 shows that the continuum from leisure to physical recreation narrows as less people are involved. Will it get narrower still when we look at sport? This narrowing process could be due to personal choice. More probably though, it is due to lack of **opportunity, provision** or **esteem**. This could be based on insufficient time to take part, unavailability of suitable activities or lack of physical competence. It could also be due to inadequacy of local facilities or a low disposable income. Some may lack self-confidence or feel discriminated against – due possibly to lack of appropriate role models. In theory, physical recreation should be for everyone irrespective of age, ability or disability, gender, race or class. For many years the various home country Sports Councils have run campaigns to try to promote 'Sport For All' – another way of saying physical recreation.

TASK 2

In pairs, make a list of activities whose descriptive word or phrase (e.g. jogging) tells us that it is being practised as a recreational pastime rather than as something more serious or competitive. What words or phrases are there for recreational horse riding, swimming, playing tennis, playing football, fitness training? Can you think of some more?

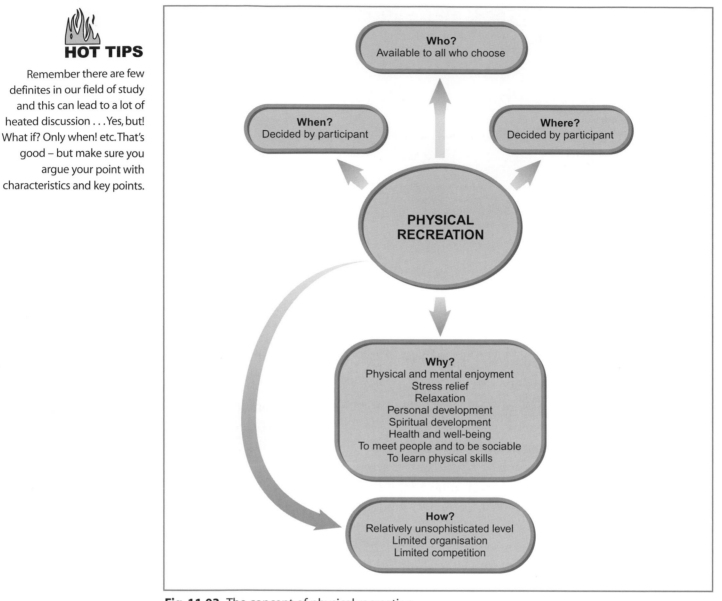

Fig. 11.03 The concept of physical recreation.

Figure 11.03 shows that the activity being pursued may have the positive outcome of promoting health and developing physical skills in a friendly and enjoyable atmosphere, but also that physical recreation goes far beyond the physical. It also provides the opportunity to learn about ourselves and others. It is clear that it is, like leisure, more than just an activity – it is also a potentially valuable experience.

TASK 3

Survey up to ten people to find out what motivates them to take part in their chosen physical recreation activities. Illustrate your finding in a pie chart or tally chart.

Outdoor Recreation

In his book *The Adventure Alternative*, Colin Mortlock superbly explains the potential of outdoor recreation as follows:

> ❛ *ADVENTURE WAYS*
> *The following journeys, providing you take any of them to the outer limits of your capabilities in a self-reliant manner, can take you along the road to truth and beauty, freedom and happiness.* ❜

Wow – that is some claim! – truth, beauty, freedom and happiness to be gained through what exactly? Mortlock explains:

> ❛ *Up a mountain or down a river, across an ocean or along a coastline, across the wilderness or along the outdoor way, through the air or under the surface of the earth.* ❜

Fig. 11.04 Hill walking – an aspect of outdoor recreation.

TASK 4

Discuss as a class any outdoor recreation experiences you have had. Where did you go? What did you do? What did you gain that was valuable from the experience?

It seems that by recreating in the beauty of the natural environment during our free time we can learn several valuable lessons. Let's take each of the items from our specification in turn.

To Appreciate the Beauty of Nature

Our natural landscape is beautiful – ideal surroundings for recreation. Some people live in beautiful rural areas, whilst others need to travel to find and enjoy them. Whether climbing, walking, canoeing or orienteering, the scenery of the countryside rewards our senses with beauty and variety. We get to see, feel, smell and hear things that are way outside of our normal day-to-day existence. We are able to leave behind the clutter of urban life and get in touch with the natural world. We get 'back to nature'. Life can seem simple again. Importantly, we can also get in touch with ourselves. We might feel very small and in awe of the surrounding splendour. Poets, artists and writers certainly seem to – but the beauty is there for all of us to enjoy. Outdoor recreation can indeed be a spiritual experience – a time when we tune in to our deepest thoughts and feelings. And of course to have great fun too! But all stimulated by the landscape.

To Respect the Natural Environment

Having been moved by the remarkable beauty of the natural environment, we are likely to value it and want to preserve its uniqueness for others to enjoy. We may not actually join the Green Party, but will probably admire its principles and agree that the countryside needs to be treasured and kept safe. We may feel concerned about issues such as conservation and pollution, and have a greater interest in and understanding of the work of the Countryside Agency. As more people escape to national parks and green-belt areas for refreshment and renewal they create new problems. Some areas of the UK are already suffering from land erosion and disturbances to the natural world caused by increased numbers of visitors.

To Feel a Sense of Adventure and Perhaps Risk

The natural environment is certainly beautiful, but it is also unpredictable. The weather can change suddenly, and tides might be erratic; the paths might be steep and uneven. Each of these situations is potentially risky, worrying and even hazardous. We can feel exhilarated, challenged and even frightened. The key to a positive experience of outdoor recreation is to avoid all real risk by using commonsense and by abiding strictly to safety codes. Any remaining worries can then be embraced with a feeling of excitement and adventure. Benefits can then be found – including a feel-good factor and a real sense of personal achievement.

HOT TIPS

Remember that outdoor recreation means using the outdoor/natural environment, e.g. hills, lakes and rivers for relaxation and pleasure, and is not just playing a game of hockey outside.

Historically, there have been two conflicting views of recreation. Those who have traditionally said that recreation is only for the privileged and that it has no particular use outside of itself, and those who have thought that it is useful – or has a purpose. The same beliefs have been held about outdoor recreation. Increasingly, however, as the values of outdoor recreation have been more widely accepted, the privilege of the few has become right of the majority. As Davis argues, '*The key democratic factors are the right to choose; the opportunity to participate, and the provision to facilitate that freedom.*' (Davis et al, *Physical Education and the Study of Sport*, Mosby, London, 2000)

Sport

❝ *Serious sport has nothing to do with Fair Play. It is bound up with hatred, jealousy, boastfulness, disregard of all rules and sadistic pleasure in witnessing violence. In other words, it is war minus the shooting.* ❞

George Orwell

Isn't George Orwell's view of sport of over half a century ago a little depressing? Is it really that bad? Is sport really a global opportunity for violence, deviance and hatred? Or at its best, is it the place where we can learn to make moral decisions, test ourselves physically and mentally, excel, make lifelong friends, influence and inspire others as a positive role model, create memories and even be part of a celebration of compelling drama and exhilarating passion?

Maybe it depends on where in the world you are taking part in sport (i.e. your society or culture) and whether you take part as an amateur or as a professional.

KEY WORDS

Nationalism

Loyalty and patriotism to one's country.

Nation building

Using sport as a way of building the nation in the eyes of the country's citizens or in the eyes of the rest of the world.

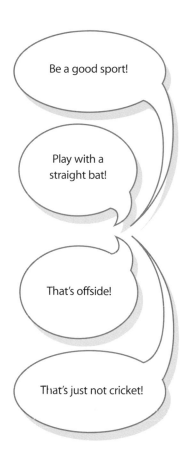

Be a good sport!

Play with a straight bat!

That's offside!

That's just not cricket!

Sport and Culture

Sport is part of every culture or society and is as old as time. It can be found in the ancient records of the earliest civilisations and exists in countless forms in every inhabited corner of the planet. It can be the almost unknown local custom of a tribal society, whose roots stem from a need such as hunting for food. In contrast, sport can be a massive global experience of huge proportions such as the most recent Olympic Games. In France and Australia, sport is all to do with **nationalism** or feeling good and patriotic about your country, whereas in developing countries it is to do with **nation building** or making your country look good to the rest of the world. Sport seems to be different depending on where in the world it occurs. Sport and culture is covered more fully in Chapter 12.

Amateurism and Professionalism

Today, sport is a multi-million pound industry where the word 'amateur' can be used in a slightly derogatory way to describe something that is great fun but rather unsophisticated and unpolished – a bit like amateur dramatics. But where does the word come from? It stems from the Latin word *amare* which means 'to love'. Amateurs take part in sport for the love of it rather than for monetary reward. Successful athletes in Ancient Greece were highly trained and committed, but they needed specialist equipment and food in order to achieve their success. So, although they received no payment, and just a laurel wreath as their prize, they were supported and sponsored by their employers or wealthy individuals. Were they amateurs?

The concept of amateurism really evolved in nineteenth-century England among the privileged upper classes whose sons attended elite boarding schools such as Charterhouse and Eton. At the beginning of the nineteenth century these schools were rowdy even riotous institutions, where the boys behaved like hooligans and where the teachers had little control outside the classroom. This rowdy behaviour actually reflected society as a whole, which was rather uncivilised by twenty-first century standards. Headmasters used team games to control the boys and to channel their excess energy so that they were too exhausted to cause trouble. This strategy seemed to work and over time, games became important in their own right. By the 1860s games became the ideal setting for boys to learn valuable lessons such as self-control, teamwork and fair play. In short, the games field was the place that your character was formed. Certain phrases still in use today stem from an era when games were the most important elements of public school life.

'Gentleman amateurs'

Certain wealthy individuals who excelled in games were referred to as 'gentleman amateurs'. They were from the upper and upper-middle classes and could afford to spend a lot of time away from their work playing sport for enjoyment. Working-class men, however, could not afford to miss work in order to play, so at a time

KEY WORDS

Amateur

Someone who plays or competes for pleasure not for financial gain.

Professional

Someone who plays or competes for payment – it is their job.

HOT TIPS

Remember that it was class not payment that originally determined one's status as amateur or professional.

'Professional' doesn't just mean that you excel in sport – it means you get paid!

when spectator sport was growing, if they were good enough, they played full time for payment. Sport became their job and they were very much looked down on by the 'gentleman amateurs'. It is very important to understand that at this time the primary distinction between amateurism and professionalism was social status or class, not payment. Being an amateur was all to do with a set of unwritten rules about how life should be lived as well as how sport should be played.

In cricket, both 'gentleman amateurs' and working class professionals would play in the same team, but they:

- had different titles ('gentleman' v 'players')
- appeared differently in the programme (either Bloggs, J. or J. Bloggs Esq. depending on status)
- ate and travelled separately
- changed separately and dressed differently
- walked on to the field of play from different entrances
- had different roles – the professionals were likely to be the hard-working bowlers, not the stylish batsmen.

Not until the 1960s was the annual 'gentlemen versus players' match at Lords cricket ground abolished.

In Chapter 13 we shall look at some of the many issues relating to contemporary sport. Issues such as sponsorship and the role of the media, as well as more challenging concerns, where sport seems to have become tarnished in its role as a money-spinner. Stories of drug taking by performers, violence by performers and spectators, corruption by some judges and administrators at top level all seem to get into the newspapers on a regular basis. For now, we will stick with sport as a concept and consider what it *ought* to be like.

What are the Characteristics and True Potential of Pure Sport?

The Dutch historian and philosopher of sport, J. Huizinga emphasised sport's most appealing quality – its playfulness. Let's see what some other people have said:

❝a rational playful activity . . . an attitude of mind.❞

Luschen (1960)

❝fair-play is the essence . . . of any game or sport that is worthy of the name.❞

Noel-Baker (1965)

❝sport is a highly organized game requiring physical prowess.❞

Loy (1970)

❝an athletic activity requiring physical prowess of skill and usually of a competitive nature.❞

Michener (1976)

If we take the key words from the definitions above it seems fairly safe to say that in theory sport is likely to be highly organised, skilful and competitive with fair play as a central feature. Some argue that all sport stems from play.

TASK 5

Study the pictures on the left. Can you think of any other characteristics of sport?

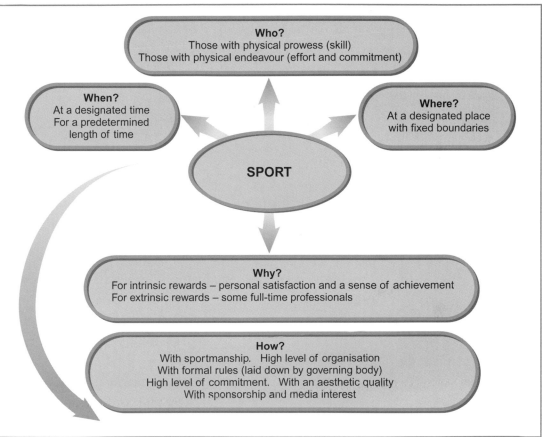

Fig. 11.05 Views of sport.

Fig. 11.06 Keyword model for the concept of sport.

 KEY WORDS

Aesthetic

Movement that is beautiful to watch.

What makes a Sport a Sport?

We would all probably agree that the winner of the London Marathon, the competitor in the winter Olympics, and the regular league netball player are all taking part in sport. But what about the person who comes last in the London Marathon whilst dressed as a carrot for charity? And what about aerobics, chess, skipping, body building, fishing or ballroom dancing?

In analysing these activities it might help to consider the following.
*   Tradition – do we traditionally call the activity a sport in this country?
*   Physical exertion – does the activity involve strenuous movement?

- Competition – does the activity involve competition against oneself or others?
- Administration – does the activity follow National Governing Body rules?
- Behaviour – does the performer show commitment, skill and fair play?

The more often that these features fit a particular activity, the more likely it is that the activity could be classified as sport.

KEY WORDS

Functional

When sport is played in the spirit of the game, where rules are abided by and referees decisions are unreservedly accepted.

Dysfunctional

When rules are broken on purpose, players argue with the referee and aggression is shown towards others.

Sportsmanship

Treating your opponent with respect and as an equal, showing fair play and good behaviour.

Gamesmanship

The practice of beating your opponent by gaining an unfair or psychological advantage, without actually breaking the letter of the law, e.g. time wasting.

Fair Play/Sportsmanship

The essence of the 'gentleman amateur' was fair play. Gary Lineker and Jimmy White have been recent models of fair play.

> *What places Gary Lineker head and shoulders above the world's best is his sportsmanship: a total dedication to fair play that rubs off on the crowds watching the game . . . while some players spend a whole match trying to get even, he refuses to retaliate. He knows that the best answer to aggression is to score goals.*

Readers' Digest

Even though performing as a highly pressurised professional, positive sporting attitudes were Gary Lineker's trademark. It could be said that he was not only playing to the letter of the rules, but also to the spirit of the rules. Even though he certainly wanted to win, he did not seem to hold the 'win-at-all costs' view, which is usually associated with American sport.

The opposite of **sportsmanship** is **gamesmanship**. Here the performer will stretch the rules to the absolute limit in order to gain an unfair advantage.

TASK 6

In small groups, try to think of examples of sportsmanship and gamesmanship in both amateur and professional sport. Make notes of your discussion.

Fig. 11.07 Sportsmanship – respect for your opponent.

Sport For All and Elite Sport

The twin concepts of **Sport For All** (where everyone is encouraged and has the opportunity to take part in the sport of their choice, irrespective of any social or cultural differences such as wealth, gender or age) and **Sporting Excellence** (where the very best performers are given additional support so that they may reach international success) can effectively be shown in the framework of a performance pyramid.

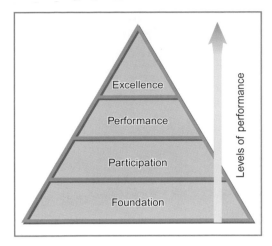

Fig. 11.08 The Performance Pyramid.

HOT TIPS

Be able to name and explain each level of the performance pyramid.

The Performance Pyramid

A pyramid structure illustrates a continuum of development from mass participation at the base of the pyramid to excellence at the top. The broader the base, the more likely it is that some will achieve excellence.

At Foundation Level – young children are introduced to sport and learn basic movement skills and a positive attitude to physical activity through a wide variety of activities, possibly through their school's PE programme.

At Participation Level – youngsters choose to take part in selected activities for enjoyment and friendships, as well as for health and fitness. This may be through extra-curricular school activities, local centres or clubs.

At Performance Level – participants are committed to performing in formally organised activities at higher club and regional levels. They are keen to improve their standard, train regularly and receive coaching.

At Excellence Level – elite performers represent their country in national and international competition. They will be fully committed to their sport, and will, in some cases, train full time and receive financial, administrative, medical and personal support.

The Role of the Coach

It has been argued that within any group there is a division of labour, a ranking structure, rules, punishments for breaking rules, special language and gestures, and co-operation to achieve group goals. It seems that within groups or social situations, people behave in a certain way and have different functions.

Being a coach involves far more than choosing and training a squad or team – effective coaches have many functions and need to be adaptable. They have diverse roles to play in order to meet the many and ever-changing needs of their students and performers.

TASK 7

In threes, list all of the tasks that a coach might have to complete before, during and after a five-day combined netball and rugby tour to Dublin.

Fig. 11.09 Coaches wear many 'hats' in the course of their work!

TASK 8

Identify the various roles a coach might have to adopt to help a performer who:

1 has a new and painful injury
2 is homesick during a sports tour
3 is turning up late, wasting time and appearing disinterested at training
4 hopes to qualify for 'World Class Potential' funding
5 attends a specialist sports college and has been selected to attend a UKSI centre for extra/specialist coaching.

More than one role is likely to be needed in each case.

Figure 11.09 shows the various relationships between a coach and a performer. The three central roles are instructor, trainer and educator. We need to analyse each of these in terms of what is being communicated, the lines of communication, and the relative importance of experience and outcome.

The **instructor** gives instructions often concerning rules or safety – 'Don't throw the javelin until I say,' or 'Don't step out of the front of the discus circle.' The lines of communication are one way in that there is nothing to discuss. The instructor is not interested in any feedback or how the student feels about the instruction.

The **trainer** is interested in outcome. He or she will give advice on technique, training or diet that directly relates to improved performance. There is two-way communication, especially if the performer is highly motivated and skilful. Steven Redgrave, the Olympic rower, was certainly involved in and consulted about his training programme.

The **educator** or teacher is interested in and keen to help develop the whole person. There is a two-way relationship here and the experience or process outweighs the outcome or product. The educator knows that all aspects of a child's life impinge on performance and so will support and empathise with the *individual* rather than purely instruct or train the *performer*.

Revise as you go! Test your knowledge and understanding

- Why, other than for enjoyment, do people take part in physical recreation activities?
- Make a list of who takes part in physical recreation, when and where it is pursued, and the likely level of organisation.
- Name three different outdoor recreation activities.
- What are the main characteristics of sport?
- Explain how a performer may have a recreative attitude while taking part in sport.
- Compare amateurism with professionalism.
- Argue for and against aerobics being classed as a sport.
- What features can help identify whether an activity can be classed as a sport?
- What is meant by the term 'sportsmanship?'
- How might pupils experience sport, physical recreation and education during one swimming or gymnastics lesson?
- Name and explain the four levels of the performance pyramid.

Sharpen up your exam technique!

1 How does outdoor recreation lead to an appreciation of nature, a respect for the environment and a sense of adventure? (3 marks)

2 Children experience physical activity in different ways. How might pupils experience sport, physical recreation and education through different aspects of their school PE programme? (3 marks)

3 Use a swimming, athletics or gymnastics situation to explain when a coach might adopt the role of an instructor, a trainer and an educator. (3 marks)

4 Identify three roles the coach might have to play with a performer and give examples of these in operation. (3 marks)

Chapter 12 **Sport and Culture**

Learning Objectives

At the end of this chapter you should be able to:
- Give examples and characteristics of traditional ethnic sports that survive in the UK and suggest reasons for their survival.
- Understand the global significance of sport in different cultures.
- Identify characteristics of sports and pastimes in tribal and emergent societies.
- Understand why emergent societies seek sporting success and be able to identify and explain their strategies for achieving success.
- Explain the 'American Dream' and the 'shop window' as the different approaches that capitalist multi-party democracies (e.g. the US) and socialist one-party states (e.g. China) have towards sport.

Introduction

Sport is part of culture and reflects a community's true nature. Sociologists are interested in human social behaviour and in what happens to groups when they interact over time. In this chapter, we will study sporting groups from different parts of the world. We will look at tribal, emergent and advanced societies, with a view to identifying and analysing their sports and pastimes.

Survival of Traditional Sports and Festivals in Britain

Do you think that Morris dancers are strange, laugh at the idea of wassailing your apple trees and think that people who turn up for annual pancake races are a bit weird? What about eating hot-cross buns on Good Friday, hanging up mistletoe at Christmas, and going to Halloween parties?

The British Isles are rich in surviving festivals and customs that are bound up with the changing seasons of the year and the rhythm of country life. Many are of medieval or pagan origin, such as the Furry Dance at Helston in Cornwall. There are numerous mob football games, for example, the Haxey Hood Game in Leicestershire. Then there is the danger and excitement of chasing a wheel of cheese down Cooper's Hill in Gloucestershire. Some, such as the Doggett Coat and Badge sculling race on the Thames, stem from the participants' occupations as watermen nearly 300 years ago.

'Town and county, do your best for in this parish I must rest.'

Hurling is an ancient Cornish sport that survives in the villages of St Columb Major, St Columb Minor and St Ives. It is played on Shrove Tuesday by two teams of Townsmen and Countrymen, which can have up to 500 a side. The game is extremely rough and involves rugby-type tackling, but throwing, not kicking of the ball. The goals are a mile apart and the ball, encased in silver, is inscribed (see left).

In Ashbourne in Derbyshire, the annual Shrovetide mob football game has survived, despite several attempts to abolish it since medieval times. Here, the Up'ards play the Down'ards in a game centred on the River Henmore. The game has few rules, any number of players and mill wheels form the goals that are three miles apart. The game is played over two days and only rarely is a goal scored, possibly because the ball is filled with cork dust to make it heavy and the game more static. The ball is hardly ever kicked, but mostly 'hugged' by a scrum, which tries to move forward.

Fig. 12.01 The Ashbourne football match.

In addition to these single sport occasions, there are surviving multi-sport festivals, notably the Lakeland and Highland Games. There are over 50 different Highland Games meetings each summer, with Royal Braemar being the most famous. These games are a representation of Gaelic heritage and include activities such as tossing the caber, throwing the hammer, putting the stone, foot racing and wrestling. The celebrations involve bagpipe music and sword dancing. They are grand social occasions as well as a display of athleticism in-keeping with the needs of a hardy lifestyle in remote and sometimes severe conditions.

Fig. 12.02 The Highland Games.

Robert Dover's Cotswold Olympics is a multi-sport occasion originally established by permission of James I in 1605 and was an annual event until 1851 when it was disrupted by hooligan behaviour. The games were revived in Chipping Campden, Gloucestershire in 1963 and continue today. An engraving from 1636 (see Figure 12.03) shows that the original activities ranged from throwing the sledgehammer, hare coursing, sword fighting and horse riding, to shin kicking, dancing, fireworks and picnicking. Today the celebrations include wrestling, Morris dancers, cross-country running, hot air ballooning, marching bands, fireworks and a torchlight procession with dancing in the square at the end of the day.

Fig. 12.03 Robert Dover's Cotswold Olympics.

Traditional festivals have a history of criticism and attack, for example due to:
- the Reformation (which took power from the Church to the Crown)
- Puritanism in the early seventeenth century, which discouraged folk games and festivals
- the weakening of traditional, rural community life due to nineteenth-century industrialisation
- the First World War – which wiped out a generation and changed people's views about stability and tradition
- the Second World War, followed by a modern age of improved technology
- hooliganism, which caused some festivals to be banned
- concern over danger to participants.

ALL BLACKS PSYCHED OUT BY ENGLISH HAKA

DEFINITELY A DRY BLACKTHORN DAY.

Fig. 12.04 Morris dancers in a new light.

Nonetheless, there has been an overwhelming desire and enthusiasm for celebrating simple amusements and so many have survived throughout the UK. Most of them show some or all of the following characteristics.

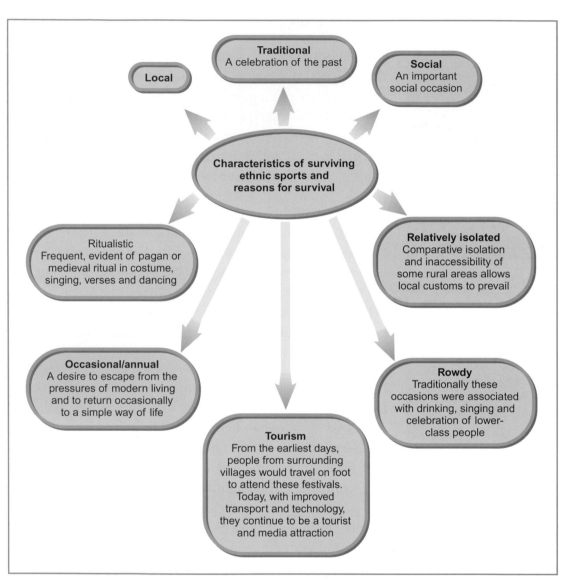

Fig. 12.05

TASK 1

Research any surviving ethnic sport in the UK, for example, the Lakeland and Highland Games or Cumberland and Devonian Wrestling, then answer the following questions.

1 What is it called?
2 What are its origins?
3 Where does it take place?
4 When and how regularly does it take place?
5 Does it have any special festival or cultural features?
6 Why do you think that it still exists?
7 Present your work as a poster.

Tribal Societies

Do you think of tribal peoples as having a relatively unsophisticated lifestyle and living in a natural environment with survival dependent on hunting? Certainly this was the case historically, and in analysing the physical activities of tribal cultures we do need to look back in time. In doing so, we will focus on the following phases of development and emergence.

Fig. 12.06 Tribal society.

1   Pre-colonial (the inherent activities of a society, before the arrival and influence of British and other colonialists).
2   Colonial (reform due to the imposition of foreign customs and behaviour).
3   Post-colonial (the contemporary scene with possible re-emergence of traditional ethnic identity).

KEY WORDS

First though, we must consider what *is* and *was* the influence of **colonialisation**, and what are the characteristics of physical activities in tribal cultures?

Ethnic identity

Unique behaviour and characteristics of a group often based on tradition and ritual.

Colonialisation

The nineteenth-century building of empires by dominant nations who took over and governed previously independent regions of the world.

Spread of Imperialism and Team Games Around the World

Throughout Queen Victoria's reign (1837–1901), British life became more civilised, transport and communications improved and large numbers of upper-class public schoolboys were nurtured for future leadership roles by way of their obsession with team games (which supposedly endowed them with qualities such as courage, endurance, self-reliance and self-control). Britain also gathered and governed a vast empire of sovereign states around the world at this time – and the ex-public schoolboys went abroad to administer them. Missionaries, intent on proclaiming and spreading Christianity, joined them too. Among other places, these late Victorian and Edwardian imperial administrators, educators and disciples went to the tropical rain forests of Africa, the islands of the Pacific, the plains of India and the prairies of Canada. They took their games and the games' associated qualities and values with them in a mission to create loyal, brave, truthful Christian gentlemen! We need to be aware of the positive and negative effects of an alien culture being imposed upon selected tribal cultures in sporting terms. British and other Colonial schools, for example, certainly had a big impact.

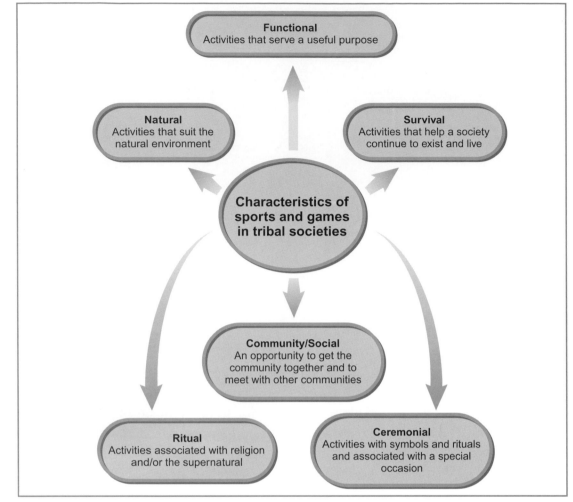

Fig. 12.07 Sports and games in tribal societies.

HOT TIPS

Make sure that you understand the meaning of each of these characteristics and can link them with tribal activities.

Sports and pastimes develop through the needs of the society in which they exist. Historically, tribal cultures have needed to survive in a frequently unpredictable natural environment. They needed the security of military proficiency as well as everyday skills of finding and catching food. Work-related skills such as building and farming also had to be nurtured. Social relationships, co-operation and group harmony were necessary in these societies because they depended on each other for survival. All of these qualities were often promoted through physical activities. The Timbira tribe of South America, for example, has a river festival which includes a log race where several teams manoeuvre logs downstream. The intention is not to win, but to ensure that as many teams as possible successfully complete the course. The focus is on group co-operation rather than internal competition.

With widespread access to technology impossible, simple, inexpensive and unsophisticated, activities emerged in tribal cultures to suit their environment. Any sports later adopted or adapted from colonialists also had to fit in with the limitations of local environmental conditions. You will know that the ancient Greeks and Romans used their sports to praise and to please their gods in order to achieve security and eternal happiness. The same is true of tribal cultures. Several traditional physical activities had ritualistic elements that reinforced religious customs. The ball in many games was a symbol of the supernatural, while ritual dancing featured in ceremonies associated with special occasions such as births, marriages and deaths. Erotic dancing was believed to inspire the gods to produce fertility in all of nature.

We need to be aware of the changes brought about by the arrival of an alien culture.

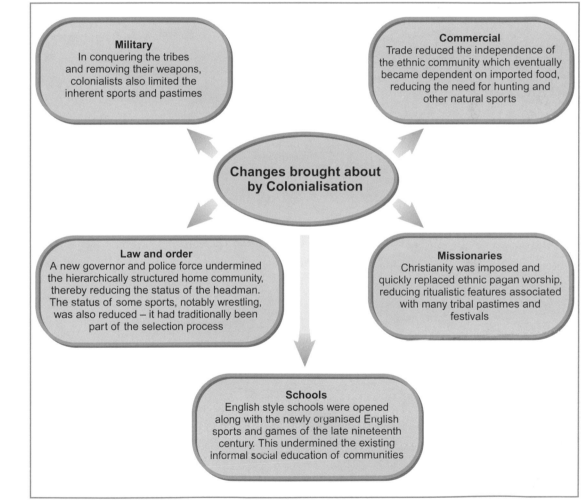

Fig. 12.08 The impact of Colonialisation.

We should now look at some case studies.

Polynesians: Samoan Culture and Physical Activity

The inhabitants of Samoa live on fourteen isolated islands known as Polynesia in the southwestern Pacific, discovered in 1722, but not really explored until 1830.

Pre-Colonial

In 1838 a visitor to Samoa observed that nothing was so important to a Samoan that couldn't be cancelled immediately if a sporting opportunity came up! As an island race, the physical activities of the Samoans were both land and sea based. At sea they enjoyed turtle-riding, diving, swimming, surf-riding and canoeing, while on land they took part in kicking matches, fishing, tug-of-war, juggling, stick throwing for distance, spear throwing for accuracy, wrestling, dart throwing, racing and dancing. These activities ranged from a few members of one village playing informally, to a whole village or district competing in a multi-activity championship. Importantly, success and prestige were always sought for the village, not for the individual. These were great social and ceremonial occasions involving speeches, dancing and feasting. Fierce stick fights were fought in praise of the gods, and ritualistic mock battles (from stories handed down through the generations) were ceremoniously re-enacted. Tribal war was common making courage, strength and resilience prized qualities, essential for success in both games and war.

TASK 2

Match the pre-colonial Samoan physical activities to a characteristic from Figure 12.07.

Colonial

When Samoa became part of the British Empire and missionaries brought Christianity to the islands, the native people had to succumb to outside influences, customs and sports. Traditional Samoan rituals, particularly their erotic dances and many festivals, were either banned or undermined. Instead, the high-ranking Samoans (and over time the lower orders too) adopted and modified the newly acquired team games of cricket, rugby and baseball. These games, rugby especially, appealed to the lifestyle, temperament, flair and physique of the islanders.

Fig. 12.09 The Western Samoan 'Haka'.

Post-Colonial

By 1930 American and New Zealand officials were in control of Samoa. They continued to regulate inter-village ceremonies and sports meetings, but one social anthropologist noted that after one hundred years of foreign influence, Samoan culture had not changed greatly from what it had been like when the missionaries first arrived. Amusements of a vigorous physical nature remained highly important. Rugby unified villages as the old sports had done and was an ideal medium for inter-village rivalry and celebration. It took the place of inter-village stick fighting! With numbers relatively low, the 7s game was an ideal adaptation and one where the

Western Samoans have achieved international success and acclaim. The Western Samoan 'Haka' or ritual war dance is significant for many reasons. Firstly, it represents an expression and re-emergence of traditional Western Samoan ethnic identity. It calls upon the war gods and acts as a link between pre-colonial primitive pastimes and modern sport. It unites the players, all Western Samoans, and perhaps most significantly psyches out the opposition!

Melanesians (Indonesia): Trobriand Island Cricket

The Trobriand Islands lie just off Papua New Guinea in the South Pacific.

Pre-Colonial

As with the Samoans, the Trobriand Islanders participated in ethnic physical activities on both land and sea as part of their tribal existence. These games, sports and dances were predominantly a functional and/or ritualistic part of community ceremonies and celebrations.

Colonial

The invasive influence of British colonialists led to an enforcement of new ways of worship, fighting and play, and diluted the uniqueness of traditional culture. Sophisticated sports, including cricket, were brought to the islands and either adopted or adapted to suit their new environment.

Post-Colonial

The Trobriand Islands became a part of Australia in 1904. When the British left, the game of cricket stayed, but was remoulded to suit its cultural setting. The main features of cricket are still evident in the Trobriand Island version in that there are batting and fielding teams with runs being scored and essential rules in place, but it is fundamentally a tribal experience (see the points below).

Fig. 12.10 Trobriand Island cricket.

Clearly, the game is not just for enjoyment, but serves a useful purpose.

- Players have to clear the jungle before they can play (natural).
- The equipment is made by the players (natural).
- Scoring is kept by pulling leaves from a palm tree (natural).
- The home team always wins as an act of courtesy (ritual, functional).
- It is a community festival involving the whole village (functional, survival).
- It involves dancing, singing and chanting (ritual).
- It integrates different villages (functional, survival).

Aboriginal culture

The word 'Aboriginal' was a general term given by colonialists to all native Australians.

Pre-Colonial

Research shows that physical activities in pre-colonial aboriginal culture could be divided into team games (e.g. football), group games (e.g. hide and seek), group pastimes (e.g. dancing) and individual pastimes (e.g. swimming). These inherent activities of the native Australians were frequently functional, natural and a form of ritual needed for survival. There were ceremonial festivals to honour births, marriages and deaths, and corroboree dances and mock battles to commemorate previously fought encounters. Activities suited the hostile environment and were functional in that hunting with a spear and boomerang throwing were necessary skills, which children were taught from an early age. The game of hide and seek, as played by Aboriginal children, is often cited as an example of functional play. In contrast to the non-serious competitive 'one against the masses' version played in the relatively safe British environment, Aboriginal children practised life skills and worked together to hunt out a lone hidden playmate.

Colonial

Colonialists and missionaries brought games, customs and Christianity to the indigenous population of Australia and oppressed them to the extent that between 1800 and 1830 a population of 10,000 Aboriginals in Victoria was reduced to 2,000. Some moved to a life of poverty and alcohol abuse in towns, while many children were taken from their natural families and brought up in orphanages as second-class English children. As a result of this oppression, a tough mentality or 'bush ethos' developed – a determination and ability to withstand the rigours of life and the outback. It has been argued that the perceived characteristics of the Australian male as being tough, independent, practical, lacking in emotion and diligently loyal to his friends stems from this.

Post-Colonial

KEY WORDS

Glass ceiling

The perceived highest level to which certain groups in society can rise. When individuals break through it, they may become role models.

The authentic ethnic identity and traditional tribal customs of the Aboriginals are now only evident in the least populated desert areas of the country, but they also survive as part of folklore and as a tourist attraction. In the 1970s, Evonne Goolagong broke through the glass ceiling of discrimination to become a role model for Aboriginal women in contemporary Australian sport and more recently, the athlete Cathy Freeman has successfully taken on the role.

Emergent Societies

Emergent countries are less economically developed countries. They are mainly in Africa, the Far East, and Central and South America, and all have experienced colonisation by wealthier countries at some time in their history. The UK has emerged from tribal origins. It has progressed by way of the Industrial Revolution and the empire-building spree of the eighteenth and nineteenth centuries, to the technological boom of the twentieth and now twenty-first centuries. As a so-called advanced society, the UK now has relative wealth, world status and political stability. Meanwhile, emergent countries strive to improve their quality of life, and to develop politically and socio-economically. They are often still emerging from a tribal level. Sport can be their way of achieving their goals.

We are interested in how countries use sport as a vehicle for advancement. Research has shown that certain general principles can be associated with this process. As general principles, they will not necessarily fit each nation's profile precisely. Their emphasis will also alter, sometimes quite quickly, as the process of change and emergence takes place and as success in an original sport prompts adoption of and success in others. They still continue to be important guiding characteristics.

Firstly, we need to understand the meaning of the characteristics of sport in emergent societies and secondly, we need to look at selected emergent countries in relation to them.

Political Motives

Nation building – the goals of attaining economic progress and establishing a strong cultural identity can be achieved through sporting excellence. The 'shop-window' effect operates, whereby the world becomes aware of a nation through its sporting success. Recognition can then attract respect, financial support and even tourists, all of which can help to improve the country's economy.

Stability – in order to retain power and create wealth, new governments strive to establish stability and social control in their countries. In theory, sport can appease the population, divert attention from the realities and problems of life and reduce the likelihood of internal conflict.

Integration – countries with a tribal history often experience internal disputes. Strong leaders, authoritarian governments and military power have alternatively been used to suppress them. Sport can bring different tribes, islands or ethnic groups together under one national flag, it can also be used to calm tension.

Health – a healthy workforce is needed for any nation hoping to emerge into the modern industrialised world. An improved standard of living for the majority, based on economic and political efficiency, can only be achieved if citizens are free from disease. Sport and physical activity can help to promote a health-conscious society and be an alternative to dangerous or undesirable activities such as drug taking or alcohol abuse. International sporting success can also be achieved more readily by the few if the masses from whom they come are in good health.

Defence – emergent nations have military, economic and political battles to fight. A strong army and police force are needed to maintain stability, ease internal disorder and establish a high profile defence in the face of potential external conflict. The military and police often organise sport, and successful athletes are frequently given token jobs in the army, police force or government.

Strategies for Success

Selection (sometimes referred to as elitism) – initially, emergent societies will select and specialise in one sport. Perhaps this is one that is already popular in the country or which suits the climate, landscape, altitude, lifestyle or physique of the people. Once success and recognition have been won, there is likely to be a greater selection of sports, pursued by a greater number of people (e.g. from different tribes, areas, gender or ethnic groups).

Unequal funding (also called disproportionate funding) – an emergent society will not initially have the resources to reach excellence in a variety of activities, resulting in much more money being spent on one sport than others. Sometimes, huge sums of money are spent on the few, while the majority remain neglected and impoverished.

High profile/low technology – the Olympic Games is a global sporting extravaganza and the Olympic rostrum is the ultimate stage. A country that seeks international recognition will choose a high status, world-renowned sport to achieve maximum exposure. With technology largely underdeveloped, sports that are simple, natural and require a minimum of technical expertise or expensive equipment will be selected. Athletics and football are commonly chosen.

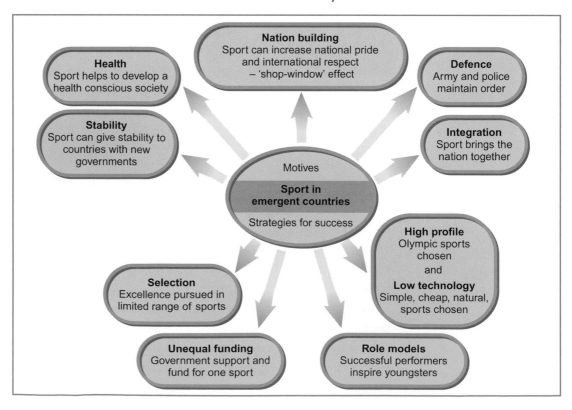

Fig. 12.11 Sport in emergent countries.

Role models – world champions become local and national heroes and give the people a feeling of pride and well-being. Children will copy role models and may in their turn achieve sporting excellence and international recognition.

Kenya – Middle and Long Distance Running

By the 1880s, British, American, French and German explorers and missionaries had travelled into the part of Africa now known as Kenya. By the early twentieth century, some Europeans had settled in the region, big game hunters had been attracted by the Kenyan wildlife and civil servants were in place to administer the new British colony. British culture became the norm in high-ranking circles. In the 1950s, however, native discontent became apparent and an uprising by a terrorist organisation resulted in large-scale reforms. Kenya gained its independence in 1963.

Before the influence of colonialists in Kenya, physical activities were tribal in nature. There was dancing, 'whipping' (an activity associated with cattle-herding) and a variety of fighting games. The early colonialists then brought their organised and rationalised sports and until the 1960s, Kenya's policies reflected the needs of the colonialists rather than the native people.

In the Mexico Olympics, 1968, Kenya competed for the first time as an independent nation. Its amazing athletic victories (nine medals, including three gold) ensured instant international recognition and respect. The country produced a string of middle and long distance runners including 'Kip' Keino, Naftali Temu, Ben Kogo, Henry Rono and Amos Biwott. Kenya was well and truly on the world sporting stage.

How did Kenya achieve its remarkable success? Was it politically motivated? Here are some of the possible reasons for success.

- Living and training 6000ft above sea level. High altitude helps runners take in and utilise oxygen very efficiently.
- Running is part of the natural lifestyle in Kenya. A tradition has developed and role models inspire all children to believe they too can be champions.
- Middle and long distance running suits the physique of Kenyans.
- They have a well-balanced diet of high quality protein and carbohydrates and a wide variety of fruit and vegetables.
- Expert coaching and training (initially from abroad).
- Dedication and commitment.

Without doubt, the aim of the newly established independent Kenyan government in the late 1960s and 1970s was to raise the profile of the country worldwide and to attract foreign financial investment. It selected a low tech, but high profile Olympic sport. It then channelled large amounts of money towards a small number of male athletes from privileged tribes who excelled in particular events.

Once the primary motive of achieving international recognition was achieved, the Kenyan government could broaden its focus. A wide variety of sports is now played in Kenya and women have also achieved sporting recognition and success. In 1996 Kenya beat the West Indies in the cricket World Cup, soccer is widely played, and both the men's and women's national basketball teams are highly rated among African nations. There is a National League for Basketball from which some players gain sports scholarships to American universities with a few playing professionally in Canada, South Africa and India. The result of this contemporary situation is the emergence of role models from a greater number of events and sports who influence greater numbers of aspiring young people.

An article from *Runners World* in August 1995 sums up the situation perfectly:

> *As the Western world becomes more affluent physical standards will continue to decline. We shall count our successes in other arenas where the toys are more expensive and prestigious – motor racing, yachting, skiing, even computer games. The simple sports where success depends on strength of mind and body rather than the price of the equipment will be dominated by Third World athletes – people who are accustomed to fighting for survival. This is right and proper.*
>
> *In the long term, the way to beat the Kenyans is to build them more schools (so they don't have so far to run), subsidise their buses, set up chains of burger bars and export lots of sliced bread! Dragging them down to our level will take a long time. Until then, they'll keep on scooping the prizes.*

TASK 3

Read the extract from *Runners World* and identify key characteristics of sport in emergent countries.

Fig. 12.12 The victorious Brazilian football team of 2002.

Brazil – Football

Brazil won the World Cup in 1958, 1962, 1970, 1994 and most recently in 2002. More than 30 million Brazilians play football regularly. There are 2,500 professional teams and 10,000 amateur sides. Even Indian tribes in the Amazon have officially recognised teams. Even though volleyball and basketball are now also widely played, and very successful women's teams compete, football still dominates Brazilian culture. What are the roots of and reasons for this success?

Carlos Alberto, skipper of the 1970 world cup team explains:

' *Like the Americans constantly produce natural basketball players, we create footballers who play like no one else in the world. It's in the blood. It comes from our culture. We call it "Jeitinho", a piece of Brazilian magic that exists only in our culture.* '

The Sun, Saturday 29 June, 2002

Although Spain and Portugal colonised South America, the British game of football was adopted as the national game of the people. One story is that the game was first introduced to Brazil in the late 1890s by the son of an English São Paulo aristocrat who was sent to boarding school in Nottingham. He returned with the football rules and two footballs and organised matches at an exclusive club for expatriate railway and gas engineers in the town's affluent suburbs. The game then spread to the factory workers and the slaves of the sugar and coffee plantations by word of mouth. Barred from practising *capoeira* – a martial dance with African roots – the poor blacks adopted football en masse, but made it their own.

Brazil has a large underprivileged population in its major cities and football became the natural street game. It was a simple, cheap and healthy pastime and a positive alternative to crime or drugs. Inspired by role models such as Pele, children dreamed of being spotted by professional clubs and finding a way out of poverty, first as players and later as coaches and managers. Football also allows each South American nation to express its identity and to appease its people. Football leagues and championships can integrate communities in a competitive but relatively unthreatening way.

Extracts from a *Times* newspaper article (27 June 1998) illustrate the situation very well:

Fig. 12.13 Ronaldo – a role model for Brazilian children.

' *On a Sunday afternoon, far away from Rio de Janeiro's huge world-class stadiums where Brazil's first-division matches are being held, a hearty crowd of about 500 has gathered in the centre of the favela Rocinha to watch their local third-division team perform in a practice match. Each time the ball zooms through the imaginary goal posts, marked by pairs of flip-flops, the fans fall into delirious cheering. In the sprawling favelas, the Brazilians' renowned passion for football is at its rawest . . . for many who live in the sprawl of urban squalor, football is the only thing . . . a chance to play for the local side could also mean a way out . . . Hundreds of youngsters spend all day, every day, on nearby beaches learning ball tricks . . . they start playing almost after they learn to walk . . . most of them don't have boots . . . but there is still the hope of being spotted one day . . . "it became a means to affirm our identity and boost our low self-esteem" . . . for the people in the favelas it is a way to participate in national issues . . . it has been argued that the game has been used to appease the public and make them forget about* ' *social and economic crisis . . . back in the narrow, open sewage alleys that connect the precariously built brick home in Rocinha, dozens of children proudly point to their green-and-yellow "Ronaldinho" shirts.* ❯

TASK 4
Read this newspaper extract and identify evidence of characteristics of sport in emergent cultures, for example, nation building, stability, role modelling.

West Indies – Cricket

The West Indies is a collection of independent islands and mainland Commonwealth territories in the Caribbean. The sports there range from the tribal activities of the original population, to the Afro-Caribbean activities developed by the slave population and to the sports, notably cricket, that were introduced by colonialists. Today, baseball and basketball rival the popularity and funding of cricket.

In recent history, cricket has helped to establish a national identity for a multi-dimensional culture made up of many islands. It united the islands so that they could take on the rest of the Commonwealth and achieve success that would not have been possible individually. Cricket integrated the islands and the different races within the islands. As a highly structured and codified game it also had the potential to establish a sense of team loyalty and stability within the community. Cricket became central to West Indian culture and countless children continue to play the game with makeshift equipment on the beaches, inspired by their role models and driven by a desire to achieve and earn. With the influence of American sports, they now have a variety of possible avenues for success, but diversification may also mean national sporting mediocrity.

Indonesia – Badminton

Indonesia is made up of thousands of small islands, plus larger islands such as Java and Sumatra, each of which has different tribal cultures. There is evidence that Japan and India have an ancient shuttlecock game and that the Chinese played shuttlecock with their feet 2,000 years ago! When the British introduced their game of badminton into India, Malaya and Singapore in the late nineteenth century, it therefore had roots to cling to.

Badminton developed as a popular game in India and Malaysia and has been played at a high level in Indonesia since the 1950s. It suits the physical make-up and dexterity of the people and requires only limited numbers, space and equipment. The original gentle pace of the game also suited the tropical conditions. As an Olympic sport, success brought international recognition.

Capitalist economies

Where private ownership dominates and is encouraged. Private wealth is used to produce and distribute goods and services.

Socialist economies

Where state ownership dominates and controls commercial activities, policy and practice.

Mixed economies

Where both private and public enterprise operates together.

Democracy

A system where the people have the right to participate in public affairs.

Centrality

When the dominant roles in sport are taken by the dominant group of society.

The Links between Sport and Commercialism, and Sport and Politics

Here, we are looking at what could be called advanced cultures – those with economic and technological superiority over others.

When countries compete internationally they want to succeed. International sporting success gives status to a country in the eyes of the rest of the world. It can inspire or appease, be a political tool or a multi-million pound commodity. Sporting success can unify citizens and create national pride, and at a blanket level it can increase the nation's health.

We need to understand that a nation's politics affects its approach to sport, so in this section we will take a sociological view of both western **democracies** (which reflect **capitalist economies**) and eastern democracies (which reflect **socialist economies**). We need to assess how differently and for what reasons they promote sport. Do they put the individual or the community first? It is important to understand that although we study the two contrasting eastern and western models, most western European countries do, in fact, lie somewhere between these two extremes. They have their own versions of either socialist or conservative governments within a mixed economy where there is both state and commercial support for sport.

Characteristics of Sport and Commercialism – the 'American Dream'

In the US sport means business! At every level it is driven by commercialism. Both private and corporate business use sport to promote their products and to achieve goodwill.

US school sport has a very high profile and attracts big sponsorship. Entire towns ritualistically throng to the pomp and ceremony of the Friday night ball game, where the band plays and cheerleaders dance and rouse the crowd's excitement and support. Players become heroes or villains overnight and are either praised or mercilessly criticised in the local newspapers the following day. The most promising performers compete for athletic scholarships to colleges and universities.

College players receive top level coaching and support and are under enormous pressure to win in a highly competitive field, which is heavily funded by TV and sponsorship deals. The best college athletes are drafted into professional sport.

Professional sport receives enormous public interest in the US and is inextricably linked with and dependent upon commercialism. TV and advertising not only fund professional sport, but also govern procedures and influence its rules.

The US sporting event is a superb reflection of US culture where the 'win ethic' dominates. In the nineteenth century, European games were adopted and quickly moulded to suit their new environment and rapidly evolving culture. Other games were invented. This was a new society – the 'land of opportunity' where the groundbreaking 'Pioneer spirit' of determination, enterprise and drive was respected. Games are high scoring, action packed and with exciting short bursts of activity which are followed by commercial breaks.

The top US professional sports stars are the richest in the world. The 'American dream' assumes that anyone can be a success in society, irrespective of age, gender or ethnic background and sport is a particularly useful vehicle for success. Through sport, stereotypical views can be defied, the restricting glass ceiling of opportunity can be smashed and role models for future generations can be created. Top professional sportsmen and women are on multi-million dollar playing contracts and can earn even more from advertising and sponsorship deals. Professional sport dominates in US society and reflects its competitive and capitalist nature.

Positive outcomes of commercialism	Negative outcomes of commercialism
• Funding gives athletes a better chance of success.	• Performers become mobile adverts.
• Commercial sponsorship leads to events which otherwise might not happen.	• Money determines the location, timings and nature of events.
• It matches the 'win ethic' of US culture.	• Sporting values can be lost.
	• Only high profit sports and the most successful performers benefit.

Sport and Politics – the 'Shop Window'

It seems universally accepted that sport and politics are interwoven. As eastern European countries showed in the 1970s and 80s, sport can be used for internal and external political motives and with both functional and dysfunctional outcomes.

Here we are concerned with authoritarian one-party states, such as China, where sport is controlled and encouraged by the state in order to increase political prestige and morale among the workforce. As the reforms of the Soviet Union did not mean an end to Communism or to 'socialist' influences in the world, we can also usefully refer to the old eastern European socialist countries that were dominated by the USSR before the disintegration of the communist system in the early 1990s.

From 1917, after the Russian monarchy was overthrown, the Communist party abolished class division and private ownership and in theory established an egalitarian system – equality for all. Whether or not this happened in practice, and in sport in particular, is not the central issue here. We are concerned with motive. Politicians used sport to promote their country and their political system worldwide. And the Olympic Games was their chosen stage. The entire population was tested, and talented children were selected and given the best facilities, coaching, diet and even drugs to ensure international success and perceived political superiority. Athletes were given token jobs in the army or industry, so that they could devote themselves full time to sport. The government centrally controlled all of this. In reality, the minority were funded at the expense of 'equality for all'.

This drive for success and political superiority is evident in China and other advanced eastern cultures today, even though the west and the east have a lot in common. The issue is not so much between right wing and left wing politics, but between multi-party democracies and single-party authoritarianism.

TASK 5
Discuss possible positive and negative outcomes of sport being used as a political tool.

HOT TIPS

All advanced societies use sport to reflect their supposed superiority. Make sure that you know how commercialism and politics alternatively drive countries.

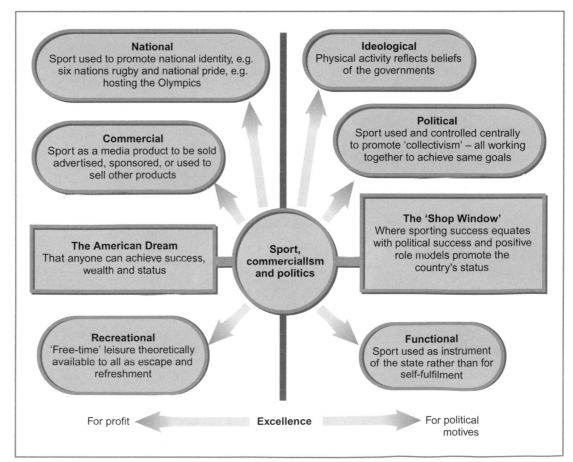

Fig. 12.14 Commercial and political approaches to sport.

Revise as you go! Test your knowledge and understanding

- Name a traditional or ethnic sport that still takes place in the UK today.
- Identify four characteristics of traditional ethnic sports.
- Why do some traditional sports and festivals still occur in the UK today?
- How do tribal societies show their traditional ethnic identity in their sports?
- Why was co-operation more common that competition in tribal societies?
- What is meant by the term 'nation building'?
- What was significant about 'hide and seek' in Aboriginal culture?
- What is the significance of the Western Samoan Haka?
- How does commercialism affect sport in the West, particularly in the US?
- What is meant by the term 'shop window effect'?

Sharpen up your exam technique!

1   In many cases, sports and pastimes in tribal societies have gone through three developmental stages: pre-colonial, colonial and post-colonial. Identify three characteristics of sports and pastimes tribal societies before colonialism took place.   (3 marks)

2   Explain the development of a sporting activity from a tribal culture of your choice, for example, rugby in Western Samoa.   (3 marks)

3   Name an emergent country. Discuss the nature of sporting activities in emergent societies.   (6 marks)

4   'Nation building, integration, health and defence are key motives for the selection and unequal funding of one sport in emergent countries.' Discuss this statement with reference to one particular emergent country.   (4 marks)

5   Identify the significance of role models in emergent societies.   (4 marks)

6   Identify key features of sport in each of the following:

    (a)   capitalist multi-party democracies, for example, the US
    (b)   socialist one-party states, for example, China.   (5 marks)

Chapter 13 **Sporting Issues Analysis**

Learning Objectives

At the end of this chapter you should be able to:
- Understand the influence of various organisational agencies involved with increasing mass participation and sporting excellence in the UK.
- Identify organisations' initiatives and strategies which target a) minority groups and mass participation and b) sporting excellence in the UK.
- Identify potential problems associated with high-level sport, for example, administrative inefficiency, inadequate funding and a lack of comprehensive, professional coaching policies.
- Consider ethical issues in high level sport such as corruption, violence and the temptation to cheat.
- Analyse professional sport as a business and the role of the media and sponsorship in promoting the business.
- Examine discrimination in sport and participation by minority groups.

Introduction

Figure 13.01 on page 220 shows the main themes and issues that will be covered in this chapter.

What is Sporting Excellence?

A dictionary definition of excellence is 'a state of exceptional merit or quality'. Here we are concerned with the identification, support and development of sports performers of distinction. The issue involves:
- the moral debate about whether pursuing excellence for the best is unfair to the rest
- an analysis of current political views and policies regarding elite sport
- a review of administrative procedures aimed at its achievement.

The issue can usefully be discussed under the headings of policy, provision and administration.

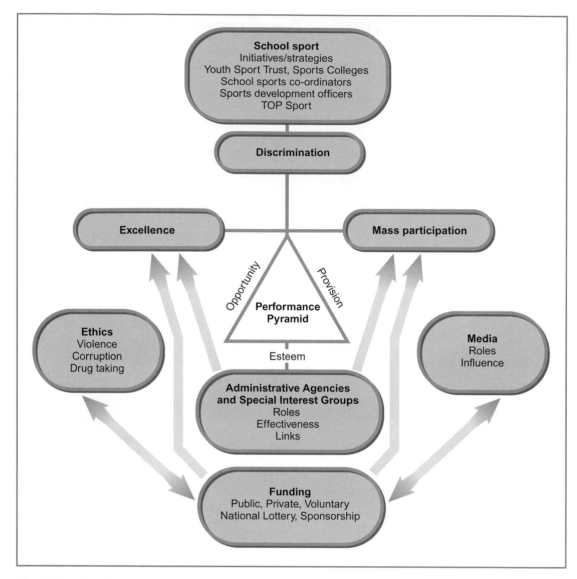

Fig. 13.01 Sporting issues.

Policy

Policy includes government initiatives and government support. It is also to do with the concept of amateurism. Policy influences and is clearly linked with provision and administration.

Political **ideology**, or dominant beliefs and values, determine policy. We have already established that many countries want Olympic medals in order to build their reputation. Some countries, notably the German Democratic Republic in the 1970s and 1980s, pursued this goal at the expense of the majority. In Britain, however, success at international level has traditionally been left to the National Governing Bodies. On the one hand, many politicians believed that sport and politics just did not mix, and on the other, the governing bodies wanted to retain their autonomy. Everyone, including politicians, applauded our winners, but left them and their sports to their own devices. There was little drive to attract world-class events, time for PE in state schools has been eroded and the traditional amateur approach to sport has held us back. More recently, however, some aspects of the ideology have changed. Following our disappointing performance in the Barcelona Olympics in 1992, and particularly in Atlanta in 1996, politicians, notably John Major in the early 1990s, have shown greater interest, involvement and support. Financial aid has been channelled into the pursuit of excellence, particularly from the National Lottery. The status of high-level sport has risen in line with increasingly professional attitudes and approaches from National Governing Bodies (NGBs) and other organisational agencies. Visionary policy has the potential to change the sporting culture of the UK.

Provision

What do performers need in order to reach their potential? Specialist sports schools and the more recent sports colleges fulfill a particular role here. Elite performers need the best training venues with the best facilities and highly qualified and committed coaches who themselves enjoy respect, security and support. They also need the added support of nutritionists, sports scientists, psychologists, physiotherapists and mentors to guide on personal and career issues.

Administration

We need to be aware of how sport in Britain is structured, organised and funded and what each organisation does in the pursuit of sporting excellence. Starting at the base of the pyramid, schools, clubs and NGBs need an efficient structure, to channel talent to the top.

Structure and Organisation of Sport in the UK

The structure of sport in the UK is very complicated. Figure 13.02 is one way of illustrating the various organisations that link together and affect both mass participation and sporting excellence. The situation has emerged over the last 150 years, which adds to its complexity and inter-connected nature.

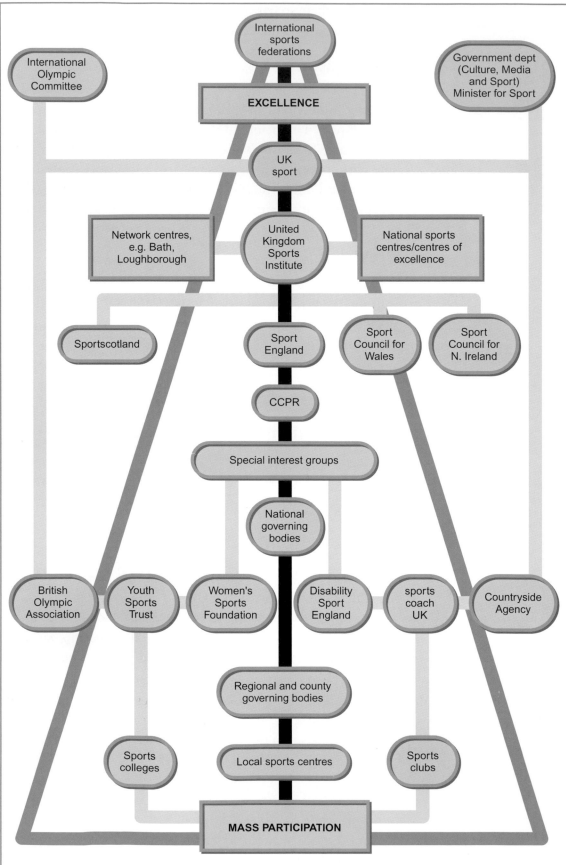

Fig. 13.02 Organisations influencing mass participation and sporting excellence in the UK.

KEY WORDS

Centralised

A system where power is held by central government.

Decentralised

A system where power and control are locally held.

The UK has a decentralised system of sports administration. Grass-roots clubs and local associations are self-governing, with central government providing very little in terms of overall sporting policy. A decentralised sporting system has both positive and negative consequences. On the positive side, limited outside interference allows sporting associations to build on tradition and to use their initiative to meet individual needs. On the negative side, a decentralised system can be inefficient, in spite of UK Sport's recent efforts to minimise organisational inefficiency in the system as a whole. Historically, keen and committed volunteers have run sport in the UK. From small local clubs to NGBs and major associations, unpaid staff have run the system. With no overall policy, a lack of professional training and an insignificant number of full-time paid administrators, there has been inconsistency of effectiveness both in and between organisations. Excessive bureaucracy has also been an issue. In recent years, there has been a period of organisational change. While small private clubs continue to depend on volunteers, the larger and more determined clubs are taking a more businesslike and professional approach.

What do various organisations do for mass participation and sporting excellence?

Government

The Department for Culture, Media and Sport (DCMS) appoints the Minister for Sport and gives an annual grant to UK Sport, Sport England, the Sports Council for Wales, Sportscotland and the Sports Council for Northern Ireland.

The Department for Education and Employment (DfEE) is responsible for PE in schools and works through the Youth Sport Trust to improve school sport and PE.

Fig. 13.03

UK Sport

UK Sport is responsible for developing elite sport in the UK. It is funded by the government and distributes National Lottery money to support excellence. Specifically it:

- identifies sporting policies for the UK as a whole
- supports our best performers through the World Class Programme
- runs the ACE UK (Athlete Career and Education Services) programme which aims to maximise career opportunities for athletes both during and after their sporting career by giving them access to educational programmes, career advice, training in personal finance and media management. The programme has been developed with the British Olympic Association, the Scottish Institute of Sport and the home country sports councils
- oversees the UK Sports Institute (UKSI)
- promotes international status by attracting major sporting events, for example, world cups
- promotes ethical standards of behaviour and administers an anti-doping programme

Fig. 13.04

Fig. 13.05

• co-ordinates all organisations within the national framework and encourages administrative efficiency.

The United Kingdom Sports Institute (UKSI)

The idea of an institute was outlined in the 1995 government statement *Raising the Game*. The aim of the UKSI is to provide Britain's best sportsmen and women with everything they need to compete and win at international level. Each home country has its own institute (e.g. the English Institute of Sport, split into nine regions) and there is a network of centres throughout the UK. £120 million of Sport England

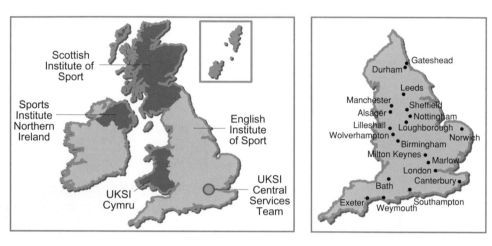

Fig. 13.06 UKSI's home country institutes.

Fig. 13.07 The network centres of the English Institute of Sport.

Lottery money is earmarked to develop facilities at England's network centres.

HOT TIPS

The UKSI network emerged from the idea of having a British Academy of sport, which was initially intended to be similar to the Academy in Australia.

More specifically, the UKSI:
• provides coaching, sports science and medical support to elite athletes
• has a central services team based in UK Sport's London office
• works closely with NGBs and other organisations.

TASK 1

Explain, under the headings 'policy', 'provision' and 'administration', what elite performers get from attending a UKSI network centre.

SPORT ENGLAND

Fig. 13.08

Sport England

Sport England is accountable to Parliament through the Secretary of State for Culture, Media and Sport. It is funded by the Exchequer and through the National Lottery. It has a London head office and nine regional offices whose staff work closely with local authorities, NGBs, and other national and regional organisations concerned with sport. Sport England is responsible for:

- developing and maintaining the infrastructure of sport in England
- distributing National Lottery funds,

and aims to get:

- **more people** involved in sport
- **more places** to play sport
- **more medals** through higher standards of performance.

More People

Over the years there have been several campaigns to encourage mass participation. Today, mass participation is encouraged through the *More People* campaign, which is divided into three elements: 1 Active Schools, 2 Active Sports, 3 Active Communities.

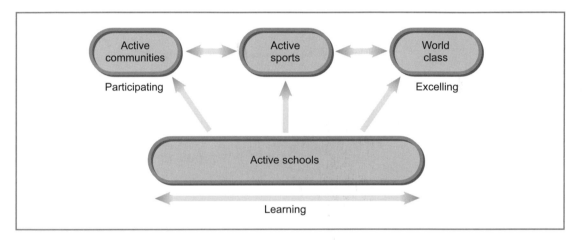

Fig. 13.09

The Active Schools Project:

- follows on from the National Junior Sports Programme of the 1990s
- aims to provide every school child with the opportunity to learn skills and to participate in the sport of their choice.

It includes:

- **Activemark** (and Activemark Gold) and **Sportsmark** (and Sportsmark Gold) awards which are given to primary and secondary schools respectively that reach targets for PE in school and sport in the community
- Coaching for teachers
- Sportsearch
- the TOPS programmes – a series of linked programmes all aimed at developing sport for young people and which include TOP Tots, TOP Play, TOP Sport and TOP Skill (see pages 183–4).

The Active Sports Project:

- follows on from the Champion Coaching project of the 1990s
- aims to help young people to achieve more from their chosen sport.

How does it operate?

- Sport England has targeted nine sports through which it hopes to encourage more young people to take part in, improve in and benefit from extra-curricular sport
- interested participants will be introduced to clubs and talented performers will be guided towards development squads.

The Active Communities Project:
- has emerged from the 'Sport For All' campaigns of the last 30 years
- aims to get more people from all communities, especially from minority or disadvantaged groups, to have opportunities to take part in regular physical activity.

How does it operate?
- Sports Development Officers work in communities
- 'Sports action zones' have been created and targeted
- the 'Active Communities Development Fund' is a funding programme to increase participation among:
  - ethnic communities
  - people with disabilities
  - women and girls
  - people on low incomes
- it focuses on projects that tackle rural and urban deprivation, for example, in March 2001 the Waltham Forest Sikh group was awarded £150,000 (the largest sum to date) to improve sporting opportunities in its community.

More Places

Sport England wants efficient management of the right facilities in the right places. Thus they:
- plan – by identifying the needs of the area and the best possible location for facilities
- develop – to make sure that their objectives are effectively met
- design – to make sure that the facility is suitable for the intended purpose
- manage – to make sure that the facility runs smoothly.

More Medals

In conjunction with UK Sport, Sport England supports elite performers in the pursuit of excellence. It does this through the:
- English Institute of Sport network
- National Sports Centres (Bisham Abbey, Holme Pierrepont, Lilleshall, Crystal Palace, and the National Velodrome in Manchester), which form part of the network
- World Class Programme, which provides lottery funding to outstanding performers to help with their training and preparation. The programme includes:

  - World Class Start – for promising young performers
  - World Class Potential – for talented performers with the potential to represent their country

KEY WORDS

Sport action zone

Up to 20 areas have been earmarked by Sport England as being of high social and economic deprivation, where local sporting needs are identified and action plans implemented.

– World Class Performance – for elite performers at international level
– World Class Events – which aims to attract and stage major sporting events to the UK.

In 2000, the World Class Programme received £20.5 million from the National Lottery. At £3.05 million, athletics received the most, an investment repaid with two gold, two silver and two bronze medals by track and field athletes in the Sydney 2000 Olympics.

TASK 2

	Excellence	Mass participation
UK Sport		
Sport England		
Sportscotland		
Sports Council for Wales		
Sports Council for Northern Ireland		

Chart how UK Sport and home country organisations aim to increase mass participation and sporting excellence in the UK. Further research can be done on www.uksport.org.uk and home country websites.

National Governing Bodies

Every sport is controlled by its own National Governing Body (NGB), for example, the Lawn Tennis Association (LTA). With an increased desire for international success, some full time professional administrators are taking up positions, where they can be afforded.

TASK 3

In groups, research a number of different NGBs and identify:
• to what extent their roles fit the model in Figure 13.10
• how many paid employees they have
• how they specifically influence their sports
• evidence of efficiency or inefficiency.

Fig. 13.11

The Central Council of Physical Recreation

The Central Council of Physical Recreation (CCPR) represents more than 300 governing bodies. It is funded by Sport England, by sponsorship, from the sale of goods and from members' donations. It is largely a pressure group representing and working on behalf of sports, but specifically it:

• promotes participation
• runs campaigns, e.g. Fair Play in Sport
• runs the Sports Leader Award scheme
• gives advice on sports sponsorship.

Fig. 13.10 NGBs select all world class funded performers.

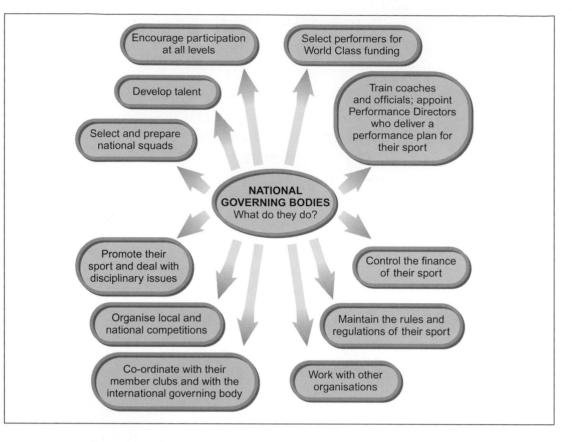

Special Interest Groups

These voluntary organisations represent and encourage particular societal groups to take part in and have equality of sporting opportunity and provision, for example, women or people with disabilities.

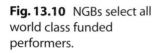

Fig. 13.12

The Women's Sports Foundation

The Women's Sports Foundation (WSF) is funded by Sport England and by subscriptions and sponsors. Its functions include:

- combating inequality in sport
- getting women and girls involved in sport at all levels
- encouraging better access to sport for women and girls
- raising the profile of all British sportswomen
- advising sports organisations on women's sporting issues.

Fig. 13.13

Disability Sport England

Disability Sport England (DSE) receives money from fundraising and from sponsorship. Its functions include:

- working to improve awareness of and the image of disability sport
- educating the general public about the abilities of disabled people
- providing opportunities for disabled people to take part in sport
- promoting the benefits of sport and physical activity to disabled people

- encouraging disabled people to play an active role in the development of their sport.

sports coach UK (formerly the National Coaching Foundation)

One of the problems faced by coaches in this country is that many are unpaid volunteers and so may not have the time or finances to keep up to date with their qualifications. In relation to coaches from some other countries, many also have less status and security and so morale can be comparatively low. **sports coach UK (scUK)** is the only single organisation in the UK that is solely dedicated to providing an infrastructure that is geared towards producing better coaches. Through a programme of education and continuing professional development at all levels, it is taking a long term approach to British sport, concentrating efforts at the very heart of sport – the coach.

Fig. 13.14

scUK is a charitable organisation, funded by UK Sport, Sport England and earned income. It is concerned with:

- supporting individual coaches by offering workshops and resources covering a wide range of subjects, applicable to all levels
- working with other sporting organisations and the Home Country Sports Councils to promote coach education and improve coaching standards
- providing a network of Coaching Development Officers within England to offer support in the regions
- producing Faster Higher Stronger (a quarterly coaching publication) which is held in high esteem throughout the world
- supporting the activities of Coachwise Limited, the trading subsidiary of **scUK**
- running workshops and training sessions for those coaches in the high performance environment
- running the *Coaching for Teachers* scheme, which is funded by Sport England, to improve the standard of coaching within schools.

Funding for Sport

Sport makes money and costs money. Gold medals cost a lot of money. British politicians have long regarded sport as a low status activity. Historically, sport has received insufficient state funding (public sector funding), resulting in the need for cash from private and voluntary sources. Increasingly, however, the vote winning potential of providing quality facilities for all and of achieving international success has led to some change of political heart.

Fig. 13.15 The funding pie is made up of public, private and voluntary sectors.

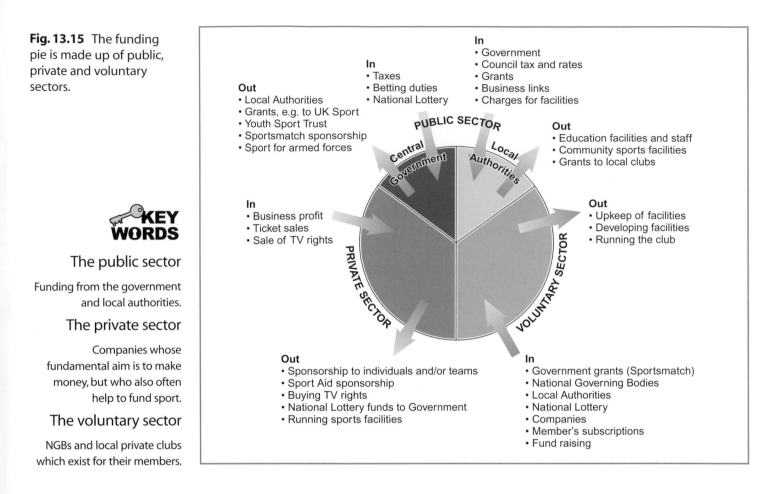

In
• Taxes
• Betting duties
• National Lottery

In
• Government
• Council tax and rates
• Grants
• Business links
• Charges for facilities

Out
• Local Authorities
• Grants, e.g. to UK Sport
• Youth Sport Trust
• Sportsmatch sponsorship
• Sport for armed forces

Out
• Education facilities and staff
• Community sports facilities
• Grants to local clubs

In
• Business profit
• Ticket sales
• Sale of TV rights

Out
• Upkeep of facilities
• Developing facilities
• Running the club

PUBLIC SECTOR

Central Government

Local Authorities

PRIVATE SECTOR

VOLUNTARY SECTOR

Out
• Sponsorship to individuals and/or teams
• Sport Aid sponsorship
• Buying TV rights
• National Lottery funds to Government
• Running sports facilities

In
• Government grants (Sportsmatch)
• National Governing Bodies
• Local Authorities
• National Lottery
• Companies
• Member's subscriptions
• Fund raising

KEY WORDS

The public sector

Funding from the government and local authorities.

The private sector

Companies whose fundamental aim is to make money, but who also often help to fund sport.

The voluntary sector

NGBs and local private clubs which exist for their members.

There are both good and bad features of sports funding in the UK.

GOOD	BAD
• National Lottery money is available for excellence.	• Lottery money needs to be evenly distributed.
• Some clubs are very wealthy, e.g. Manchester United.	• There is lack of financial equality between clubs.
• As a relatively newly professionalised game, Rugby Union can now compete on even terms with southern hemisphere sides.	• When ambition outweighs financial resources, smaller clubs can go bankrupt.
• In 1999 the government put £125 million into a scheme to 'bring back our playing fields' and is committed into putting lottery money into a 'green space' initiative.	• NGBs need to be careful when 'selling' their sport for commercial reasons. They can lose their autonomy.
	• Limited government aid means that commercialism has a greater role to play in British sport. This can lead to lack of control by clubs over their own destiny.
	• A balance should be sought between public and private funding.
	• The complexity of funding sources in Britain has led to an imbalance between activities and provision on levels of the performance pyramid.

KEY WORDS

Sportsmatch

A grass roots sponsorship scheme run by the Institute of Sports sponsorship, whereby the government matches the sponsor's donation, thereby doubling the value of grass-roots sponsorship.

SportsAid Sponsorship

SportsAid is a charity, set up in 1998 to replace the Sports Aid Foundation (SAF). It is funded by the Foundation for Sport and the Arts, sponsorship from companies, and donations from individuals and companies. It gives grants to talented able-bodied and disabled performers who are outside of the World Class Programme.

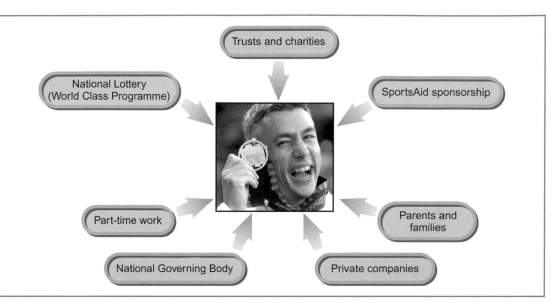

Fig. 13.17

Fig. 13.16 Possible sources of funding for elite performers.

National Lottery

Since 1994, the National Lottery has had a huge impact on British sport and is now the primary source of sports funding in the UK. The Lottery was set up to raise money for five good causes, with the New Opportunities fund for health and education projects (including healthy living centres and after-school clubs) added in 1998.

Fig. 13.18

The Lottery Sports Fund provides grants of more than £200 million annually. These are distributed by the five sports councils to support and encourage sporting excellence and mass participation. The councils make their own funding decisions without political interference.

The National Lottery and Excellence

UK Sport distributes £25 million of lottery funding each year to the NGBs' World Class Performance Programmes (WCPP). It also funds the UKSI and its coaches, sports science back up, warm weather and acclimatisation training, travel and accommodation for competition, athlete development programmes and training facilities. Performance directors co-ordinate the project. Funding is aligned to success. If performers are not achieving targets, they lose their funding.

> *We have the talented athletes who can be winners on the world stage and we must give them the best services and facilities in the world so they have the best possible chance to succeed.*

Steve Redgrave (UKSI board member)

The National Lottery and Mass Participation

The Sports Councils encourage sports development and the provision of facilities by providing funding for individuals, sports clubs, local government and the NGBs of sport. To date, over £1 billion of lottery money has been awarded to over 3,000 community sports projects in all parts of the country. Sport England is particularly focused on increasing participation by young people and improving sports provision in schools. Other priorities are to support deprived areas, ethnic minorities, people with disabilities and women via Sport England's sport action zones.

Sport – a challenge for body and mind or a celebrity circus?

Sport is now a mass consumer spectacle.

> *When I stopped playing in 1990 football was still a game,' said Alan Hansen in 1997, 'now it's an industry.*

Sport in Britain 1945–2000, Holt and Mason

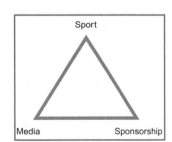

Fig. 13.19 The 'golden triangle'.

This is a far cry from the notion of sport preached by the 'gentlemen amateurs' of the late nineteenth and twentieth centuries. The sport of the middle-class gentleman amateur was pursued for fun, was not taken too seriously, and certainly did not involve training. All that would turn sport into work, a pursuit fit only for the working classes!

Times have changed, however, and now we have what Hargreaves (1986) identified as an axis or 'golden triangle' between professional sport, the media and advertisers. Whether this is a match made in heaven or an unholy alliance is debatable. Either way, there is no doubt that sport and the media (and therefore sponsorship, which depends on the media) are inextricably linked. And TV is the most powerful aspect of the media.

In all sports with strong media links, professionalism is a reality. Professionalism in this sense means a shift of power from unpaid amateur administrators to paid professionals who increasingly bring business methods and management techniques to the running of voluntary sports associations. Professionalism also refers to the high level of commitment by everyone involved and to the amount of income generated. Sports have had to change their rules, format and scheduling in order to meet the demands of the TV companies and sponsors. As sport becomes more commercialised and 'Americanised', it is increasingly powered by a 'win-at-all-costs' ethic. As the stakes get higher and the result becomes more significant, there is increased pressure on everyone involved. This can intensify ethical problems such as corruption, cheating, violence and drug abuse, which are of course highlighted by the ever-increasing media coverage. The next part of this chapter will focus on these issues arising from the pursuit of excellence in high-level sport.

TASK 4

In small groups, discuss and record the possible advantages and disadvantages of a sport such as hockey becoming professional to:

1   the performer   3   the sponsor
2   the spectator   4   the media.

Present your results to the rest of the class.

Influence of the Media

> ❝ *Spectator sport and the media have fused together. The one is inconceivable without the other.* ❞

Sport Britain 1945–2000, Holt and Mason

The media, especially TV, has had as profound an effect on contemporary sport as the railways had on Victorian sport. In the early 1950s, fewer than 10% of British households had a TV. By the late 1960s, only 10% did not. TV companies once paid relatively small sums to sports bodies to entertain and inform their new audience.

Roles of the Media

Sport is a central feature of TV and radio, of newspapers and magazines, of the Internet, books, films and videos. Sport related TV programmes range from live coverage, recorded highlights and quiz shows to educative documentaries and the latest news. Newspaper articles feature pre-event predictions and post-event analysis, news on the size and behaviour of the crowd, the state of the facilities and behind the scenes stories about the celebrity sport stars. There are also scores of specialist sports magazines, which not only give information on skill development, but also feature personalities and events. An ever-increasing number of biographical and autobiographical books is also being published.

The media has four main roles: to **inform**, **entertain**, **educate** and **advertise**. In any particular media feature, programme or report, one role can dominate or elements of each can be evident. Improvements in recording and editing technology, camera angles and interactive features have all increased the potential of TV to fulfill its roles.

The Informative Role

The media gives live coverage, factual information and analysis of what is happening and what has happened in sport. Results, reports, rules and rule changes, team analysis, analysis of performers' behaviour, highlights and comments feature in newspapers and magazines, and on radio and TV. School sport and developments in PE are also reported.

The Entertainment Role

We read about sports stars' private lives and watch televised sport for its drama, skill and intensity of emotion while some are seriously committed to supporting a particular sport or team. Sport is central to the increasingly popular home-entertainment industry; people even argue that Britain is now a nation of armchair supporters. On 4 July 1990, when the potential audience for any programme was 52.8 million, 25,210,000 viewers (the biggest audience for any single event in British TV history) watched the World Cup semi-final between England and West Germany. Nearly half of the nation shared in the intense emotion of an international soccer penalty shootout.

The Educative Role

Documentary programmes give the opportunity for greater understanding of global sport. In addition, the public can be educated about sporting skills, coaching techniques, contemporary sporting issues (such as the use of drugs by some performers), and developments in school and community sport. Ethics of fair play can be reinforced through comment and behaviour of role models.

The Advertising Role

Sport is used either directly to advertise products (from sports goods to crisps, beer and hair gel), or indirectly through sponsorship. Companies sponsor individuals, teams, leagues and events to heighten corporate awareness. Preview programmes also promote events. In contrast to the BBC, independent TV has always had to sell advertising in order to pay for itself.

What is the Real Issue?

How can sport retain its true nature and values while benefitting from the money offered by commercialism?

In the nineteenth century, sport was seen as a valuable experience in its own right. In the latter part of the twentieth century, it became part of the entertainment industry. Is it now just a branch of the advertising industry? Has money corrupted sport or has the media saved sport from economic disaster at a time when it was becoming more expensive and fewer people were paying at the gate? Has sport benefitted from its relationship with the media? Colour TV revived activities such as

TASK 5

Find examples of programmes or articles that predominantly either inform, educate, entertain or advertise. As a class, research from the following sources:

- one tabloid newspaper (e.g. the *Mirror*)
- one broadsheet (e.g. *The Times*)
- a specialist sports magazine (e.g. *Ace Tennis Magazine*)
- BBC sports related coverage (in the *Radio Times*)
- ITV and Sky sports related coverage
- Radio 5 sports coverage.

	Tabloid	Broadsheet	Specialist magazine	BBC	ITV/SKY	Radio 5
Inform						
Educate						
Entertain						
Advertise						

darts, snooker and even tennis, while Gladiators and Strongest Man competitions were invented. But has the price been too high? Has sport been manipulated for the sake of sponsors, advertisers and passive armchair spectators, at the expense of the paying punter? Modern commercial sport earns millions for the very best performers in the most media exposed sports, yet others are exploited in the interests of profit. We are left with the same concern of 150 years ago when professionalism worked its way into amateur cricket, athletics and rowing – that the need to win for money might lead to corruption and the temptation to cheat.

Professional sport is certainly a media commodity driven by market forces, but can sport also benefit from its mutually dependent relationship with the media? With careful management, the unique qualities and potential of sport as an educational and entertainment tool can hopefully be retained.

What about Sky, Cable TV and Pay per View TV?

In the 1950s, the Government, the BBC and ITV identified and agreed on ten sporting events that should 'belong' to everyone and not be given exclusive coverage by any one TV organisation. They wanted exclusive coverage to be avoided. The listed events were the Olympics, the World Cup, the Commonwealth Games, the FA cup final, Wimbledon, Test Match cricket, the Derby, the Grand National and the Boat Race. At first there was not much competition between ITV and BBC and the viewer was not threatened. The threat came with the rise of satellite TV 30 years later.

British Satellite Broadcasting began in 1988, and used sport to attract a mass audience. The Broadcasting Act of 1990 declared that all rights to broadcast sport could be sold to the highest bidder and in November 1990 British Satellite Broadcasting merged with Sky to create BSkyB. Exclusivity now forced fans to sign up to the entire channel. BSkyB paid £304 million for a five-year deal with the top clubs, who then broke away from the Football League and formed the Premiership. BSkyB had turned soccer, historically the game of 'the people', into a big business. Channel 4 paid £50 million for the rights to televise Test Matches from 1999–2002 and ITV had to pay £44 million in 1992 for a four-year deal for exclusive live coverage and recorded highlights of league football, forcing it to drop coverage of other sports. By 1997, when two-thirds of Football League clubs were losing money, Premier League clubs were massing around £8 million a year from broadcasting and sponsorship rights. Relegation is now a serious business involving loss of media revenue and reduced demand for merchandising.

In summer 2002, the BBC and BSkyB stepped in when ITV Digital's short-lived coverage of League football ended in disaster. ITV Digital collapsed owing nearly £200 million to football clubs, many of whom faced economic ruin having contracted expensive players on the promise of their slice of the multi-million pound financial cake. This not only illustrates the mutually dependent relationship between sport and the media, but also the firm control and profound effect that television can have over one particular sport.

TASK 6

In small groups, discuss the potential value of the following actual or proposed changes to rules and format:

- to the players
- to the game
- to spectators.

1 Rugby Union – five points for a try. Change from two halves to four quarters.

2 Association football – increase the size of the goal. Goal-less draws replaced by a 15-minute period of first-to-score-wins extra time, followed by a penalty shoot-out.

3 Squash – limit the length of rallies – score on every point.

4 Netball – move the goalposts off the back line and allow 360-degree shooting. Change to two instead of three zones for greater movement and freedom.

5 Cricket – one day games, floodlit games with multi-coloured strips, restrictions of field placings to discourage defensive play and encourage big hitting.

6 Tennis – the tie break.

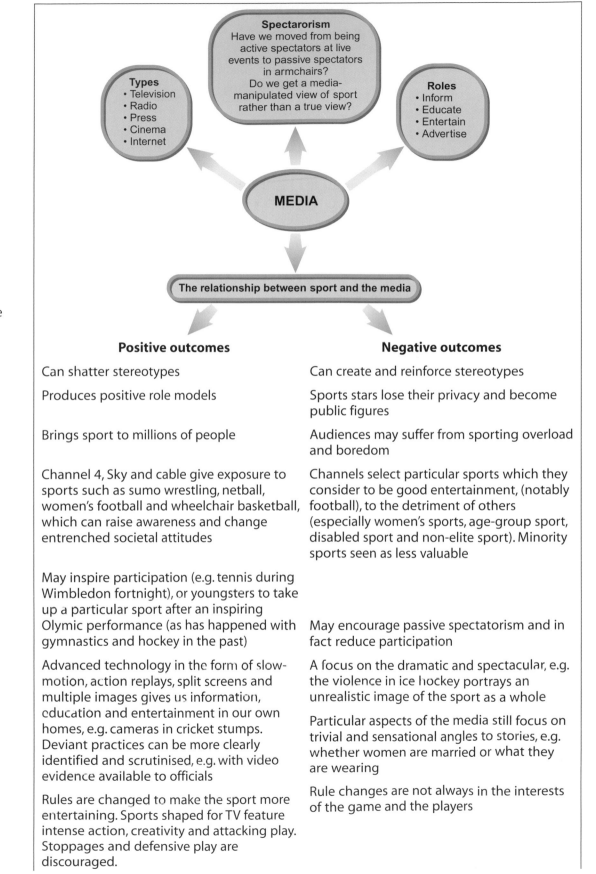

Fig. 13.20 Sport and the media.

Spectarorism
Have we moved from being active spectators at live events to passive spectators in armchairs?
Do we get a media-manipulated view of sport rather than a true view?

Types
• Television
• Radio
• Press
• Cinema
• Internet

Roles
• Inform
• Educate
• Entertain
• Advertise

MEDIA

The relationship between sport and the media

Positive outcomes

Can shatter stereotypes

Produces positive role models

Brings sport to millions of people

Channel 4, Sky and cable give exposure to sports such as sumo wrestling, netball, women's football and wheelchair basketball, which can raise awareness and change entrenched societal attitudes

May inspire participation (e.g. tennis during Wimbledon fortnight), or youngsters to take up a particular sport after an inspiring Olymic performance (as has happened with gymnastics and hockey in the past)

Advanced technology in the form of slow-motion, action replays, split screens and multiple images gives us information, education and entertainment in our own homes, e.g. cameras in cricket stumps. Deviant practices can be more clearly identified and scrutinised, e.g. with video evidence available to officials

Rules are changed to make the sport more entertaining. Sports shaped for TV feature intense action, creativity and attacking play. Stoppages and defensive play are discouraged.

Negative outcomes

Can create and reinforce stereotypes

Sports stars lose their privacy and become public figures

Audiences may suffer from sporting overload and boredom

Channels select particular sports which they consider to be good entertainment, (notably football), to the detriment of others (especially women's sports, age-group sport, disabled sport and non-elite sport). Minority sports seen as less valuable

May encourage passive spectatorism and in fact reduce participation

A focus on the dramatic and spectacular, e.g. the violence in ice hockey portrays an unrealistic image of the sport as a whole

Particular aspects of the media still focus on trivial and sensational angles to stories, e.g. whether women are married or what they are wearing

Rule changes are not always in the interests of the game and the players

Key events appear on our screens at prime time	Performers' needs are secondary to media requirements. The men's marathon in the Los Angeles Olympics was scheduled at the hottest part of the day. Similarly, rugby and soccer matches sometimes go ahead when pitches are flooded or snow covered to meet media demands
Sports provide world rankings and championship events, which are compelling and entertaining The public can be educated about minority global sports and pastimes and develop a positive sense of national pride Elite performers, their agents and a small number of sports promoters in selected spots can become millionaires Sports benefit from large amounts of money, which can be used for grass roots development	It has been suggested that, in boxing, rankings lists are manipulated to stage 'world' title fights. In tennis there is widespread allegation of corruption. Players will allegedly lose matches in order to move on to higher paid tournaments, or share the first two sets and play a legitimate third set to fill a particular TV time slot. Another accusation is that umpires are directed by tournament organisers to treat big-name players well to ensure their continued involvement National prejudice can be encouraged by bigoted and sensational headlines Financial rewards diminish below the very top of the pyramid and also differ greatly between sports. Some performers may be under pressure to perform more frequently than is physically or mentally desirable

TASK 7

Analyse the amount of space devoted to sport in a variety of tabloid and broadsheet newspapers. How much space is given to:

- women's sport?
- sport for people with disabilities?
- veterans' or children's sport?

TASK 8

1 In groups of four, two people find and compare a report in a tabloid with a broadsheet newspaper on a men's sporting event and two people do the same for a women's event.

 Do the reports differ between newspapers? Between men's and women's coverage? Language used? Reference to personal life, clothes worn, skilfulness, personality, looks, training regime? Suggest reasons for your findings.

2 Has the reporting of women's events improved in recent years? Give reasons for your answer.

TASK 9

Analyse sporting photographs in a variety of tabloid and broadsheet newspapers. What percentage are of men, women, athletes with disabilities? Are the photographs of minority sporting groups different in any way from those of the dominant group in society? Suggest reasons for your findings.

Influence of Sponsorship

Features of sponsorship

Fig. 13.21 Formula One – Sponsorship at its height?

- Sponsorship is the provision of funds or other support to individuals, teams, events and organisations in order to get favourable publicity and a commercial return.
- Sponsorship agencies bring sponsors and sports bodies together to organise events or programmes.
- Agents promote particular competitors for their mutual financial benefit.
- Athletes endorse, or give their backing to products by displaying the company name on their clothing or equipment while performing.
- They also use their celebrity status to advertise products away from the sport.
- Companies invest in perimeter advertising around and on pitches.

In 1908, OXO sponsored the Olympic marathon. Now companies are prepared to pay vast sums of money to secure sponsorship, for example, Carling's Premiership sponsorship cost £12 million over four years and Beefeater Gin spent £1.35 million to sponsor the Oxford and Cambridge Boat Race over three years – an event that lasts for less than half an hour a year!

Sponsorship has been called 'the most visible relationship between sport and business in the modern world' (Mason, *Only a Game*) with company names and logos appearing on shirtfronts, hoardings and playing areas. We regularly see top performers purposefully turning drinks, skis and kit bags towards conveniently positioned cameras in order to maximise their sponsors' media coverage. At one point in 1996 a newspaper included information on: the FA's Carling Premiership, the Nationwide League, the Tennants Cup and the GM Vauxhall conference in football; the Texaco cup, the AXA Equity and Law League, and the Britannic Assurance Country Championship in cricket; the Johnnie Walker PGA Cup in golf; the Benson and Hedges Cup in ice hockey; the Auto Trader RAC Touring Car Championship in motor racing; the Courage Clubs' Championship National League in rugby union; and the Land Rover British Horse Trials in equestrianism!

What is the Real Issue?

Top-level sport is inextricably linked with big business. Although the aim of both sport and business is to win, the drive to win at any price undermines the true ethic of

KEY WORDS

Sponsorship

The funding of sport to gain recognition and increased income.

The Institute of Sports Sponsorship (ISS)

A national non-profit-making organisation comprised of a group of companies which sponsor sport. They work to: protect the traditional nature of sport, help companies to get fair returns on their outlay, cooperate with the sports councils, CCPR and NGBs and run the Sportsmatch scheme for the government.

HOT TIPS

Be able to give one or two examples of different types of sponsorship, sponsored events, leagues or teams. Examiners like examples!

sport whose traditional values of enjoyment, participation, fair play and a fair chance may struggle to survive a wholesale business takeover. There is also the problem that sponsorship is uneven across sports, with high-profile sports attracting generous sponsorship and low-profile ones next to nothing. A vicious circle ensues: if low-profile sports, such as volleyball or those pursued by minority groups, such as netball, fail to attract media attention they also fail to attract sponsorship; if they do not get sponsorship they cannot market themselves, improve or compete on an even playing field with those that do. Some performers may be driven to trivial, sensational articles that have nothing to do with their skilfulness or commitment, just to attract the sponsorship they need. International bodies and NGBs strive to retain autonomy and to safeguard their sports against their profit orientated colleagues.

TASK 10

With unambiguous evidence that drinking and smoking damage physical and social health, the Labour government banned tobacco advertising at sporting events in the UK in 1997. In 1998, the European Union voted to ban all sponsorship of sport by tobacco companies in magazines and newspapers by 2002, at normal cultural and sporting events by 2003 and at world level sporting events, including Formula One, by 2006.

In your class, present a moral debate: 'Should tobacco and alcohol companies be allowed to sponsor sport?' Propose a motion and elect speakers to plan and deliver short arguments for and against the motion.

Sponsorship should benefit both the sponsor and the performer, but there can be negative outcomes.

Advantages of sponsorship for the performer	Disadvantages of sponsorship for the performer
At its best, sponsorhip can:	But sponsorship can also:
• Allow for full-time training and cover living and travelling expenses, clothing, equipment and coaching.	• Make performers reliant on a particular sponsor.
• Provide financial security for when a performer's competitive career is over.	• Be withdrawn or given only for a limited time leading to insecurity.
• Allow performers to concentrate on their sport without worrying about money.	• Give a bad image to sport and the performer, e.g. tobacco or alcohol sponsorship.
	• Control and manipulate individuals, teams or events to the detriment of performers and true supporters.
	• Lead to the performer or team feeling exploited.
	• Being imbalanced. Generous sponsorship is only available to the very best performers.

Advantages of sponsorship for the sponsor	Disadvantages of sponsorship for the sponsor
At its best, sponsorhip can:	But sponsorship can also:
• Give a positive and healthy image to the sponsor.	• Reflect badly on the company if their performer or team behaves badly.
• Be tax deductible.	• Be uncertain – the success of an individual or team cannot be guaranteed so outlay may be 'wasted'.
• Increase goodwill.	
• Be a relatively inexpensive form of advertising for massive exposure and positive income generation.	
• Lead to hospitality for sponsors and their customers at big sporting events.	• Be wasted – if bad weather disrupts the event and media exposure is lost.
• Have a positive impact on sales and profit.	

TASK 11

You are a company wishing to invest £500,000 in sponsoring a sports team. Will you invest in:

• the national netball team?
• the national Paralympics team?
• a Division 2 men's football team?

What is your product? In threes, discuss the issue at a company board meeting with each group member supporting a different team. Give reasons to support your view. You must come to a decision.

Ethics and High-level Sport

Fig. 13.22 An example of deviance in sport.

Controlled aggression is a fundamental part of many sports. Sometimes, however, this spills over into an uncontrolled situation where legs and fists fly and where serious physical injury is caused. Notably, when similar violence occurs on the streets, rather than in the name of sport, it is a crime.

This is not new. The occasional mob football games of pre-industrial days, some of which survive today, were characterised by severe violence and brutality. With the onset of Victorianism, however, and the more civilised ethics that emerged from the English public schools of the nineteenth century, games became inextricably linked with fair play and sportsmanship. The beliefs were that games should not be taken too seriously, that honesty was the only policy, and even though physical determination and courage were applauded, they must always go hand in hand with gentlemanly behaviour, courteous attitudes and respect for the opposition. The late Victorian public schoolboy and his descendants, played games to the *letter* of the law, but also to their *spirit* or underlying unwritten principles of good manners.

Rudyard Kipling wrote in this famous poem *If*, which greets players on a plaque as they enter Wimbledon's centre court.

Times seem to have changed and the middle class amateur attitudes of the nineteenth century were all but squeezed out of high-level professional sport by the late twentieth century. The stakes became high, the outcome imperative, the pressure intense, and the stadium like a cauldron. Gamesmanship, or the stretching of rules to the absolute limit in order to gain an advantage, became commonplace.

❛If you can keep your head when all about you Are losing theirs and blaming it on you; . . . If you can meet with triumph and disaster And treat those two impostors just the same; Yours is the Earth and everything that's in it, And – which is more – you'll be a Man my son!❜

TASK 12

Look up and make a note of definitions or meanings of the following words or phrases:

- deviance
- sportsmanship
- gamesmanship
- fair play
- etiquette
- the letter and spirit of the law.

TASK 13

Identify, discuss and make a note of incidents of both sportsmanship and gamesmanship at club level and national or international level sport.

HOT TIPS

Be sure you understand the difference between sportsmanship and gamesmanship and be able to identify how each might affect a sporting situation.

Here we are concerned with the social rather than the psychological causes of violence and aggression in sport.

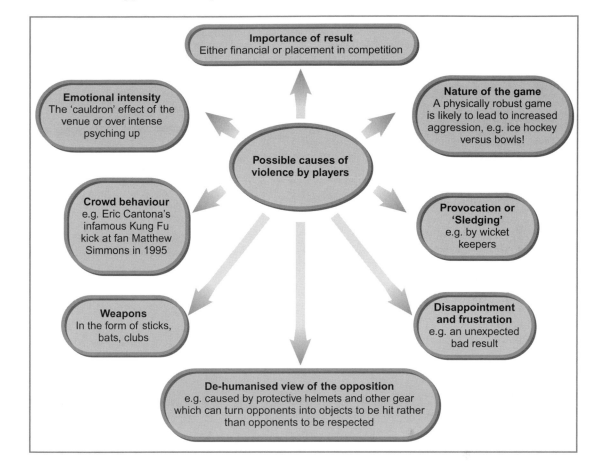

Fig. 13.23 The possible causes of violence by players.

Violence by sports performers can be explained, but it is wrong. It can be analysed in terms of:

Cheating - it is a blatant infringement of agreed sporting codes and a disregard of the true values of sport as an experience

Health - it causes injury and physical damage, which can be life threatening

Legality – physical violence is against the law of the land and is increasingly being punished with legal action when it occurs in sport

Role modelling – elite sports performers have a responsibility to take advantage of their media exposure as positive role models, especially to young people.

Fig. 13.24 Possible solutions to the problem of violence by some performers.

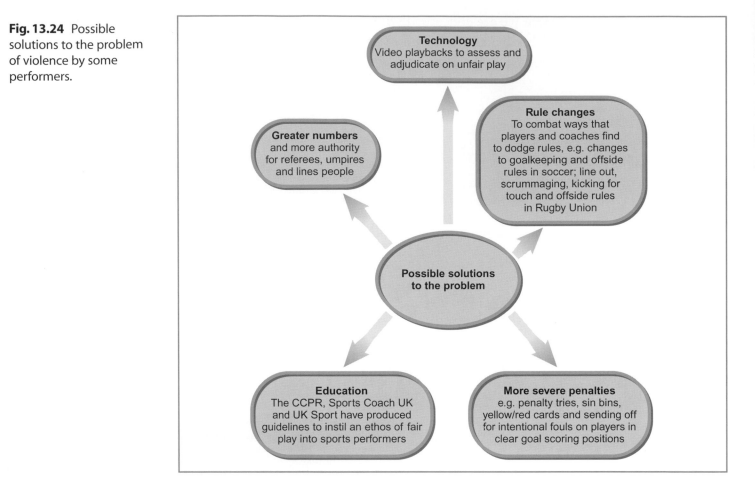

Violence by Spectators

❝*Peace, Peace is what I seek and public calm; Endless extinction of unhappy hates.* ❞

Matthew Arnold, quoted by Mr Justice Popplewell, interim report on football in 1985, after the Heysel Stadium disaster

Aggressive and rebellious behaviour at sporting events is not new. As Holt argues 'hooliganism exemplifies to perfection the difficulty of disentangling what is new from what is old in social history' (Holt, *Sport and The British*). The problem was around in pre-industrial days and throughout the Victorian period, when the constant fighting of the Irish immigrant Hooligan family added a new word to the language of the 1890s. Hooliganism forcefully raised its head as a major social problem again in the 1960s in connection with the collective, aggressive behaviour of predominantly white, urban, unskilled teenage males at football matches.

There has been much research and debate about the nature and reasons for football hooliganism. Some say that the phenomenon arose due to exaggerated and sensational reporting of incidents by the press, which included headlines such as 'Smash the Thugs!' which instilled anger and resentment in the 'thugs', who willingly rose to the challenge. Others say that a chauvinistic and primitive desire to assert maleness is at the heart of the issue. Groups dress the same in order to be easily identified, but wear different boots or socks or differently tied scarves to identify their rank in the group, just as the public school 'hearties' did in the 1890s. Other possible causes of violence by spectators are illustrated in the model on below.

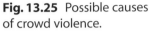

Fig. 13.25 Possible causes of crowd violence.

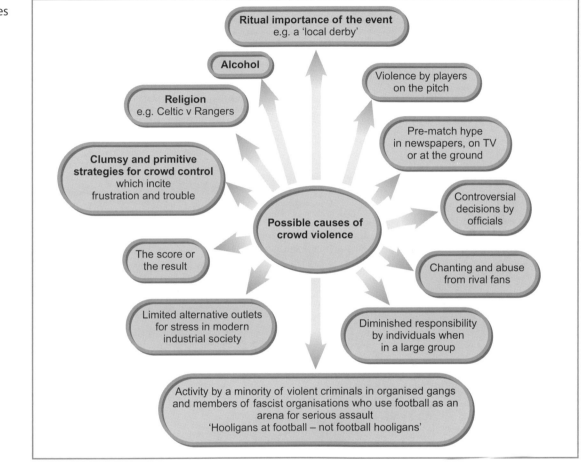

Despite criminal incidents of beatings and stabbings, it has been argued that the chanting, charges and threatening behaviour are just symbolic rituals and that injury or worse is a result of panic rushes to escape attack, rather than as a result of attack itself. This was certainly the case in the Heysel stadium disaster of 1985 when 39 spectators, including 31 Juventus fans were crushed or trampled to death when trying to escape a charge by Liverpool supporters. More than 250 others were injured when violence erupted between rival fans – all in front of a huge European TV audience. The Italian Prime Minister, Bettino Craxi, said Britain was 'a country submerged in disgrace by the criminal actions of violent and irresponsible groups'. Britain was banned from European football for five years.

Another major football tragedy, which had nothing to do with hooliganism, occurred at Hillsborough in Sheffield in 1989, when Liverpool were playing Nottingham Forest in the FA Cup semi-final. Hundreds of Liverpool fans were channelled into an already crowded section of the ground, resulting in a catastrophic crush at the front, which caused 95 deaths. Prime Minister Margaret Thatcher immediately instructed a thorough investigation. The resulting Taylor report identified overcrowding and poor facilities as central to the problem.

What has been done to make stadiums safer and to prevent and control violence by spectators at football matches?

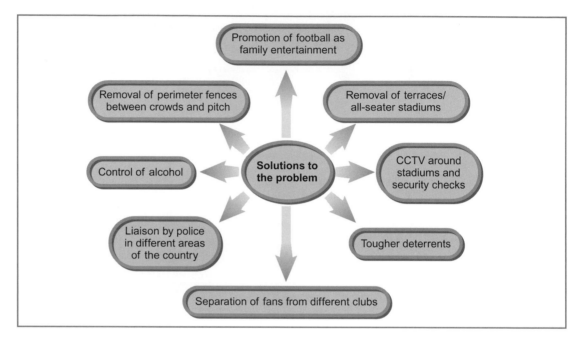

Fig. 13.26 Safety at football matches.

Drugs and Sport

The oath sworn on behalf of Olympic athletes states:

' In the name of all competitors, I promise that we shall take part in these Olympic Games . . . without doping and without drugs in the true spirit of sportsmanship. '

IOC, September 2000

It seems that not all Olympic performers keep their promises. The Sydney Olympics of 2000 and the Salt Lake City Winter Olympics of 2002 surprised very few people with their drug scandals. There is now a covert, regular, systematised and multi-million pound drugs industry operating whose sole purpose is to enable some sportsmen and women to illegally enhance their performance. It is a very expensive, serious and dangerous game of cat and mouse. As testing systems and random testing intensify and known drugs become more easily detectable, new drugs become available and improved masking drugs help users to avoid detection. Naïve performers and corrupt or inefficient testing laboratories leave the careers and

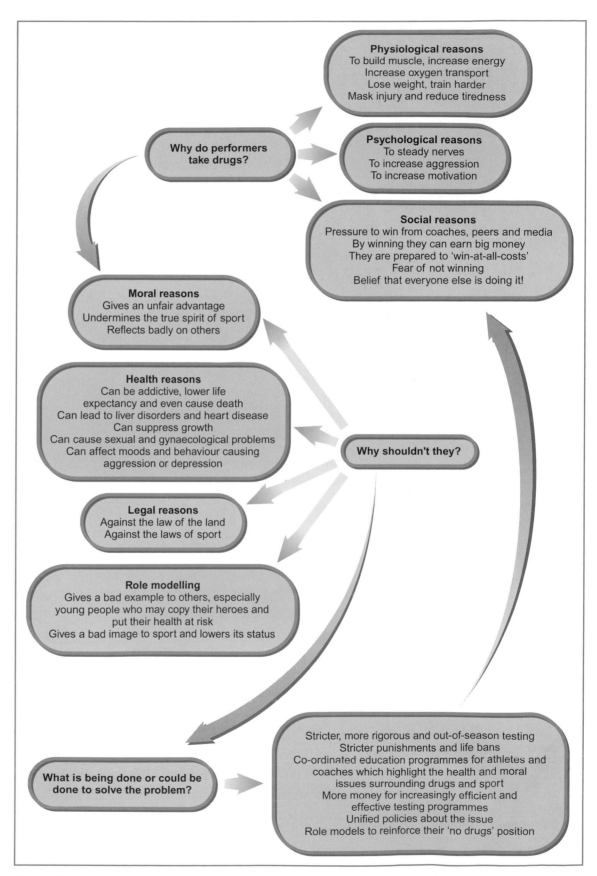

Fig. 13.27 The issue of drugs and sport.

personal lives of some innocent performers in tatters, while guilty competitors go free. The radical 'counter-culture' suggestion to even up the playing field and legalise and carefully monitor the use of performance enhancing drugs would not solve the problem. The richest countries would remain ahead of the game, athletes may become victims in a power system and their lives would continue to be put at risk. Meanwhile, young people would receive the wrong messages about drug abuse and the true spirit of sport would finally be buried. Our task is to analyse why some performers are tempted to take drugs, to identify reasons why they should avoid temptation and to suggest ways of solving the existing problem.

TASK 14

Research and prepare a short role play of an appeal hearing for an athlete who has been correctly tested positive for taking a banned substance. The characters can be from the following:

- the athlete
- the coach
- the team doctor
- UK Sport representative
- a team mate
- the athlete's mum

Consider the following in your role play:

1 Why did s/he take the drugs?
2 Did the team doctor and/or the family know?
3 Put forwards their arguments against drugs.
4 What about team mates?
5 What does the UK Sport representative say about their policy on and strategies for overcoming the problem?

Sport and Mass Participation

Mass participation and its ensuing policy of 'Sport For All' is the idea that everyone should have the chance to take part in sport, as regularly as they wish and at whatever level they choose, irrespective of where they live, the school they attend, their ability, age, wealth, gender, race or religion. Fundamentally, participation at recreative level is the aim, though some individuals may strive to reach their personal peak performance. The key intention is that everyone should reap the benefits of regular physical exercise, such as stress relief, sociability and improved health, fitness and self-esteem. Another benefit of mass participation is that it enlarges the pool from which talent can be trawled and helped to the top of the performance pyramid. For these reasons, UK sports councils have been campaigning for 'Sport For All' since 1972. They have concentrated on attracting certain target groups such as ethnic minorities and people with disabilities. We have already noted that more people are currently being encouraged through Sport England's Active Schools, Active Sports and Active Communities programmes and that more places are being designed and developed with the help of lottery funding.

Facilities for Mass Participation

Within Britain, sports facilities are provided by private, voluntary and public sectors. The nature and purpose of such provision affects mass participation.

Private or entrepreneurial facilities exist to make money, using sport as their commodity. They will be owned either by individuals or groups of individuals. Mass participation will be sought, but for financial rather than for ideological reasons. An example of a private facility is a David Lloyd tennis centre or Living Well health club.

Voluntary facilities exist for their members. They charge subscriptions to cover costs with any surplus being ploughed back for the benefit of members. The committee is a voluntary body of keen and committed amateurs. NGBs are encouraging voluntary clubs to promote mass participation, especially among junior members, but clubs still retain their autonomy.

Public facilities are funded by local authorities and exist for the community, but must also meet performance targets. It is through these public facilities that the 'Sport For All' campaigns have been most widely operated.

Why is 'Sport For All' not a Reality?

Although opportunities for mass participation should exist in all democracies, the reality is that not everyone is able to take up the sport of their choice. Constraints act upon people, which limit their chances of regular participation. These constraints are illustrated in Figure 13.28 and can be usefully discussed under the headings: opportunity, provision and esteem.

Opportunity

The chance of taking part in sport can be determined by the attitude of friends and the amount of time and money available. To minimise some of these problems, sports centres offer reduced entry rates for groups such as senior citizens, provide crèches for childcare and run campaigns to project an upbeat and user-friendly image of sport.

Provision

Provision relates to more tangible features that influence participation. Provision includes the presence or absence of appropriate activities, space, transport, equipment and specialist facilities. It also relates to accessibility in terms of, for example, wheelchair ramps or the availability of public transport. In addition, well-maintained and equipped, private and clean changing and social areas are important. Sports organisations have spent a lot of time surveying and consulting

HOT TIPS

Private and voluntary provision can be a bit confusing – especially as the voluntary sector incorporates 'private members clubs', such as local village cricket clubs. Remember though, voluntary clubs are run by volunteers who are not seeking financial profit.

KEY WORDS

Joint Provision Schemes

'Sports for All' campaigns include:

· Disabled people – 1981
· Over 50s – 1983
· Women – 1990

with their potential customers to identify their needs and wants. For 'Sport For All' to become a reality, it needs to be attractive.

Esteem

Levels of self-confidence and the perception that others have of an individual or group will affect the likelihood of their participation. Society is stratified, which means that it has imaginary layers or stacks into which each group falls. Stacking is most evident in societies or areas of high immigration. The dominant group in society (in the UK, the white, middle-class male) is at the top of the stack and enjoys the greatest freedom and opportunity, while others such as Asian women are lower down in the pecking-order and have less opportunity. It is important to note that no group is homogenous, meaning that not everyone within a particular societal group has the same needs and wants. In addition, combinations of aspects of exclusion lead to double deprivation and a greater likelihood of under-representation. A disabled, black female's constraints are clearly multiplied. Esteem is affected by one's status within a stratified society. It can lead to a reinforcement of societal views and a **self-fulfilling prophecy** of low expectation, uneven participation and under achievement.

TASK 15

Study the programme at your local sports centre. What, if any, strategies are in place for attracting target groups?

TASK 16

With reference to opportunity, provision and esteem, identify three specific reasons why each of the following target groups may be under represented in terms of mass participation:

- the elderly
- people with disabilities
- the unemployed
- women.

What else can be done to bring about Mass Participation?

Schemes, projects and publicity focused at particular societal groups continue to operate. There must be continued co-operation between organisational agencies such as local authorities, sports coach UK and NGBs to work at grass roots level. Elite performers visit schools as motivating role models who can challenge traditional stereotypes, begin to change attitudes and encourage participation by a particular group. Schools and community club links are also being forged and the influence of School Sport Co-ordinators is being felt. School PE programmes are under pressure to provide a worthwhile but appealing curricular and extra-curricular programmes when curriculum time and resources are limited. Attitudes,

KEY WORDS

Myths

Myths are untruths, such as views that males cannot perform cartwheels or females cannot park cars.

Apartheid

'Apartness' or racial segregation – an official policy in South Africa until the 1990s. Since 1956 sport had been a formal part of the South African Government's apartheid policy with non-whites being excluded. This resulted in a world ban on South African sport in 1964 although South Africa went to great lengths to attract world class competition.

especially of teenage girls, to sport can only be changed if the time, resources and expertise are available.

Discrimination in Sport

Discrimination occurs when a particular societal group is constrained or held back by factors that are not applied to the dominant group. They receive less favourable treatment. In a stratified society where **stacking** occurs, minority groups will be the ones who experience discrimination, and this is likely to be noticeable in sport. The concept of targeting policy towards certain groups in order to raise participation levels reflects this social ranking. Discrimination often occurs unofficially, but is sometimes part of an official policy, for example, Apartheid in South Africa or the constraint on free recreation placed upon some Muslim women.

Attitudes ⟶ Stereotypes ⟶ Myths ⟶ Discrimination ⟶ Self-fulfilling prophecy

The issues surrounding discrimination are to do with stereotypical images of groups of people and an imbalance of power and resources between groups.

Social Class/Wealth

The term 'social class' refers to income, background, societal status and education. Playing and watching sport costs money. The more money you have, the greater the opportunities of taking part in or watching different sports. You will also have a free choice of whether to participate at public, private or voluntarily run facilities.

In Britain, social class, wealth discrimination and the consequent inequality of opportunity are hundreds of years old. In pre-industrial times, the upper and lower classes pursued separate sports (e.g. hunting for the upper class and mob football for the lower class), or had different roles and status in those that they shared. In prize fighting for example, the upper class 'patrons' or 'sponsors' supported the lower class bare-fist fighter.

As a result of the Industrial Revolution, a new middle class emerged which then created three broad tiers or classes in British society. The upper class retained their exclusiveness and privilege to hunt, shoot and fish. The new middle class took part in sport for the love of the game and for social reasons, and founded the vast majority of NGBs and sports clubs. Working-class males, meanwhile, had to wait until the end of the nineteenth century when their living and working conditions improved, to find their niche, predominantly as spectators, although some became professionals. Working-class females had even less freedom and opportunity. They suffered from double discrimination. This three-tier society is still broadly in evidence in the UK today with polo and even golf remaining very expensive and exclusive while (in spite of many Premier League and Division 1 Clubs attracting

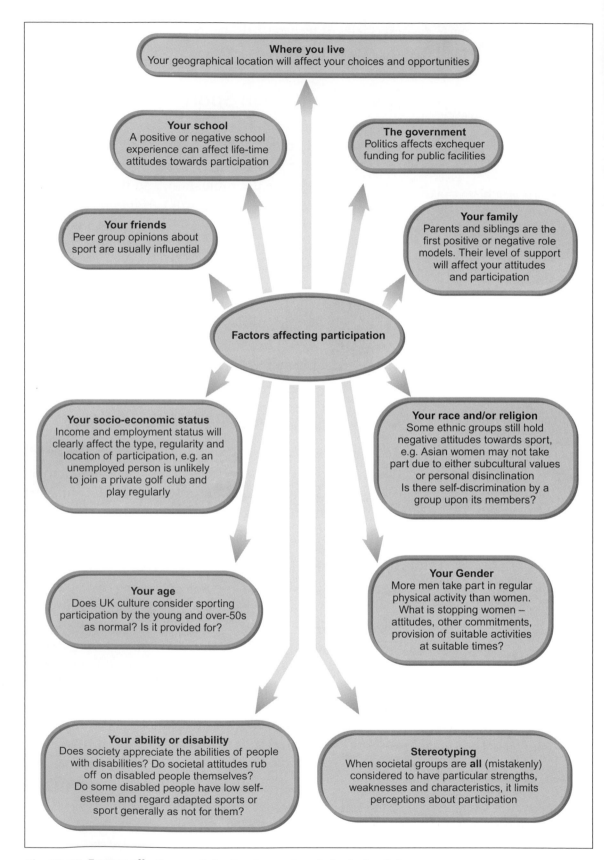

Fig. 13.28 Factors affecting participation in sport and physical activity.

the support of families, politician and celebrities) football's hard core support still comes predominantly from working-class males.

Evidence shows that lower socio-economic backgrounds lead to lower sports participation. This is due to cost, lower levels of health and fitness, low self-esteem and lack of opportunites to take it up or become role models in leadership positions. There could also be feelings that 'sport is not for me' and an aversion to the dominant middle-class culture surrounding sports centres.

Women

There are obvious differences between men and women, just as there are between some women and other women. Consequently not all sports are for all women. The issue here is that gender stereotypes need to be broken and that girls and women need the freedom to choose, and equal opportunities and provision to both participate and to excel. Figure 13.29 illustrates the various factors influencing participation and achievement of women and girls in sport.

Attitudes

A major league baseball player in America is quoted as saying: 'Women were not created by God to be physical. God created women to be feminine.' Over time, gender roles are formed within societies, which become the socially accepted ways for each sex to behave – stereotypical models for masculinity and femininity. These stereotypes can lead to myths. A myth finally overcome by women in the late nineteenth century was that cycling would ruin their chances of having children. Gender roles take a long time to develop and even longer to change. They still suggest dominant characteristics such as creativity and sensitivity for females and aggression, determination and confidence for males. This has a profound effect on how children are socialised (learn how to behave and fit into their environment), and on how a society views their participation in sport. It also gives some women a problem, in that competitive sport needs the attributes more normally associated with masculinity. A society might support women's participation in gymnastics and dance, which highlight traditionally perceived female characteristics, but oppose their participation in traditionally male activities such as rugby or boxing, for example. Males and females alike often disapprove of the image of successful female body builders who are highly committed to rigorous training programmes and who reach the top of their sport.

KEY WORDS

Socialisation

The process by which people learn acceptable cultural beliefs and behaviour including how to interact with people who are different from themselves.

Media

Women receive less than 5% of men's coverage in national newspapers and are still under represented in all areas of the media. This has been the case since the first publication of *Bell's Life* in 1822. The media creates a public image of sport generally and in individual sports in particular. It creates role models and influences finance. The issue is about quality as well as quantity.

The sporting audience is predominantly male and these viewers seem to prefer the power, speed and dynamism often associated with traditional male sports, rather than the aesthetic and technical brilliance of some women's sports or women performers. The majority of presenters, as well as editors and sports journalists are also male. Even with Sue Barker and other females now in the limelight, sports reporting is still a male driven and dominated industry whose individual newspapers and channels generally cannot afford to be different. (Channel 4 and Sky, however, have covered some minority activities such as Kabaddi and Sumo wrestling.) Again we have the problem of self-fulfilling prophecies. The media creates superstars who become role models and increase participation, but unless minorities receive airtime in the first place, this opportunity is lost. Similarly, sports with large audiences attract media attention, advertising and sponsorship, which all generate income and increase opportunities for excellence and interest by the masses. Sports with small audiences are consequently constrained.

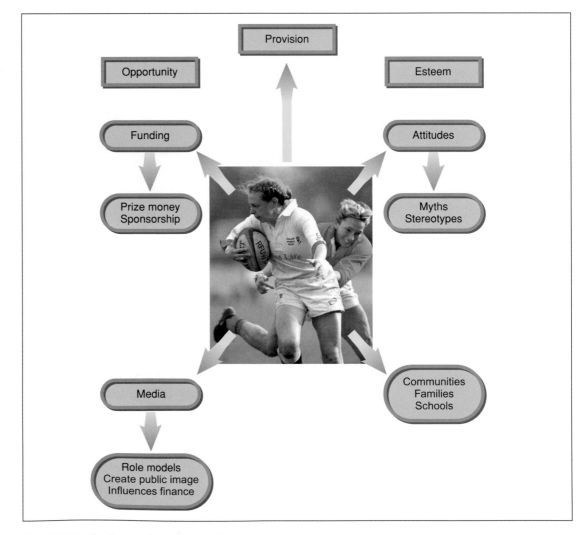

Fig. 13.29 The issue of women and sport.

Funding

In the British Open golf championship, women get just 10% of male prize money. If women receive less prize money for doing the same job as men, is that discrimination? If female sports receive less sponsorship than male sports their opportunities for development are clearly unequal and restricted.

Families, Schools and Communities

It is interesting to consider whether families, school sports clubs and communities discriminate. Do parents offer the same amount of support to their female as to their male children? Do schools work to make the image of girls' PE upbeat, attractive and positive or are girls put off by asexual kit and compulsory communal showers? Do communities offer the same opportunities for girls as for boys? If not, why not – could it be something to do with the disproportionate number of dads rather than mums who are involved with community sport? Why is that?

Other constraints to women's participation might be lack of time and disposable income, access in terms of transport, inappropriate role models in terms of coaches and leaders as well as the timings of sessions at local centres.

HOT TIPS

Remember the role of the WSF in pursuing and promoting opportunities for women and girls in and through sport.

Ethnic Minorities

Britain is a multi-cultural and multi-racial society. The population of non-white groups rose from less than 1% in 1951 to approximately 5.5% by 1990. 70% of the non-white population is concentrated in Greater London, West Midlands, West Yorkshire and Greater Manchester. Over 60% is under the age of 30, compared with 43% in the population as a whole, while only 5% are over 60, compared with over 20% of the general population. This all affects sporting needs, opportunity and provision.

Racism stems from prejudice linked with the power of one racial group over another. This leads to discrimination, or unfairness. Although illegal, discrimination still exists on the grounds of colour, language and cultural differences. The Professional Football Association (PFA) set up a campaign in 1993 with the Commission for Racial Equality to 'Kick Racism out of Football'. This now operates independently and is called *Kick it Out*. The Sports Council and NGBs encourage non-discriminatory attitudes to fight racism.

Here's the situation . . .	But consider that . . .
The participation of black people in sport is often considered not to be an issue because of their comparative over representation.	In fact, black participation in sport is limited by stereotyping which systematically channels people into certain sports or certain positions within sports teams.
This over representation of black athletes in some national sports teams seems to indicate equality of opportunity.	Black athletes become what Cashmore (1982) referred to as sporting 'gladiators' for white society and are, in fact, a result of institutional racism. Channelling towards sport might channel away from other equally valuable experiences and opportunities such as educational qualifications.
Black sportspeople are encouraged into competitive and professional sport to make a living and as an avenue for upward social mobility.	Ethnic minorities need equally to be encouraged into recreative mass participation.
Successful black athletes become positive role models.	Hundreds of young black people find that sporting success is very rare.
Ethnic groups are still under represented in coaching, managerial and organisational roles as a result of stacking, but also perhaps due to lack of educational opportunity and aspiration.	Positive discrimination might be a workable short-term strategy.
Ethnic groups are still under represented in terms of participation.	Group leaders who may encourage others to take part should be trained. Information about provision needs to be readily available.
The majority of ethnic communities use inner city, public facilities.	These need to be improved in order to raise participation. Sport development officers from ethnic minorities should be appointed. Single-sex provision must also be improved in order to attract Asian women to centres.

What else can be done to solve the problem of discrimination in sport? Stereotypical thinking can be challenged through race-awareness training and opportunities can be provided for different cultural groups to pursue their own cultural activities, for example Kabbadi.

In 1993 the then Sports Council stated its objectives in working towards the elimination of racial disadvantage and discrimination. They wanted to:
- raise awareness of racial inequality in sport
- increase sporting opportunities for black and ethnic minority people
- improve skill levels in, and positive attitudes towards, sport by black and ethnic minority people
- increase the number of black and ethnic minority decision makers and organisers in sport.

Sport, Ability and Disability

Society continues to discriminate against, handicap and impose barriers on disabled people. Significantly, as three quarters of disabled adults rely on state benefits as their main source of income they are also financially disadvantaged, which multiples barriers to participation. Our task is to recognise sources of discrimination and to identify measures that have been or could be taken to bring about fairer opportunity and provision for people with disabilities.

Frank Kew argues (in *Sport, Social Problems and Issues*, Butterworth Heinemann,1997) that:

> ❛*The key issue for disabled people . . . is not to mimic the non-disabled in sport, but rather to celebrate difference, acknowledge abilities in modified sports, and to recognise, on the basis of those abilities, outstanding sporting achievement.* ❜

Background

Six million of the British population have some form of sensory, physical or mental impairment. Clearly, not all disabled people have the same needs.

Fig. 13.30 People with disabilities have different abilities and needs.

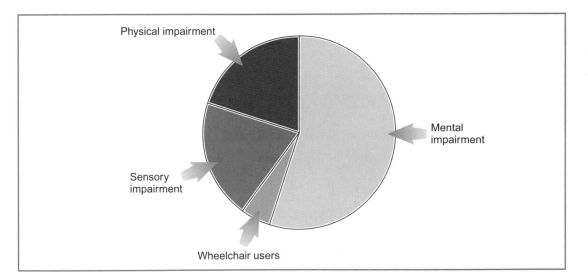

There are currently seven national disability sports associations, which are united by the English Federation of Disability Sport, a charity founded in 1999. The associations are: Disability Sport England (DSE), formerly the British Sports Association for the Disabled (BSAD), British Deaf Sports Council, British Blind Sport, Cerebral Palsy Sport, British Wheelchair Sports Foundation, British Amputee and Les Autres Sports Organisation, the English Sports Association for People with a Learning Disability.

HOT TIPS

Remember the role of DSE and other special interest groups in pursuing and promoting opportunity and provision for people with disabilities.

Traditionally, disability has been viewed from a medical perspective. People with disabilities have been considered as dependent and passive rather than independent and self-governing, probably because they have been supported by various carers and professionals. This limited and limiting view has more recently been updated with a social view which recognises that attitudes, assumptions, myths and stereotyping, along with inadequately designed environments all impose limitations on disabled people. Organisations, which are developed by and for non-disabled people, are now seen as the main sources of discrimination.

'Building on Ability' was the 1989 government report, whose name clearly identifies the need to emphasise abilities rather disabilities and to crush myths, fears or ignorance. The report included recommendations for NGBs, Local Authorities, disability sports organisations and the media. The themes were:

- integration
- specialist training for coaches
- adequate provision of facilities at local level
- the promotion of positive images of disabled sportsmen and women.

In short, the aims are:

- to increase participation by people with disabilities at all levels of the performance pyramid
- to ensure equality of access to facilities, competitions, training and coaching.

A lot of progress has been made. There has been a general shift towards more inclusive rather than exclusive or segregated provision. Campaigns such as Every body Active and Pro-Motion have raised awareness and flagged the need for training, resources and liaison between organisations. Access has been improved as a result of the Disabled Persons Act (1981), which required local authorities' sports facilities to conform to minimum access requirements. Improved technology for producing highly efficient wheelchairs and other specialist equipment has been developed. There has been improved training and coaching techniques and a gradual increase in the number of coaches with disabilities. There are specialist sports centres, for example the Ludwig Guttman Sports Centre at Stoke Mandeville and the Midland Sports Centre for the disabled in Coventry. The Paralympics, a parallel set of Olympic events in which elite athletes compete according to a profile system, raises awareness of elite sport for people with disabilities, focuses on sport rather than disability, and exposes positive role models, for example, Tanni Grey. The system groups competitors with particular functional abilities to allow fair competition. However, it still receives minimal publicity in comparison with the traditional event. At the Commonwealth Games of 2002 in Manchester, a positive step was taken by integrating the events of the able-bodied and disabled performers. However, more can still be done.

Awareness

Disabled people need to be aware of sports facilities and organisations which cater for their needs. Teachers need to be aware that children with disabilities need to learn basic movement abilities which can be developed into sports-specific skills later on. Sports providers and organisers need to be aware of the specific challenges facing disabled people.

Attitudes

Attitudes need to be challenged and myths need to be confronted so that misconceptions about disability are corrected. Individual differences and abilities need to be emphasised.

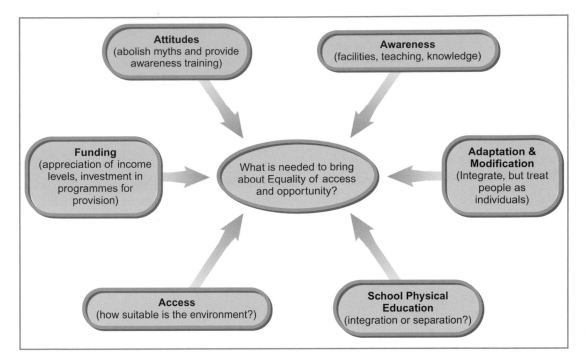

Fig. 13.31 The issue of sport, ability and disability.

Access

All of the following need to be considered: toilet and changing facilities, ramps, lifts, wide car-parking bays, hand rails on stair flights, lever taps on wash basins, automatic doors, non-slip floor, signs in Braille, signs in a colour appropriate for partially-sighted, accessible bar counters, lift control buttons, vending machine.

Funding

Unemployment among disabled people is particularly high, and those in employment earn, on average, only 80% of the salaries of able-bodied peers. Sports organisations must continue to invest, perhaps disproportionately, in provision for people with disabilities.

Adaptation and Modification

Although there are sports in which disabled people compete equally with able-bodied people, for example, archery, others need to be modified and adapted to make them accessible, for example, wheelchair basketball and tennis. Other games, for example, goalball for blind people, have been specifically designed.

Disability Sport England has suggested the following ways of adapting team games:
- use larger, smaller, lighter coloured balls and shorter handled racquets and sticks
- lower net height and limit playing areas
- increase team numbers

- give participant-specific play areas to avoid intimidation by more able performers
- use foam equipment to limit bounce heights
- use beanbags and other easy grip equipment
- use callers for direction control
- use everyday items to help participation, for example, guttering for bowls.

School PE

As a result of the Education Act of 1988 many disabled young people have been integrated into mainstream schools. There are both advantages and disadvantages to integration or separation in PE.

Integration		Separation	
Advantages	**Disadvantages**	**Advantages**	**Disadvantages**
• Increases awareness.	• Could lead to cruelty and bullying.	• Specialist teachers focus on specific needs.	• Disabled children are more likely to see themselves as different.
• A better reflection of society, which integrates rather than separates.	• It is expensive to get specialist teachers for each school and difficult for one PE teacher to cope with a great diversity of abilities in one class.	• Specialist equipment is more likely to be available. • All levels of the performance pyramid more easily established.	• Might make it harder for integration later in life. • Presumes that all disabilities are the same.
	• It is expensive to provide for adapting or modifying sports and providing specialist facilities.		• Reduces opportunities for disabled children to mix with able-bodied children when, in many cases, the disability is irrelevant.

TASK 17

With reference to sporting participation and the terms opportunity, provision and esteem, identify what should be done to overcome the problems of discrimination faced by people with disabilities.

Older People

What is the Issue?

There has been a tradition of low or non-involvement in sport by older people in this country. All age groups should enjoy the same opportunity and provision for sport based on equal respect and status, yet the media portrays the image that sport is for young people. Older people have always had a place in sport as spectators and voluntary administrators, but they need to be encouraged to stay active even when their performance levels decline. The reality is that ageing normally takes effect around the age of 30. As we have seen with other minority groups, combined inequalities increase constraints so that elderly women, elderly people on low incomes, and elderly people from ethnic minority groups will suffer greater limitations to participation.

What's so good about Sport for Older People?

In 1983 the then Sports Council began a campaign called 'Sport For All – 50+ All to Play For' which encouraged participation by emphasising the benefits of regular sports participation.

- *Health benefits* – participation can aid cardio-vascular function, strength and flexibility and increase a sense of well being.
- *Social benefits* – sport can increase self-confidence, be enjoyable and lead to friendships.
- *Psychological benefits* – sports participation can give focus to older people who may feel lost after forced retirement or redundancy.

What are the Problems?

- Older people may be put off by the ideal that physical activity is for the young.
- There are relatively few leaders and coaches in the older age range.
- Younger instructors and coaches may be unclear of the abilities and needs of their older clients or may not specialise in working with older people.
- If older people have been ill or injured they need to be cautious and seek advice from specialist coaches.
- Local centres may fail to consult with their potential customers and offer restricted or unappealing programmes. Taster programmes of new activities need to be provided.
- Older people on pensions may have limited money for recreation and may not have their own transport.
- Some older people may not have had opportunities to learn skills and lifetime sports such as badminton when they were young. Others may have had a poor experience of physical activity at school and be reluctant to give it another go.
- If people have been inactive for years, it can be harder to become active again.
- There is insufficient media coverage of veteran's events, results and accomplishments resulting in few role models.

TASK 18

1 Research your local sports or leisure centres to see whether there are any classes and sessions particularly for the over 50s. What do you think are the advantages and disadvantages of separating older people for sports provision?
2 In pairs, identify and record what can be done to increase regular recreative participation by older people.

Young people

What are the Issues?

In 1960 the Wolfenden Report identified a post-school gap of non-participation into which many school leavers fell as they progressed from school and childhood to work and adulthood. School age children need to have a positive experience of PE to ensure continued participation in physical activity when they leave school. They must be respected, cared for and provided for according to individual needs and abilities so that all levels of the performance pyramid are accessible.

TASK 19

Identify reasons why school leavers may drop out of sport. How can the problem be solved?

Issues associated with young people and sport are the moral questions of an emphasis on sportsmanship or gamesmanship in competitive sport for young people, while those associated with elite performers are:

- the advantages and disadvantages of early specialisation
- the dangers of some intense training methods
- an awareness of the needs for child protection in the light of some evidence of abuse by coaches.

TASK 20

Write a letter to your local leisure centre on behalf of either the women/people with disabilities/over 50s or unemployed in your community. You are writing about the problem of low participation by one of these groups. Suggest why the problem exists and what the centre can do to solve the problem.

Revise as you go! Test your knowledge and understanding

- How does UK Sport support sporting excellence?
- Name an NGB and identify four of its functions.
- How does sports coach UK influence both mass participation and excellence in British sport?
- Give specific examples of how the media fulfils each of its main roles of informing, educating, entertaining and advertising.
- What is meant by sponsorship in sport?
- Give three reasons why performance-enhancing drugs are banned by International Sports Federations and NGBs.
- What measures are being or could be taken to solve the continuing problem of drugs and sport?
- Identify five socio-cultural factors that might limit participation.
- What is the difference between a stereotype and a role model?

Sharpen up your exam technique!

1 UK Sport is concerned with sport and sports performance in the UK. Each home country also has its own sports council. Identify two key functions of UK sport and two different functions of any home country sports council.   (4 marks)

2 Sports funding is central to the pursuit of excellence. Describe public, private and voluntary sources of funding for sport in the UK.   (3 marks)

3 The United Kingdom Sports Institute (UKSI) is one initiative for increasing sporting excellence in the UK.
   (a) Describe the structure of the UKSI network.   (1 marks)
   (b) What are the functions of the UKSI network?   (3 marks)

4 Traditionally, keen and committed amateurs have run British sport. With reference to policy, provision and administration, describe how British sport is still dominated by this traditional amateur approach.   (5 marks)

5 Sport in the UK has become increasingly commercialised. Why has this occurred, and how is it evident in contemporary sport?   (6 marks)

6 Give reasons why female team games have not become fully professionalised in the UK.   (4 marks)

7 Identify some essential requirements for coaches and administrators in sports that change from amateur to professional status.   (4 marks)

8 Explain how the media can affect and influence sport.   (3 marks)

9 Explain the increase in the media coverage of women's sport in recent years.   (4 marks)

10 Why is media coverage of sport still male dominated?   (4 marks)

11 Sponsorship of sport is an important contemporary issue. Outline possible advantages and disadvantages of sponsorship to both the performer and to the sponsor.   (6 marks)

12 Sport cannot justify a drug culture. Explain this in the context of cheating, risk to health and role modelling.   (5 marks)

13 Discuss the problems faced by wheelchair athletes in the UK in achieving excellence in sport.   (5 marks)

Chapter 14 **Performance and its Improvement through Critical Analysis**

Learning Objectives

At the end of this chapter you should be able to:
- Understand which practical activities you can choose to be assessed in.
- Understand how you will be assessed.
- Understand the terms 'standardisation' and 'moderation'.
- Appreciate how you can improve your performances.
- Understand the structure and contents of the Personal Performance Portfolio (PPP).
- Successfully complete your PPP.

Introduction

Advanced level PE has as its central aim the linking of theory to practical and practical to theory. This means that we use practical activities to help us gain knowledge, understanding and appreciation of theoretical concepts whilst also applying those concepts to our practical activities to help us to improve their performance. Advanced level PE recognises that students should be able to capitalise on their practical talents by being assessed in practical activities with the marks gained contributing to their examination grade.

In this chapter we will explore the opportunities that you have within AS PE to be assessed in practical activities and ways in which you can improve the marks you can achieve. Closely linked to your practical activity assessment is the **Personal Performance Portfolio** (PPP) in which you are required to apply a range of theoretical concepts to one of your chosen activities. You then evaluate your performance in this activity by identifying your strengths and weaknesses. Based on this evaluation you will produce an action plan designed to improve your performance and help you gain more marks when you are assessed in this activity.

Participation and assessment in your activities also prepares you for your A2 practical work when you will apply your skills in a more open situation. Your PPP helps prepare you for the Evaluation and Appreciation of Performance element of your A2 assessment. You will find useful information in this chapter, but to improve your practical performance there is no substitute for actual practice which can be performed both in and outside your centre.

This chapter is divided into two sections: the practical activities and the PPP.

Your practical performance, knowledge and understanding will be assessed by your performance in two practical activities together with a piece of written coursework, the PPP. In each of these three components you will be assessed out of 30 marks which enables you to score a maximum of 90 marks in this unit.

The Selection and Application of Acquired and Developed Skills (Practical Activities)

Module Content

The activities are grouped together by profile into ten categories. You must choose two activities, each from a different category. For example, you could choose judo and basketball but not hockey and basketball.

Activity category	Activity
Athletic activities	Track and field athletics
Combat activities	Judo
Dance activities	Educational dance
Invasion game activities	Association football, basketball, field hockey, Gaelic football, hurling, netball, rugby league, rugby union
Net/wall game activities	Badminton, squash, tennis, volleyball
Striking/fielding game activities	Cricket
Target games activities	Golf
Gymnastic activities	Gymnastics, trampolining
Outdoor and adventurous activities	Mountain walking, canoeing, skiing, sailing
Swimming activities	Competitive swimming

The activities above are those that appear in the specification, but there are some additional activities which your centre may allow you to take part in and be assessed on. You can find a list of these activities on the OCR website.

Assessment

Your teacher will assess you throughout your practical activity course. This will enable them to accurately assess you rather than have just one assessment session towards the end of the course when you may have an 'off' day. This will ensure that if you are injured they will have some marks on which to base your assessment. The final assessed marks have to be sent to the exam board by 31 March. In some instances you may have to be videoed doing your practical activity.

The teachers in your centre will consult with each other to check that activities assessed by different teachers or coaches in your centre are all at the same standard. Standardisation is particularly important for many activities which cannot be done in your centre and are sometimes taught by coaches who are based at clubs. In cases such as these, the PE teacher responsible for A level will liaise with the coach to ensure that they are aware of what you need to do in your activity. This teacher will assess you with the help and advice of the coach.

Sometime between Easter and Whitsuntide some students in your centre will be chosen to perform their practical activities alongside students from other centres in your area. A moderator from the exam board will look at all these students' performances to check that they have been assessed correctly and that marks awarded by the different centres are all at the same level. The moderator knows the correct levels and standards of performance.

Content of the Practical Activities

The specification indicates that the focus of your activities will be on 'acquired and developed skills'. This means that you will have to work specifically on the techniques and skills of your activities. These skills, however, will not be performed in isolation but in a situation where you are put under some pressure either from opponents or have to apply them to circumstances relevant to that particular activity. These are called **conditioned competitive situations**.

KEY WORDS

Conditioned competitive situation

A situation where you apply your skills and tactics under pressure. You will have to select the correct skills to use as well as apply them accurately, fluently and with control.

Conditioned competitive situations allow you to show that you are able to:

- select the correct skill for a particular situation, e.g. choose the correct stroke when batting in cricket
- repeat skills consistently, e.g. get the skill right each time you perform it
- adapt skills where and when required, e.g. adjust your pass in netball to avoid the opponent marking you intercepting it
- show some tactical awareness
- perform all the above when under pressure.

The conditioned competitive situations also allow you to show how well learned your skills are and how well they stand up to the pressure provided by these situations. It is important to realise that the pressure of competition is not the same for all activities and that the conditioned competitive situations will differ according to the category the activity belongs to. For example, in gymnastics, in the conditioned competitive situation, students have to perform vaults and agility sequences. The 'competition' is to get your vaults and agilities as close as possible to the perfect model, and to flow and look aesthetically pleasing when linked together.

In invasion games the competition will be from opponents in a small sided game, whilst in outdoor adventurous activities it will be a situation where you have to combine your skills in an amended version of the 'normal' situation. For example, in mountain walking you will complete a six-hour walk.

Fig. 14.01 One of the conditioned competitive situations for gymnasts is to perform the perfect vault.

Examples of conditioned competitive situations for each category are given below.

Athletic activities (sprinting) – sprint starts, sprint action, finishes.
Combat activities (judo) – contests limited in terms of techniques permitted, size of mat area and time allowed.
Dance activities (educational dance) – choreograph and perform a solo dance routine lasting 2–3 minutes and containing leaps, balances and rolls.
Invasion games (association football/soccer) – half pitch game of 5 attackers and 3 or 4 defenders with a goalkeeper.
Striking/fielding games (cricket) – feeder to a batter who has to play one of 3 shots and score runs off them. Fielders will try to run batsman out.
Net/wall games – shot rallies, shot accuracy, short games.
Target games (golf) – series of targets of different distances and sizes to test club selection and accuracy of shot.
Gymnastics activities (trampolining) – a ten-contact sequence to include a jump, a twist and a drop.
Outdoor adventurous activities (canoeing) – five hours of paddling on appropriate water.
Swimming activities (competitive swimming) – racing starts, stroke technique in short race, racing finish.

Fig. 14.02 The conditioned competitive situation for mountain walking is a six-hour walk.

These conditioned competitive situations will allow you to practise your skills whilst also permitting you to develop your strategies and tactics. Strategies and tactics are more obvious and applicable in some activities than others. For instance, in invasion games you will need to develop an awareness of such things as support for team mates, width in attack and depth in defence. In other activities, for example, outdoor adventurous, they will take the form of awareness of safety aspects and appropriate codes, for example, the Country Code. In gymnastics your strategy may be to include only movements that you can perform really well and place them in the order that allows your sequence to flow.

> **TASK 1**
> Find out what the conditioned competitive situations are for each of your two assessed activities.

You need to focus on building up the range of your skills as well as their quality and consistency. You will remember from your studies of skill acquisition that skills are perfected through practice and receiving feedback on the results of your practice. It is therefore important for you to get as much practice as possible with the appropriate people to advise you.

What are the Assessment Criteria?

There are several areas that your teacher will be looking at as follows:
- how good your skills are and the accuracy, control and fluency with which you perform them
- if you have any advanced skills and can use them when appropriate with accuracy, control and fluency
- your understanding of tactics and strategies, shown by your use of them
- your overall standard of performance.

Your teacher will use these criteria to put you into one of five bands (0–6, 7–12, 13–18, 19–24, 25–30) before they finally decide the exact mark you will be given.

Your teacher will do this assessment over a period of time, but might have one last assessment session to finalise your mark. It may be that in this session they decide where to place you in a band to confirm your actual mark.

What will I be required to do for my Assessment?

How you will be assessed and what the focus of the assessment will be has been identified for each practical activity. Conditioned competitive situations are used to determine how you will be assessed and we identified some examples earlier. The list below shows the focus of assessment for each specific activity or the focus for all activities in a category where this is more appropriate.

Track and field athletics – two events from two of the following areas: track, jumps, throws.

Educational dance – leaps, balances and rolls.

Invasion games – passing and receiving in attack or defence.

Golf – club selection and distance; stroke action and target accuracy.

Gymnastics – through vault and straddle vault (cross-box): three short sequences each containing a roll, a jump, a balance and an agility.

Trampolining – a ten-contact sequence containing a jump, a twist and a drop.

Mountain walking – use of maps and their symbols, navigation, planning the route, calculation of distance, organisation of equipment, application of safety principles, obtaining bearings.

Competitive swimming – two strokes from: front crawl, back stroke, breast stroke, butterfly.

More detail, including the focus for additional activities can be found in 'Teacher Support – Coursework Guidance' on the OCR website, which can be accessed through www.heinemann.co.uk\hotlinks.

TASK 2

Access the OCR website and identify the assessment focus for each of your two assessed activities.

How can I improve my Practical Activity Performances?

You should now be aware of how and when you will be assessed as well as the focus for your assessment. This understanding will help you plan how you should use your time to improve your performances in your practical activities and thereby increase the marks you are awarded.

In your PPP you will apply a range of theoretical concepts to one of your practical activities, identifying your strengths and weaknesses and developing an action plan. These processes will give you a better understanding of the activity and improve your ability and performance. Some of the ways you can improve your performance and identify in your PPP action plan are explained below.

Valuable additional and specific information can be found in coaching books which are normally published by the governing or organising body. You should consult these for ideas and information on improving your performance.

TASK 3

1   Find the websites of the governing/organising bodies of your two activities to see what coaching manuals are available to help you develop your skills.
2   Check in your centre's library to see if these manuals are available.

Physical Fitness

This is an important aspect in any practical activity and will be a key part of your preparation for both your activities. Different activities have different fitness requirements and through your training and by talking to your teacher/coach you should be able to identify which of the four main fitness components below are important in your activity.

- strength   • speed   • stamina   • suppleness.

You will be able to use your knowledge from your anatomy and physiology studies to help you appreciate how you can work on your fitness. You will be able to use fitness tests to measure your fitness and any improvement.

If you can increase your levels of fitness in the relevant components then you will undoubtedly improve the standard of your performance and therefore your marks.

TASK 4

For each of your activities consult your teacher/coach and the relevant manuals to establish the important physical fitness components.

Improving the Quality and Range of your Skills

If you look at expert performers they will undoubtedly have a wide range of skills which they can perform with accuracy, control and fluency. They achieve this range and a high level of performance by practising, spending a great deal of time developing and perfecting their skills.

Your knowledge of acquiring, performing and teaching movement skills will help you to plan the focus and structure of your practices. First, you should consult the coaching manuals to identify both the basic and advanced skills that are required for your activity. They will also identify the coaching points you will need to concentrate on in each of the skills. Be aware that in some activities the basic skills will require you to be proficient in a variety of ways, for example, kicking/passing with both feet or, perform forehand and backhand shots.

TASK 5

Consult your teacher/coach and the relevant coaching manuals to identify the basic and advanced skills that you will need to be proficient for each of your assessed activities.

You should start your learning by practising each skill in its simplest form. The practice situation should allow you to concentrate on the coaching points and getting the skill right. Once you have mastered this simple skill you should make the practice a little more difficult and bring in further coaching points. As the skill practices get more difficult they should also get more 'open', bringing in more decision making and opposition. An example of this is the short serve in badminton, where you could go through the following progressive practices.

1 Practise the shot concentrating on the coaching points relating to the phases: preparation (stance/body position, feet and hand position), execution (transfer of weight, contact with shuttle, follow-through), recovery (balance and return to be ready for the return shot), result (was the shot good both in terms of performance and success?), overall efficiency (general nature of the shot, fluency, closeness to technical model).
2 Increase the need for accuracy and precision – aiming to get shuttle into a target within the service area. Impose restrictions on how high above the net the shuttle may pass.
3 Practise the shot initially with an opponent just threatening the serve.

4   Practise the serve with an opponent who can attack the serve.

5   A practice which mixes short and long serves and is competitive with points for a successful serve and points for the receiver if they are able to return it.

A critical part of the practice of skills is feedback and it is important that you receive this from your teacher and coach, listen to and act upon it. This will improve the quality and rate of your learning.

Fig. 14.03 It is important that you receive, listen to and act on feedback.

Progressive practices will help you not only to improve your basic skills but also to learn advanced skills. Eventually, your practice situation will become very similar to the conditioned competitive situations in which you will be assessed.

For each activity criteria the Coursework Guidance booklet identifies the phases into which the skills will be analysed for assessment purposes. This may also help you to improve your skills and extend your range of skills. Some examples of these phases are identified in the table below.

Activity	Phases
Track and field athletics	*Track events*; posture, leg action, arm action, head carriage, overall efficiency
	Jumping events: approach, take off, flight, landing, overall efficiency
	Throwing events: initial stance, grip and preparation, travel and trunk position, throwing action, release, overall efficiency
Games	Preparation, execution, recovery, result, overall efficiency
Gymnastics	*Vaults*; shape and aesthetic quality, flight on the box, flight off the box, repulsion and landing, overall efficiency
Competitive swimming	Arm action, leg action, body position, breathing, overall efficiency

TASK 6

Access the OCR website and identify the phases into which the skills for each of your assessed activities will be analysed.

Once you have identified these phases it will allow you to structure your initial practice when you are attempting to perfect the basic skill and get it to match the model you will find in the coaching manuals.

Your skill practices can be done in a variety of ways but it is unlikely that there will be enough time in your lessons for you to perfect your skills. You must therefore look for additional opportunities to practise. Within your centre there will be clubs and teams which will offer valuable opportunities to improve your skills. Other opportunities may be found by joining a local club where you will receive coaching and playing experience. It is important that you and your teacher talk to the coaches to make them aware of exactly what you have to do in your practical activity and how you will be assessed.

Joining a local club is particularly important if you do not have the opportunity in your centre to perform your activity 'competitively'. This could be a small sided game in hockey or an expedition in mountain walking. This experience, under the guidance of a teacher or coach, is important in developing your awareness and understanding of strategies tactics.

> ## TASK 7
> Identify the basic strategies and tactics which are used in your two activities.

Personal Performance Portfolio

The **Personal Performance Portfolio** (PPP) is a piece of coursework which is specific to each student. It helps you to understand the theory which you study as you apply it to one of your practical activities. Within your anatomy and physiology, skill and contemporary studies courses, there will be several areas which you have to explain by applying them to your practical activity. An understanding of this theory will help you look at a performance in this activity and identify the areas in which you are strong as well as those in which you need to improve. You will then develop a plan to improve your performance and put this into action. The final part of your portfolio will assess whether or not your plan has led to an improvement. Hopefully your performance will have improved and you will get more marks when assessed.

When should You do your Portfolio?

You should start working on your portfolio at the beginning of your course, applying theoretical concepts to your chosen activity as you cover them. Your teacher may set homework involving applying theory to your activity and you can then use this in your PPP. This allows you to build up your portfolio as your course progresses and is a far better approach than trying to tackle it all at the end of your course.

This also means that you have to decide which activity your PPP will focus on early on in your course. Preferably, it will be one of the two that you will be assessed in as you will then benefit from any improvement in your performance.

Fig. 14.04 Start your PPP early.

TASK 8
Choose the activity which is going to be the focus of your PPP, preferably one of the two activities you are going to be assessed in.

How will your PPP be Assessed?

Your portfolio needs to be finished by the end of April. It will be marked out of 30 by your teacher and then a moderator. There are six criteria on which it will be assessed, and they are studied in more detail later in this chapter. Each of the areas has marks awarded to it.

1 Knowledge, understanding and application of anatomy and physiology.
2 Knowledge, understanding and application of acquiring and performing movement skills.
3 Knowledge, understanding and application of contemporary studies.
4 Identification of strengths and weaknesses.
5 Action plan to improve performance.
6 Overall quality of PPP.

HOT TIPS

Working on a computer will make your PPP easier to update, correct and improve if it is stored on disc. Remember to make a back-up copy. You may also be able to use it for your IT key skill assessment.

Presentation of Your PPP

The exam board have produced a structure which your PPP must follow. You may wish to produce your PPP on computer, but if it is hand written it must be neat and legible. You must also think about how to keep the pages together – a ring file is a good idea. Remember your teacher will need access to each page to mark it. Remember to number the pages as you must put them on to your table of contents.

Any material which you use from other sources such as coaching manuals should preferably be adapted to your PPP or, if it is simply photocopied material, you must acknowledge where it has come from and make reference to it.

How should I plan my PPP?

Your PPP should have the following structure:

1 Introduction   2 Section A: the theory   3 Section B: the chosen activity

Introduction

This should contain the following:

CANDIDATE'S NAME . . . .

CANDIDATE'S CENTRE NAME . . . .

CANDIDATE'S CENTRE NUMBER . . . .

THE CHOSEN ACTIVITY ON WHICH THE PORTFOLIO WILL FOCUS . . . .

DECLARATION – THIS PERSONAL PERFORMANCE PORTFOLIO REPRESENTS MY OWN ORIGINAL
WORK. ANY INFORMATION WHICH I HAVE OBTAINED FROM OTHER SOURCES IS ACKNOWLEDGED.

SIGNED . . . .

TABLE OF CONTENTS

**Page
number**

MARKING SHEET . . . .

SECTION A

a) APPLICATION OF ANATOMICAL AND PHYSIOLOGICAL KNOWLEDGE TO PERFORMANCE . . . .

b) ACQUIRING AND PERFORMING MOVEMENT SKILLS . . . .

c) CONTEMPORARY STUDIES IN PHYSICAL EDUCATION . . . .

SECTION B

a) IDENTIFICATION OF THE STRENGTHS OF MY PERFORMANCE . . . .

b) IDENTIFICATION OF THE WEAKNESSES OF MY PERFORMANCE . . . .

c) MY ACTION PLAN

   1. the goals . . . .

   2. the timescale . . . .

   3. method of achieving the goals . . . .

   4. evaluation plan . . . .

   5. record of implementation . . . .

   6. evaluation of the plan . . . .

d) REVIEW . . . .

TASK 9

Produce the introduction section of your PPP.

Section A: the theory

There are certain theoretical areas, identified below, that you *must* have in your portfolio and apply to your chosen activity. You will have already covered some of them in the tasks in this book. Each of the three theoretical areas should be presented as a separate part and should be clearly identified.

Application of Anatomical and Physiological Knowledge to improve Performance

1 The identification and justification of the components of physical fitness important in the chosen activity.

2 Give a detailed description of your personal warm up and cool down for the chosen activity. This should include an explanation of its effect on the speed and force of muscular contraction and the vascular system.

Acquiring and Performing Movement Skills

1 The major coaching points of one essential skill in the chosen activity.

2 Progressive practices for developing the essential skill identified in (1).

Contemporary Studies in PE

HOT TIPS

Check that all the areas identified are included in your PPP.

1 Information on the governing/organising body of the chosen activity, including:
- name, address, phone, website address
- regional structure
- coaching awards
- promotional/grass root schemes
- regional and national competitions
- doping control and testing.

(*Candidates using website information should adapt it to each of the above.*)

2 Your assessment of your developmental placement on the performance pyramid of the chosen activity, including a discussion on the ways in which the governing/organising body has helped you progress.

TASK 10

Check to make sure that you have completed all the PPP tasks in this book. Gather them all together ready to put in your PPP.

Section B: the chosen activity

KEY WORDS

Evaluation

Looking at a performance and identifying what is good about it and what its weaknesses are.

Strength

Part of the performance which is good and carried out correctly and efficiently.

Weakness

Part of the performance that is incorrect or carried out poorly or inefficiently.

Evaluation – identifying your strengths and weaknesses

You must look at your own performance and identify your strengths and weaknesses that will need improvement. Initially, concentrate on identifying what is good/strong about your performance. Evaluating your performance is in itself a skill that you will need to practise. You can do this by observing other students performing the same activity and evaluating their performance. Your teacher or coach will help you develop this skill.

When you wish to carry out your evaluation of your own performance you could use the following methods.

1 Watch a video recording of your performance.

2 Make notes immediately after you have performed your activity identifying what you felt you did well and what you felt did not go well.

3 Ask your teacher or coach, team mates and fellow students for their opinions on strengths and weaknesses. Remember to write them down.

Remember to make notes rather than rely on your memory. From all these sources you should be able to arrive at a realistic assessment of your strengths and weaknesses. When your portfolio is marked your teacher will look at the accuracy of your evaluation.

HOT TIPS

Use the judgements of your teacher/coach as well as your own in deciding on the strengths and weaknesses of your performance.

> ## TASK 11
> 1 Ask your teacher or coach, parents or friends to video you performing your activity.
> 2 Ask your teacher or coach what they think your strengths and weaknesses are.

What do I need to look at?

When you are observing your performance, focus on one aspect. There are three aspects you can evaluate and you should look at them one at a time. You may also decide to evaluate your performance in your PPP on just one aspect.

Skills – the basic and advanced skills. Your AS practical assessment focuses on how well you perform the skills. So evaluate them and correct any problems before your final assessment.

Strategies and tactics – how you apply basic strategies and tactics in your performance. In group activities this will involve evaluating how you play your part in group strategies.

Fitness – the fitness training to prepare for your activity will give you appreciation of the aspects that are important. You will have your own opinion as to your levels in the different components of fitness but you can confirm this by taking the standardised tests of fitness. If you improve your fitness you will improve your performance.

What do I need to know before carrying out my Evaluation?

In order to successfully carry out your evaluation you will need to:

- have a clear picture in your mind of the model with which you are comparing the aspect of your performance, for example, an agreed realistic achievement, a target you set yourself or the 'perfect' performance.
- be positive and look for your strengths first. Identify the aspects of your performance that are good and why they are.
- consider breaking down the aspect of the performance you are looking at into 'phases'. For instance, if you are looking at the quality of your skills you may want to use the phases discussed under practical activities.

Where can I find Information to help me to evaluate?

HOT TIPS

Read a coaching manual on your activity so that you know what you are looking for when you evaluate.

You will need detailed knowledge of your chosen activity from:

- information given to you by your teacher/coach when you have participated in the activity. You should make notes after each of your practical activity sessions

- coaching manuals, books and videos on this activity
- governing/organising body publications.

You should also seek help and advice from your teacher/coach.

You may find it helpful to create a form like the one below to help you.

Name of aspect you are evaluating	Strengths of the performance	Weaknesses of the performance
Gymnastic through vault	Body shape looked good because the flight onto the box was excellent.	Poor repulsion off the box resulted in very little flight off the box and an uncontrolled landing.

TASK 12
Create a form on which you can record your evaluations.

Action Planning

Once you have an accurate assessement of your performance you can start to create a plan which hopefully will lead to improvement. Your plan will normally focus on identified areas of weakness. Your action plan needs to include the following sections:

- clear realistic goals that are achievable
- a timescale in which you are going to achieve the goals
- the method by which you are going to achieve the goals
- the method by which you are going to evaluate whether or not you have achieved your goals
- record of how you put your action plan into practice
- record of how you evaluated your action plan.

HOT TIPS

PPPs scoring high marks have all these sections in their action plans.

Identifying Goals

You need to select one or more of the areas in your performance that needs to be improved as your goal; this might be skills, tactics or fitness. Choose a goal in which you are likely to succeed.

You may have found that some of your skills are weak and decide to work on improving them. Your goal to improve these skills must be realistic and achievable. For example, your shooting in netball may be weak and the improvement would be to score with more shots. This is an achievable and realistic goal, but aiming at shooting so that you never miss is not. Alternatively, you might identify improved stamina as your goal. This would be achievable if you allow yourself a realistic timescale to train, but not if you expect to improve your stamina in a week.

Planning timescales

Your timescale will be very much linked to the type of your goals. If your goal is to improve your skills you may decide to concentrate your practice five times a week for two or three weeks. You might, however, practise fewer times a week but over more weeks. If you decide to work on an aspect of fitness you would need to carry this out over a longer period of time, say six to eight weeks, to have a good chance of improving. Your timescale will depend on how long and often your sessions are, and must be long enough for you to be able to achieve your goal and show an improvement.

Recording the Methods used to achieve Goals

This section must include the detail of what you are actually going to do in your practice and training sessions in order to achieve your goals. If you are working on skills, it will include the coaching points on which you are focusing and details of the progressive practices you will do. Remember that you will have looked at these in Section A on page 275. They may come from coaching manuals or your course or coaching sessions. If you are working on fitness you will need to give details of the activities in your training sessions, including how hard you will work, the number of times you will do each activity and for how long.

Recording the Methods used to evaluate Achievements

You will need to think about how you can show that you have actually improved your performance. You could use a simple objective test. For example, if you have been working on your shooting in netball you could test yourself on how many successful shots from a set distance out of 20 shots before you begin your action plan. At the end of your action plan test yourself again and hopefully the number will have improved.

TASK 13

Think of a test that you can use to assess your performance in a skill in your practical activity.

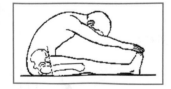

Fig. 14.05 Objective tests can be used to measure fitness.

If you are working on fitness then there are several objective tests that you could use to establish your level of fitness before and after your action plan, such as:

- Stamina – multi-stage fitness test
- Speed – 30 metre run
- Strength (power) vertical jump
- Suppleness – sit and reach test

TASK 14

Ask your teacher/coach where you can find details of fitness tests with which you can assess components of your fitness.

This type of test is simple and straightforward but may not be suitable for the goals you have set. For instance, if you have decided that your passing is weak you will need to adopt a different approach. You may get your teacher/coach to count the number of successful passes you make before and after your action plan. By comparing the two you will be able to see if your performance has improved.

You could also support these test results with subjective opinions. Record your own or your teacher/coach's opinions before and after you have completed your plan. Objective tests are easier to use as they give a clear result but opinions should also be taken into account.

Recording the Action Plan in Practice

This is simply a record of how you put your methods into practice. It should be a log/diary of what you actually did to improve your performance, rather than what you planned to do, and should also contain your feelings and opinions on how the sessions went.

Recording the Success of the Action Plan

You identified in your action plan how you would find out if it had been successful and in this section you need to record your results in two parts.

Part one – your assessment at the start of your plan, containing the results from any tests before you started and your own opinions and those of people you talked to about your performance.

Part two – your assessment at the end of your plan, containing the results from any tests during your sessions and at the end of your action plan, and any opinions, including your own, about any improvements on completion of your action plan.

As well as detailing the effects of your plan on your performance, you should also write generally about your plan. These opinions on your action plan might cover such things as whether you thought it was good, interesting, boring, too easy, too hard, etc. You should also state whether you achieved your goals and if you did not, explain the probable reasons. You might also suggest changes you would make to the plan for future use.

Important Points to Remember When Working on Your PPP

- Start your PPP early in your AS course.
- Choose one of your activities for assessment as the focus of your PPP.
- Read a coaching book on your activity to help you evaluate and action plan.
- Keep a log/diary of what you actually do when putting your plan into action.
- Remember to work out how you will test whether or not you have improved.
- Make sure you evaluate the strong and weak points of your action plan and include them in your review.

Revise as you go! Test your knowledge and understanding

- Which activity category do your two activities come from?
- What are the conditioned competitive situations for your two activities?
- Name the basic skills which are important in your two activities.
- Name two advanced skills which you are able to perform in each of your activities.
- Identify the phases into which skills in your activities are analysed.
- Describe one set of progressive practices for a skill in each of your two activities.
- Describe the basic strategies and tactics used in your two activities and describe your role in them.
- How many activities should your PPP focus on?
- What should you be looking for in the evaluation of your performance?
- What are the main elements of your action plan?
- What are the important components of fitness in your activity?
- What are the important skills in your activity?
- How many sections should your PPP be divided into?
- When does your PPP have to be completed?

Index